Thomas Harriot

Thomas Harriot

RENAISSANCE SCIENTIST

EDITED BY
JOHN W. SHIRLEY

CLARENDON PRESS · OXFORD
1974

Oxford University Press, Ely House, London W. 1

GLASGOW NEW YORK TORONTO MELBOURNE WELLINGTON
CAPE TOWN IBADAN NAIROBI DAR ES SALAAM LUSAKA ADDIS ABABA
DELHI BOMBAY CALCUTTA MADRAS KARACHI LAHORE DACCA
KUALA LUMPUR SINGAPORE HONG KONG TOKYO

ISBN 0 19 858140 8

© OXFORD UNIVERSITY PRESS 1974

PRINTED IN GREAT BRITAIN
BY HAZELL WATSON & VINEY LTD
AYLESBURY, BUCKS

To Dr. E. Arthur Trabant and Mr. J. Bruce Bredin
this book is most warmly dedicated. Without their un-
flagging interest and support, the University of
Delaware Thomas Harriot Symposium could not have
been held, and the articles contained in this volume
would not have been written. For their enthusiasm for
Harriot studies, the editor and contributors are all
grateful.

PREFACE

IT is now more than 350 years since Thomas Harriot on his deathbed considered his fame and reputation:

Item I ordayne and Constitute the aforesaid Nathaniell Thorporley ... to be Overseer of my Mathematicall Writinges ... to pervse and order and to separate the Cheife of them from my waste papers, to the end that after hee doth vnderstande them hee may make vse in penninge such doctrine that belonges vnto them for publique vse as it shall be thought Convenient ...

Alas! Though recognized by his contemporaries as England's most profound mathematician, most imaginative and methodical experimental scientist, and first of all Englishmen to make a telescope and turn it on the heavens, Harriot had not prepared his works for the use of future generations. Under the elaborate patronage of Sir Walter Ralegh and the 'Wizard Earl' of Northumberland, Harriot had toiled diligently for four decades, had achieved recognition and influenced most of his scientific friends. But he had seen through the press only one small treatise—the first English account of the new world—*A Briefe and True Report of the New Found Land of Virginia*, 1588. The thousands upon thousands of sheets of mathematics and of scientific observations which had occupied most of his waking hours were lost to sight, buried in private archives, not destined to advance the new science as he knew they were capable of doing.

Early discussions in the newly founded Royal Society of London centred around the search for Harriot's lost papers, but inquiries made from 1662 to 1669 proved fruitless, and it was finally assumed that they had been destroyed. More than a century later, in 1784, a German astronomer, Baron von Zach, startled the scientific world by announcing that he had located Harriot's astronomical observations, and that his perusal showed Harriot to anticipate and be greater in his accomplishments than either Kepler or Galileo. Though he toured Europe with such extravagant claims, von Zach produced no text or serious study of Harriot's innovations, and again the papers were returned to the dark of archival materials. Rigaud, Savilian Professor at Oxford, and Henry Stevens of Vermont, an antiquarian bookseller, both turned their hands to revealing the true Harriot in the nineteenth century. Neither fully succeeded.

Only in the second half of the twentieth century, when the significance of science has become of crucial importance and the study of the history and philosophy of science has matured, has Harriot's reputation started to come into its own. The blossoming of digital computers makes startlingly significant the fact that Harriot first explored the potential of binary numeration. The sending of man to make first-hand scientific observations on the surface of the moon renders more relevant the fact that Harriot's moon maps are the earliest-known telescopic observations of that body. The explorations of the new mathematics reinforce the importance of Harriot's gropings in number theory, combinatorics, linguistic ciphers, and the like, not to mention his high sophistication in algebra and spherical trigonometry. Now that the Harriot papers have seen the light of day, Harriot stands clear as a key figure at the time when the new science of logic, reason, mathematics, and experiment was coming into being. A man who, like Bacon, took all knowledge for his province, Harriot, through both theory and practice, has proved himself to be a true Renaissance Scientist.

Through a helpful grant from an unnamed 'favourer of all good learning, and Mecaenas of learned men', a Thomas Harriot Seminar has been held at Oxford anually since 1967, under the leadership of Dr. Alistair C. Crombie. This Seminar has brought together a sizable group of historians and philosophers to discuss Harriot and his intellectual milieu. Both the British Academy and the Royal Society have made grants to an interested group of Harrioteers (Professor Quinn is British chairman, and Professor Shirley American chairman) to acquire microfilm and photocopies of all known Harriot manuscripts and materials for deposition in the Bodleian Library, Oxford, for the use of interested scholars. A similar grant in the United States was made to Professor Shirley and the University of Delaware, and (with additional grants from two private benefactors who prefer to remain anonymous) for a Thomas Harriot Symposium to enlist the interest and support of American scholars in Harriot studies. This Symposium was held at the University of Delaware on 5, 6, and 7 April, 1971, with thirty American historians of science in attendance. The papers included in this volume, in earlier drafts, were first given at this Symposium, though they have been considerably reworked for publication.

I should like to express my own thanks and the gratitude of the University of Delaware to all who participated in making the Delaware Symposium a delightful and notable occasion. All of us, in turn, owe our gratitude to the British Academy, the Royal Society, the National Endowment for the Humanities, the University of Delaware, and our special benefactors for their assistance in bringing back to Thomas Harriot some of the fame and reputation to which he aspired so very many years ago.

The University of Delaware　　　　　　　　　　　　JOHN W. SHIRLEY
December, 1972　　　　　　　　　H. Fletcher Brown Research Professor
　　　　　　　　　　　　　　　　　　　　　　in the History of Science

CONTENTS

LIST OF PLATES   x

1. Harriot's Science, the Intellectual Background   1
   EDWARD ROSEN

2. Sir Walter Ralegh and Thomas Harriot   16
   JOHN W. SHIRLEY

3. Thomas Harriot and the New World   36
   DAVID B. QUINN

4. Harriot's Earlier Work on Mathematical Navigation: Theory and
   Practice   54
   JON V. PEPPER

5. Henry Stevens and the Associates of Thomas Harriot   91
   R. C. H. TANNER

6. Harriot, Hill, Warner and the New Philosophy   107
   JEAN JACQUOT

7. Thomas Harriot and the First Telescopic Observations of Sunspots   129
   JOHN NORTH

BIBLIOGRAPHY   166

INDEX   175

LIST OF PLATES

facing page

1. Harriot's notes on Ralegh's speech before his execution   17

2. The title-page of *A briefe and true report*   17

3. The bill mentioned in Harriot's will 'to Mr. John Bill Stationer for Books'   102–3

4. Two of Harriot's sunspot drawings. (a) The first observation, dated 8 December, 1610. (b) Observation numbers 49–52   118–19

1

HARRIOT'S SCIENCE: THE INTELLECTUAL BACKGROUND

EDWARD ROSEN

City University of New York

A s I survey the entire career of Thomas Harriot (1560–1621) and ask myself whether his life was marked by any distinctive quality, I am tempted to reply that the man who introduced into algebra the signs for 'greater than' and 'less than' and who also wrote the first original English book about the first English colony in America exemplified to a high degree in his own person that unity of thought and action which characterized his background at its best.

In *A Briefe and True Report of the New Found Land of Virginia* (London, 1588) Harriot states that 'in all our travailes which were most speciall and often in the time of winter, our lodging was in the open aire upon the grounde'. Moreover, he and his fellow-colonists obtained most of their food by their own exertions.

He put his mastery of astronomy, cartography, and navigation to use in training the pilots and sea captains employed by Sir Walter Ralegh, the English counterpart of Portugal's Prince Henry the Navigator. Whereas Harriot worked for a secular nobleman, Nicholas Copernicus (1473–1543) toiled for a collegiate chapter of canons. In other respects their careers show a striking similarity, particularly in the union of hand and brain. They both made maps of previously uncharted territory and administered landed estates. Both of them resisted the importunities of their friends and associates, who urged them to publish their findings in their lifetime. Copernicus yielded to these entreaties barely in the nick of time. His magisterial volume *On the Revolutions of the Heavenly Spheres* (*De revolutionibus orbium coelestium*, Nuremberg, 1543), which signaled the start of modern astronomy, reached him on his dying day, when he was already too ill to perceive how his masterpiece had been mal-treated by a well-intentioned but misguided editor in charge of the printing in a distant city. To the everlasting harm to his own reputation in the history of science, Harriot acceded to his admirers only in his last will and testament.

That highly informative document reveals that among his other prized possessions Harriot owned 'dishes of iron Called by the spectacle makers tooles to grinde spectacles, and other perspective glasses for trunckes'. Like

Galileo Galilei (1564–1642), who was four years younger than himself, Harriot occupied himself with the production of lenses and 'perspective trunckes', as he called his telescopes. In his correspondence with Johannes Kepler (1571–1630), who was eleven years his junior, Harriot demonstrated that he had made effective use of his scientific apparatus for the study of the refraction of light in passing through media of various densities, and he also posed serious theoretical objections to the *Additions to Witelo* (*Paralipomena ad Vitellionem,* Frankfurt am Main, 1604), the work in which Kepler laid the foundations of modern optics.

Harriot himself owned a copy of the *Ten Books on Optics* (*Opticae libri decem*) by Witelo. This most important medieval Latin writer on the subject was descended from mixed East German and Polish parentage, but studied in France and Italy. While his lengthy treatise contained a certain number of his own observations, in the main it was derived from an anonymous Latin translation of the outstanding Arabic achievement in the field. This *Kitab fi-l manazir* (*Book about Optical Objects*) had been written by Ibn al-Haitham (965–c. 1039), the greatest of the Muslim physicists, who was known in the Latin West as Alhazen. It was he who diverted the earlier investigations into the nature of light and the process of human vision from a dead-end track to the main road which has been traversed ever since. By simple yet powerful arguments Ibn al-Haitham convinced his readers that we see because our eyes are affected by something that was originally emitted by a luminous body. The opposite view had been maintained by many of the ancient Greek thinkers, who believed that visual perception occurred in whole or in part as a result of rays emanating from our eyes. *Treasury of Optics* (*Opticae thesaurus*) was the title bestowed on the Latin version of Ibn al-Haitham's *Kitab* by its editor, Friedrich Risner, who printed it in front of Witelo in the composite volume (Basel, 1572) of which a copy came into the possession of Harriot. This copy was recently identified in the library of the University of Oslo, Norway.

In both Ibn al-Haitham and Witelo, Harriot found tables for the refraction of light. These medieval tables followed the model of the first such table in the history of optics. This pioneering investigation had been conducted by the foremost astronomer of antiquity, Ptolemy, who tried to find out how a ray of light diverged from its rectilinear path when it passed from the celestial regions into the earth's atmosphere. A somewhat analogous case, closer to hand and easier to measure, was presented by the movement of light into the denser medium of water from the less dense medium of air. In Ptolemy's table for the air-into-water case, the angle of incidence at which the ray of light struck the interface between the two media ranged from 10° to 80° at intervals of 10°. The angle of refraction corresponding to each of these eight angles of incidence was recorded in a second column. The first entry therein was 8°, and the last was 50°. However, whereas in the first column the angle of incidence increased uniformly from 10° to 20° and so on by equal jumps, in the second column the angle of refraction rose nonuniformly. Had it mounted uniformly, it would have climbed from 8° to 50° in seven equal steps of 6°. But instead of 8°, 14°, 20° and so on, the second column showed a less simple sequence: 8°, $15\frac{1}{2}°$, $22\frac{1}{2}°$, 29° and so on to 50°. As the angle of refraction increased, its rate of increase was not constant, but diminished. This diminution, or second difference, as it is called, was $\frac{1}{2}°$ at each of the seven levels in the second column.

Such invariance may have indicated a sublime faith in the uniformity of nature. Yet this feature of Ptolemy's refraction table, which otherwise constitutes the high-water mark of deliberate experimentation and precise measurement in the ancient physical sciences, was not confirmed later on. By contrast, an earlier Greek discovery, that the angle of incidence equals the angle of reflection when light is thrown back by a nontransparent surface such as a mirror, stood the test of time as a sound principle. The repeated confirmation of this simple uniformity in the behaviour of light led to a search for a similar invariance in the case of refraction. Since the reported constant second difference of $\frac{1}{2}°$ in Ptolemy's table was not confirmed by his successors, a suspicion naturally has arisen that he (or perhaps some copyist) fudged his findings.

On the next to the last page in his copy of Risner, Harriot reproduced Witelo's table of refraction for the air-water case, and placed his own table alongside Witelo's. Harriot's table differs, however, from that of his medieval predecessor in two important respects. First, Harriot inserted angles of incidence not found in Witelo, namely, 5°, 65°, 75°, 85°, 86°, 87°, 88°, and 89°. Secondly, for all but one of Witelo's angles of incidence, Harriot gives not a single angle of refraction, but a pair of measurements, with the two differing by as much as 43', in the case of 30°, and as little as 2', in the case of 50°.

This table, dated 1597, represents only an early stage in Harriot's development. Later he reduced Witelo's 10° increment in the angle of incidence to 1°. Instead of advancing by 1° only in the narrow region of 85°–89°, Harriot prepared a table for the entire quadrant 1°–90° at intervals of 1°. In this later table the angles of refraction no longer coincide with those previously given by Harriot in his 1597 table. This deviation is not due to subsequent measurements. The later values for the angles of refraction do not come in pairs, but singly. They were determined by computation, not by measurement. This computation was evidently based on an invariant relation (4/3) between the sines of the incident and refracted angles. Harriot operated with the sine law of refraction, although no explicit formulation of it by him has as yet been found in his unpublished manuscripts.

Exactly what happens when light traverses media of different density was a problem that fascinated others as well as Harriot. This topic looms large in Kepler's *Optics* (his favorite short title for his *Additions to Witelo*) and also in his correspondence with Harriot. Two of their younger contemporaries, the Dutchman Willebrord Snel (1580–1626) and the Frenchman René

Descartes (1596–1650), have long been given credit for discovering, probably independently of each other, the true trigonometric relationship, formulated differently but equivalently by Snel and Descartes, between the angles of incidence and refraction. Yet Harriot knew the sine law of refraction before Snel and Descartes. Harriot's pupil and friend Sir William Lower of South Wales prophetically warned him on 6 February 1610 [Old Style; 1611, by present reckoning] that 'it is possible by to much procrastination to be prevented [anticipated] in the honor of some of your rarest inventions and speculations. Let your Countrie and frinds injoye the comforts they would have in the true and greate honor you would purchase your selfe by publishing some of your choise workes, but you know best what you have to doe.'

In conceding that Harriot knew best what he had to do, did Lower have in mind the difficulty to which Harriot had darkly alluded about eighteen months earlier in a letter to Kepler? In that half-outspoken, half-secretive communication, dispatched on 13 July 1608 (Old Style) from Syon on Thames, near the residence which had recently been acquired by Henry Percy, earl of Northumberland, a close friend of Ralegh and, like him, a generous patron of Harriot, the latter confessed to Kepler that 'our situation is such that I still may not philosophize freely; we are still stuck in the mud'.

Another correspondent of Kepler's had written to him somewhat more explicitly along similar lines about a decade before, on 1 September 1597:

Many years ago I was converted to the theory of Copernicus . . . . I wrote out many reasons in favor of it, and rebuttals of opposing arguments. But I have not yet dared to publish them. I am thoroughly frightened by the fate of our master Copernicus, who won immortal fame among some people, but among countless [others] (for so great is the number of fools) emerged a target of ridicule and abuse. I would surely have the courage to make my thinking public if there were more people like you. But since there are not, I shall avoid such involvement.

Such involvement was prudently avoided by Galileo, the author of this letter, as long as he remained professor of mathematics at the University of Padua and for two decades thereafter. But when he finally discussed Copernicanism in his magnificent *Dialogue* of 1632, he was found guilty of heresy, compelled to make a public renunciation of the new cosmology, and sentenced to life imprisonment.

Such rigorous penalties were not inflicted on Harriot, whose brush with the establishment in his own country led to less dire consequences. Nor was it his acceptance of the Copernican astronomy that drew the unwelcome attention of the investigating authorities to him. Rather, it seems to have been his favorable attitude towards the atomic theory.

In his will, mentioned above, Harriot declared:

I ordayne and Constitute the aforesaid NATHANIELL THORPERLEY first to be Overseer of my Mathematicall Writinges to be received of my Executors to peruse and order and to separate the Cheife of them from my waste papers, to the end that after hee doth understand them hee may make use in penninge such doctrine that belonges unto them for publique uses as it shall be thought Convenient by my Executors and him selfe.

As a pupil of Harriot's, the Reverend Nathaniel Torporley (1564–1632) did attempt to grapple with his deceased teacher's mathematical writings. Yet Torporley did not edit Harriot's posthumous *Artis analyticae praxis ad aequationes algebraicas nova, expedita, et generali methodo resolvendas* (London, 1631; *The Application of the Analytic Art for the Purpose of Solving Algebraic Equations by a New, Convenient, and General Method*). In fact, after this notable contribution by Harriot to the advancement of algebra was edited by others, Torporley proceeded to compose an 'Analytical Corrector of the Posthumous *Art* by Thomas Harriot. As an outstanding mathematician, he very rarely made a mistake. As a reckless philosopher, he blundered more often. As a mortal man, he erred signally. A premonitory summary, written in rebuttal and provided with examples, for the purpose of most reliably refuting the atomistical pseudophilosophy, revived by him [Harriot] and meriting stern reproach as well as anathema over and above his other tall tales.'

Harriot's revival of the atomic theory raised the hackles of Torporley, who cannot be blamed for being unaware that the holograph of the *Revolutions* written by Copernicus' own hand contained a reference (which did not appear in the editions printed in 1543, 1566, and 1617), to 'the very tiny indivisible bodies called "atoms". Being imperceptible, they do not immediately constitute a visible body when they are taken two or a few at a time. But they can be multiplied to such an extent that in the end there are enough of them to combine in a perceptible magnitude.'

The theory that was later embraced by modern science as the expression of the innermost structure of the physical universe estranged Torporley from his former teacher, whom he had once publicly praised as 'born . . . to scatter, by the clarity of undoubted truth, the philosophical clouds which have been darkening the world for many centuries'. Why did atomism so arouse Torporley's ire that he composed *A Synopsis of the Controversie of Atoms*, 'opposing chiefly T. H.' [Thomas Harriot]?

Among Harriot's twelve maxims the first place was assigned to the 'eternitie' of the atoms by Torporley, whose first refutation was 'They are not eternall.' How could eternal, and therefore uncreated, atoms be reconciled by the Reverend Nathaniel Torporley with the Biblical account of the creation of the world? 'Nothing ever arose from nothing through the action of a divinity', sang the ancient Roman poet Lucretius in zealously seeking to liberate mankind from its fear of the gods and of death. Lucretius clothed in lapidary verse the teachings of the Greek philosopher Epicurus, whose name was reviled as a synonym for 'unbeliever' and 'atheist' by orthodox Jews. Of Harriot too it was said that 'he did not like (or valued not) the old storie of the Creation of the World. He could not beleeve the old position; he would say *ex nihilo nihil fit*'. And indeed he did say: 'Out of nothing comes nothing.'

When Copernicus, a Roman Catholic canon, dedicated his *Revolutions* in June 1542 to the reigning pope, he correctly foresaw that bibliolaters would rise up in their wrath to smite him and all his works:

Perhaps there will be babblers who claim to be judges of mathematics although completely ignorant of the subject and, badly distorting some passage of Scripture to their purpose, will dare to find fault with my undertaking and censure it. I disregard them even to the extent of despising their criticism as unfounded. For it is not unknown that Lactantius, otherwise an illustrious writer but hardly a mathematician, speaks quite childishly about the earth's shape, when he mocks those who declared that the earth has the form of a globe. Hence scholars need not be surprised if any such persons will likewise ridicule me.

In 1596 Kepler was compelled to delete from his first major publication a chapter upholding the reconcilability of Copernicanism with the Bible. But he did not long remain in his obscure position as a lowly teacher, subject to censorship exercised by the faculty of Tübingen University. After rising to the lofty status of Imperial Mathematician of the Holy Roman Emperor Rudolph II, Kepler eloquently proclaimed the truth of the Copernican system in the introduction to his *New Astronomy* of 1609. In discussing Joshua 10: 12–14, Kepler did not deny that a miracle occurred, since such a denial would have undermined the authority of the Bible. On the other hand, literal acceptance of the miracle as described ('the sun stood still in the midst of heaven, and hasted not to go down about a whole day, and there was no day like that before it or after it') would have conflicted with Copernicanism, which regarded the sun's immobility not as temporary or miraculous but as its permanent and normal condition. Kepler accepted the traditional belief that God created the universe. But Kepler's God was a Copernican. When Joshua asked God to stop the sun, 'God readily understood from Joshua's words what he wanted and complied by stopping the motion of the earth, so that to Joshua the sun seemed to stand still'.

For the literal interpretation of the Bible Kepler substituted the principle that 'to teach mankind about ordinary things is not the purpose of Holy Writ, which speaks to people about these matters in a human way in order to be understood by them and uses popular concepts'. 'Piety prevents many people from agreeing with Copernicus out of fear that the Holy Ghost speaking in Scripture will be branded as a liar if we say that the earth moves and the sun stands still.' 'Having discussed the authority of Holy Writ, I reply concisely to the beliefs of the [Church] Fathers regarding these aspects of Nature. In theology, the preponderance of authority must be weighed, but in science the preponderance of reason. Therefore, revered is Lactantius who denied that the earth is round. Revered is Augustine, who admitted [the earth's] sphericity but contested [the existence of] antipodes. Revered is the modern [Holy]

Office, which concedes that the earth is small yet denies that it moves. On the other hand, the truth is revered more by me in proving scientifically, with all due respect to the Doctors of the Church, that the earth is spherical, inhabited all around by antipodes, most pitifully tiny and, finally, in motion among the celestial bodies.' 'The book of Job will appear to agree with Lactantius if it is sidetracked from the purpose of God's word to a philosophical fantasy.' 'The book of Judges was written by various authors and is confused, as is obvious at its beginning and end.'

Harriot's countryman and contemporary, Francis Bacon (1561–1626), who was no Copernican, in his *Novum Organum* declared:

Some of the moderns have with extreme levity indulged so far as to attempt to found a system of natural philosophy on the first chapter of Genesis, on the book of Job, and other parts of the sacred writings . . . which also makes the inhibition and repression of it the more important, because from this unwholesome mixture of things human and divine there arises not only a fantastic philosophy but also an heretical religion. Very meet is it therefore that we be sober-minded, and give to faith that only which is faith's.

This Aphorism 65 from the pen of England's Lord Chancellor was published in 1620, when Harriot was already suffering from his fatal illness. Nevertheless throughout his life he acted in conformity with Bacon's advice to 'give to faith that only which is faith's'. Harriot always regulated his conduct in accordance with the highest moral principles. But in the realm of thought he followed unswervingly the trumpet call of the new science: 'Free in mind must be he who desires to have understanding.' It was the lack of this freedom that Harriot lamented in his letter to Kepler, quoted above.

Also quoted above was Lower's letter to Harriot of 6 February 1610/11, in which the loyal pupil asked: 'Do you not here startle, to see every day some of your inventions taken from you? . . . Vieta prevented [anticipated] you of the gharland of the greate Invention of Algebra.' No such claim of priority over François Viète (1540–1603) was advanced publicly on behalf of Harriot by the editors of his *Artis analyticae praxis* (1631). This very title was modeled after that used forty years earlier by Viète: *In artem analyticam isagoge* (Tours, 1591; *Introduction to the Analytic Art*). The contrast between *isagoge* and *praxis* was no mere accident, for Harriot's editors plainly avowed the relationship, as they saw it, between Viète's *Isagoge* and Harriot's *Praxis*:

After the talented age of the Greeks the analytical art, which is treated here, remained undeveloped and uncultivated for a long period. Its revival was undertaken for the first time, with exceptional skill in an effort without precedent, by the Frenchman François Viète, a man of the highest renown and, by reason of his noteworthy knowledge of the mathematical sciences, the glory of the French people. . . . But while he earnestly strove to restore the analytics of old in the task which he had set himself, he seems to have handed on to us no mere restoration but something new and his own, advanced and improved by his personal discoveries. This statement in general terms should be explained in a little more detail. In this way a demonstration of what was first accomplished by Viète in carrying through his undertaking may permit a better understanding of the later contributions by our very highly informed author Thomas Harriot, who followed Viète in this pursuit of analytics.

Neither Lower nor the editors of Harriot's *Praxis* could be expected to foresee that the Egyptian hieroglyphic would be deciphered after a lapse of nearly two centuries and that the Rhind Papyrus would contain problems requiring the discovery of an unknown number by a process tantamount to solving an equation of the first degree. Nor could Harriot's editors know beforehand that some day the unraveling of the cuneiform script would disclose the ancient Babylonians doing the equivalent of solving quadratic equations and even some cubic equations. Hence, to seventeenth-century eyes, the talented age of antiquity was Greek, with its geometrical algebra, as exemplified by Euclid, and indeterminate analysis in Diophantus.

Beneath the outer layer of geometry in Euclid, a trained eye can discern in portions of his *Elements* and other writings sections that can be translated into algebra. Diophantus, on the other hand, is nakedly and starkly algebraic, the separation from geometry being virtually complete. Thus, Diophantus does not present a logical sequence of theorems rigorously proved nor even a general solution of equations. Instead, by ingeniously manipulating particular equations he solves a collection of problems concerning numbers, the problems being arranged roughly in increasing order of complexity. Only here and there, as a by-product so to say, does Diophantus generate some valid propositions in the theory of numbers.

Historically too Diophantus' legacy contrasted with Euclid's. Whereas the great geometer was studied practically without serious interruption, Diophantus disappeared from view for many centuries. Then, after a manuscript of Diophantus was discovered and its essential contents published in 1572, Viète was able to see the underlying equivalence between some of the reasoning in Euclid and other Greek geometers, on the one hand, and the numerical algebra of Diophantus and his successors.

Viète preferred the designation 'analytic art' for algebra because of its characteristic method. Ordinarily, a problem is proposed: to find an unknown quantity. In order to do so, elicit from the terms of the problem what is necessarily implied with regard to the unknown, give it a special designation, and subject it to the indicated mathematical operations. By contrast, the synthetic method started from what was assumed as known, and proceeded therefrom by strict inference to what was to be demonstrated.

Like his predecessors, Diophantus sometimes wrote out a full word for the unknown quantity, which he called the 'number'. At other times, however, he indicated it by a ligature of the first two letters of the Greek word for 'number'. Further reinforcing the trend away from the earlier entirely verbal algebra, written out in ordinary language, Diophantus moved in the direction of symbolic expression by regularly employing abbreviations for the powers of the 'number' from 2 to 6. In like manner, his sign of equality was the first letter of the Greek word meaning 'equal'. In the absence of a special sign for addition, Diophantus simply juxtaposed all the terms to be added together within the same expression. For subtraction, on the other hand, he employed a distinctive symbol, to the right of which he grouped together all the negative terms in the expression. Like addition, multiplication was an operation that lacked an indicator: Diophantus' coefficients were all definite numerals, written directly before the unknown quantity and its powers. Diophantus' symbol for the unknown quantity bore no immediately obvious relation to the various abbreviations for the higher powers of the unknown. This serious defect in Diophantus' notation was remedied by Viète, who used A for the first power of the unknown, Aq for the second power, Ac for the third, with q being the abbreviation for 'quadratus' = squared, and c for 'cubus' = cubed, and so on.

For Viète's capital letters Harriot substituted lower-case letters. To indicate the power of the unknown, he repeated it the appropriate number of times, so that his aa = our a^2, his aaa = our a^3, and so on. In this respect Harriot carried out a suggestion made by the German algebraist Michael Stifel in 1553. Extracts from his writings are found in Harriot's unpublished papers.

In manuscripts and early printed books a number was usually separated from the words in the text by means of a dot. In like manner Harriot placed a dot between the numerical coefficient in an algebraic term and the other factors which were indicated by letters. Harriot's dot has sometimes been misinterpreted as the sign for multiplication, which, however, was actually introduced nearly a century later by the distinguished German mathematician and philosopher Gottfried Wilhelm Leibniz.

Robert Recorde's *Whetstone of Witte* in 1557 had suggested our sign for equality: 'I will sette . . . a paire of parallels, or Gemowe lines of one lengthe, thus: ==, bicause noe 2. thynges, can be moare equalle.' Whereas little or no attention had been paid to Recorde's eminently useful innovation prior to Harriot, the latter adopted it and, by popularizing it, paved the way to its present universal employment. Recorde's equal sign exemplifies the trend away from readily recognizable abbreviations toward arbitrary signs having no intrinsic relationship to what they symbolize and acquiring their meaning purely by convention. A further step in this direction was taken by Harriot when he devised $>$ and $<$ to indicate 'greater than' and 'less than'. By the same token he was the first to propose the long horizontal brace $\sqrt{}$ to cover all the terms affected by a radical sign.

The term under Harriot's radical sign must be positive, since he rejected imaginary or complex numbers as 'inexplicable'. In this respect he followed Viète, who recognized no negative roots of an equation. Here their model was Diophantus, who systematically avoided equations leading to roots other than positive integers, fractions, or mixed numbers. Any result that could not be exactly expressed as a ratio of two integers was disregarded by Diophantus. For him, if a real positive root did not emerge from an equation, 'it could not be solved'. When he did solve a quadratic equation having (we should say) one positive and one negative root, the latter was ignored by Diophantus. He took account of only one root even when both were positive, rational, and real. For the negative root, which Harriot rejected as useless, his term was *radix privativa*, a designation not found in Viète but occurring in earlier German writers on algebra. Although Harriot would not admit negative roots of algebraic equations, he did accept negative numbers, which he designated by the sign for subtraction.

In the solution of a problem involving several unknown quantities, these were expressed by Diophantus in terms of a single variable, to which he was limited by the restrictions of his notation. He tried to avoid simultaneous equations of the first degree by reducing them to a single equation in a single variable by ingeniously operating with a succession of conditions. He gave only a single answer to an indeterminate problem, where modern analysis would see an unlimited number of solutions. On the other hand, Viète's method, followed by Harriot, permitted the introduction of an unlimited number of unknown quantities in the same problem.

Harriot regularly transferred all terms containing a power of the unknown to the left side of the equation, while on the right side he placed the constant term, whether this was positive, negative, or zero. In writing equations with only zero on the right side, Harriot again resumed a practice initiated by Stifel and occasionally used by that German algebraist.

Torporley, who was mentioned above as Harriot's erstwhile pupil and posthumous opponent, had once served Viète as secretary and may well have been the link between that talented Frenchman and Harriot. How Harriot viewed his own algebra in relation to Viète's may be surmised from a passage in Lower's letter to Harriot of 6 February 1610/1611: 'The last of Vieta's probleames you leave to speake of because (you say) I had a better of you, which was more universal and more easilie demonstrated, and findeth the point, E, as wel out of the plaine of the triangle given, as in the plaine.' To surpass Viète in generality and clarity was no mean feat.

In mathematics, outside the field of algebra, Harriot gazed far into the future when he wrote down the fundamental elements of the binary notation. In the absence of any known predecessor, Harriot realized that it was possible to construct an entirely workable number system based on 2 instead of on 10. Harriot's binary number $1011(2^3+2^1+2^0)$ would be equal to the decimal number 11. Of course, he could not have foreseen that the electrical investigations of his eminent contemporary William Gilbert (1544–1603) would one day lead to the invention of the electronic computer, with the on and off status of its components representing the ones and zeros of the binary system.

Harriot was alert to the swift advances being made in the science of his day. Upon receiving a copy of Kepler's *Conversation with Galileo's Sidereal Messenger*, which was published in Prague on 3 May 1610 or shortly thereafter, Harriot sent a letter to Lower reporting the exciting news of Galileo's spectacular telescopic discoveries, as discussed in Kepler's little book. Unfortunately Harriot's letter has not been preserved, but Lower's reply, dated 'the longest day of, 1610' survives. In this message of 21 June 1610 Lower told Harriot that he had been wondering

if aboute Saturn, Jupiter, Mars etc. ther move other planets also which appear not. Just as I was a saying this comes your letter. Which when I had redd, loe, quoth I what I spoke probablie, experience hath made good; so that we both with wonder and delighte fell a consideringe your letter. We are here so on fire with thes things that I must render my request & your promise to send more of all sortes of thes Cylinders. . . . Send me also one of Galileus bookes if anie yet be come over and you can get them.

In his *New Astronomy* of 1609 Kepler had demonstrated that the orbit of a planet is elliptical. In so doing, he had undermined the bimillennial prejudice that the path of a celestial body must be circular or compounded of circles. Copies of his *New Astronomy* must have reached both Harriot and Lower fairly promptly, since on 6 February 1610/11 Lower wrote to Harriot:

Kepler I read diligentlie, but therein I find what it is to be so far from you. . . . His theorie . . . me thinks . . . he establisheth soundlie and as you say overthrowes the circular Astronomie.

To observe the comet of 1607 on 22 September of that year, Harriot used his 'crosse staffe', a naked-eye instrument. But on 21 June 1610 Lower reported to him, with reference to stars seen by Galileo with his telescope but invisible to the naked eye, that

thes Starres with my Cylinder this last winter I often observed, and it was longe er I beleved that I saw them, they appearinge through the Cylinder so farre & distinctlie asunder that without I can not yet dissever. The discoverie of thes made me then observe the 7 starres also in Taurus, which before I always rather beleved to be 7 then ever could number them. Through my Cylinder I saw thes also plainelie and far asunder, and more then 7 to, but because I was prejudged with that number, I beleved not myne eyes nor was carefull to observe hou manie; the next winter now that you have opened mine eyes you shall heare much from me of this argument.

From Lower's reference to his observation of the seven Pleiades 'this last winter' of 1609–1610, it is evident that he was using his 'Cylinder' in Wales at the same time as Galileo in Florence, or at any rate not long thereafter. Since Lower obtained his 'Cylinders' or telescopes from his former teacher, Harriot must have lagged little if at all behind anyone in appreciating the utility of the remarkable new optical invention.

Just as he kept himself informed about the latest developments in instrumentation, so he acquainted himself with recent publications about the long voyages that had already begun the fateful process of redistributing the human population of the earth. In his *Report* of 1588, while discussing the plant woad, which he called 'Oade', Harriot remarked that '. . . in the Ilandes of the Asores it groweth plentifully'. Presumably he derived this information from his reading rather than from personal observation. His utilization of printed materials becomes explicit when he takes up the sassafras tree. 'For the description, the manner of using and the manifold vertues thereof, I referre you to the booke of Monardus, translated and entituled in English, *The joyfull newes from the West Indies.*' Nicolás Monardes (1512–1588), physician of Seville, published in that city his *Primera y segunda y tercera partes de la historia medicinal de las cosas que se traen de nuestras Indias Occidentales que serven en medicina* in 1574. Three years later John Frampton, formerly a British merchant in Spain, published in London his English translation of Dr. Monardes' highly popular survey of the medicaments imported from the Spanish West Indies. In Frampton's Monardes a reader who acted on Harriot's advice would have found, among other beneficial effects attributed to the infusion of sassafras,

In the disease of the stone of the Kidneis and Raines, using this Water hotte when they have this griefe, it doth greate profite, and muche more using it continually simple by it selfe, or with Wine, for that it doth preserve that the paine come not so continually nor so greevous. And also it maketh hym that dooeth use it, to caste out muche Sande, where the stones be ingendred. And also it causeth the stones that are in the Raines to be cast out, and doth staie the ingenderyng of them, for that it doth consume the fleames, of the whiche they doe principally ingender, and the windes that bee many tymes the causes of the paines.

In consulting books published originally in Spanish, Harriot did not have to resort to translations. Thus, in a confidential letter of 11 July 1596 to Sir Robert Cecil, Chief Secretary of State, shortly after the discoverer of the mouth of the Orinoco River had returned to England, Harriot mentioned 'the Spanish booke of Acosta, which . . . I have seene'. José de Acosta (1540–1600) had published his *Historia natural y moral de las Indias* at Seville in 1590 and it was not to be translated into English until 1604. Eight years earlier, referring to Acosta's *Historia* in his letter to Cecil, Harriot maintained:

Nether doth he say, or meane, that Amazones river and Orinoco is all one,—as some, I feare, do averre to your Honor; as by good profe out of that booke alone I can make manifest; and by other meanes besides then this discovery, I can put it out of all dout.

One wonders about the 'good profe out of that booke alone'. For in Book II, Chapter 6, of his *Historia* Acosta spoke of

that great river which some call the Amazon, others the Marañón, and others the Orellana, which we Spaniards discovered and sailed. . . . This river flows from the mountains of Peru . . . and at the end empties into the ocean, entering it almost opposite the islands of Margarita and Trinidad.

These islands, which owe their names to Columbus, lie near the mouths of the Orinoco and quite far from the Amazon. No wonder the readers of Acosta, who never mentions the Orinoco, presumably because he had never heard of it, were misled into identifying the two mighty streams in the north of South America.

Harriot's interest in living foreign languages was by no means confined to Spanish. He describes himself as 'beeing one that have beene in the discoverie and in dealing with the naturall inhabitantes specially imploied'. In that capacity he acquired some familiarity with what he called 'the Virginian language'. He said, for example, 'of al sortes of foule I have the names in the countrie language of fourescore and sixe'. After mentioning some familiar types of fish, he adds that there are 'very many other sortes of excellent good fish, which we have taken & eaten, whose names I know not but in the countrey language'. By the same token, 'there are many other strange trees whose names I knowe not but in the Virginian language'. Nor did Harriot fail to notice the manifold diversity of native speech: 'The language of every government is different from any other, and the farther they are distant the greater is the difference.' With respect to religion, the native priests wished 'to learne more than we had meanes for want of perfect utterance in their language to expresse'. Harriot understood the political utility of religious belief, particularly the dogma of rewards and punishments in the afterlife. Regarding the longing for eternal happiness in heaven or the fear of everlasting pain in hell, Harriot remarks:

this opinion worketh so much in manie of the common and simple sort of people that it maketh them have great respect to their Governours, and also great care what they do, to avoid torment after death, and to enjoy blisse.

In urging others to follow in his footsteps, Harriot repeatedly stressed the abundant opportunity to reap 'profit and gaine'. He took the trouble to enumerate the 'merchantable commodities', pointed out that the Indians 'trafficke for trifles', and emphasised that in enriching themselves, the 'providers' of exports from the colony to England would 'greatly profit our owne countrey men'.

In this appeal to the desire for the accumulation of personal wealth and for the promotion of his country's treasure, Harriot responded with vigor to the clamor for acquisitive individualism and national patriotism that dominated his background. The rising tide of secular interests had pushed into the hinterland any otherworldly and ascetic outlook. Papal decisions dividing all newly discovered lands between the two Catholic powers, Spain and Portugal, were disregarded by Protestant states. As Europe broke out of the narrow shell in which it had been so long confined, its boldest doers and thinkers crossed vast oceans into distant terrestrial tracts and with their minds traversed cosmic space to rearrange and expand our universe. This is the background against which Thomas Harriot played his historic role.

Although he was no physician, he would doubtless have agreed with the analysis by Andreas Vesalius (1514–1564) of the reasons why medicine had declined. In the preface of his epoch-making treatise *On the Structure of the Human Body* (*De humani corporis fabrica,* Basel, 1543) the Belgian founder of modern anatomy recalled the time when some doctors,

scorning the work of the hand, began to assign to their slaves the manual operations which they thought had to be performed for the sick, and to stand by the side of those slaves merely as their supervisors. In the course of time all the other doctors also gradually sidestepped the discomforts experienced by the practitioners of true medicine, while at the same time they relinquished none of their monetary compensation and social status. Precipitously they dropped below the [standard of the] ancient doctors. The process of cooking, and in particular the entire preparation of the patients' food, they surrendered to orderlies; the compounding of drugs, to pharmacists; and the manual manipulations, to barbers. And thus in due course the healing art was unfortunately so split up that the doctors, proclaiming themselves to be physicians, monopolized for themselves alone the prescription of drugs and diet for mysterious diseases, but turned the rest of medicine over to those whom they called 'surgeons' and scarcely regard as their servants. . . .

When the doctors themselves sloughed off the manual operations to others, they lost [the knowledge of] anatomy. For, deeming themselves to be engaged only in the treatment of internal disorders, the doctors believed that an understanding of the viscera alone was quite enough for them. They ignored the structure of the bones and muscles as well as of the nerves, veins, and arteries running through the bones and muscles as though this structure were no concern of theirs. Moreover, when operations were entirely turned over to barbers, not only did the doctors' real comprehension of the viscera die out but the practice of dissection also perished utterly. For under these circumstances the doctors did not undertake to operate, while on the other hand the barbers, to whom the work of the hands was delegated, did not have enough education to understand the writings of those authors who discussed dissection. Such men cannot possibly preserve for us a most difficult craft, when it is passed on to them kinesthetically. This regrettable disruption of the healing art unavoidably brought into the universities the execrable custom according to which some persons habitually dissect the human body while others recount the description of the parts. The latter, seated on high, with surpassing conceit caw like crows about matters with which they have never come into close contact, but merely memorize from books written by others or read from copies held before their eyes. On the other hand, the dissectors are so inarticulate that they cannot explain the dissections to the onlookers and mess up what should be demonstrated in accordance with the precepts of the doctor, whose hand never approaches the dissection. . . . In this way everything is taught wrong and some days are wasted on ridiculous questions,with the further result that fewer things are set forth before the spectators in that uproar than a butcher could teach a doctor in a meat market.

As in medicine, so in many other fields of human endeavour, hand and brain were at last reunited after having been kept apart for many centuries with dire consequences. To Harriot and the best of his contemporaries may be applied the words of Richard Hakluyt dedicating his edition of Peter Martyr's *De orbe nono . . . decades octo* to Sir Walter Ralegh in 1587, 'cum praxi theoriam non sine fructu incredibili coniungerent'—they united theory and practice not without unimaginable reward.

2

SIR WALTER RALEGH AND
THOMAS HARRIOT

JOHN W. SHIRLEY

University of Delaware

ON 23 October 1618 (old style), Sir Walter Ralegh the man was beheaded and Sir Walter Ralegh the legend was born. A public event like Ralegh's execution has naturally left many contemporary accounts, of varying degrees of accuracy. Exactly what Ralegh said can probably never be determined, since official tampering with public utterances or even court evidence was quite customary in Jacobean England. Any new, uncensored account must then, even if brief, be helpful in reconstructing the actual event.

One brief outline of Ralegh's final speech which has not previously been reproduced gives evidence that among the spectators at the execution was Ralegh's closest friend and once personal servant, Thomas Harriot. Among the scattered manuscripts of Harriot preserved in eight volumes in the British Museum exists a half-sheet of foolscap (Additional MSS 6789, folio 533[r]) which reads as follows (see Plate 1):

> Two fits of an agew
> Thankes to god.
>
> of calling god to witness
>   note

That He speaks iustly & truly.

1.) Concerning his loyalty to the
      King.   French agent.
                        & commission fro*m* the
                        french king.

2.) Of slanderus speaches touching
      his ma*jes*ty.   a french man
                        S[r]. L. Stukely.
3.) S[r] L. Stukely.   My lo: Carew
4.) S[r] L. Stukely.   My lo: of Danchaster.
5.) S. L. St: S[r] Edward Perham
6.) S. L. St.   A letter on london hyway.
                                 10,000[li]

7.) Mine of Guiana.

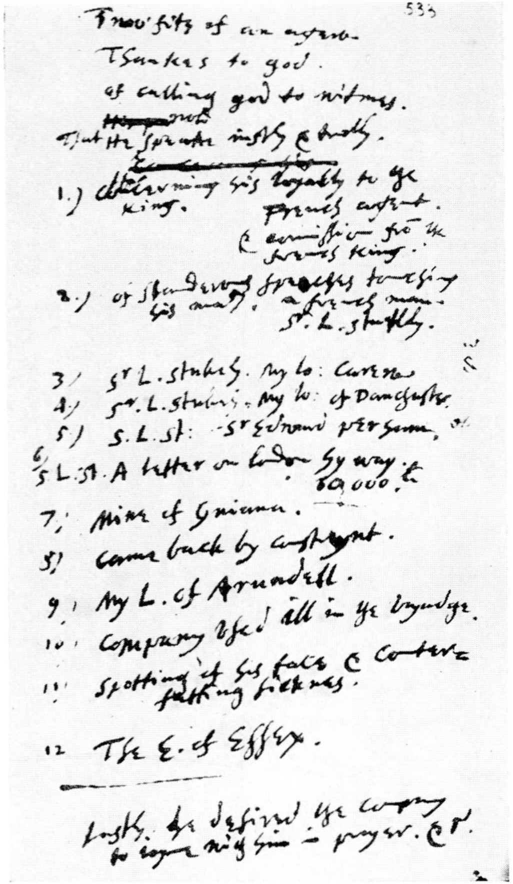

A briefe and true re-
port of the new found land of Virginia: of
the commodities there found and to be raysed, as well mar-
chantable, as others for victuall, building and other necessa-
rie vses for those that are and shalbe the planters there; and of the nature and manners of the naturall inhabitants : Discouered by the
English Colony there seated by Sir Richard Greinuile Knight in the
yeere 1585. which remained vnder the gouernment of Rafe Lane Equi-
er, one of her Maiesties Equieres, during the space of twelue monethes: at
the speciall charge and direction of the Honourable SIR
WALTER RALEIGH Knight, Lord Warden of
the stanneries; who therein hath beene fauoured and authorised by her Maiestie and
her letters patents.

Directed to the Aduenturers, Fauourers,
and Welwillers of the action, for the inhabiting and planting there:

By Thomas Hariot; seruant to the abouenamed
Sir Walter, a member of the Colony, and
there imployed in discouering.

Imprinted at London 1588.

Plate 2. The title-page of *A briefe and true report*.

Plate 1. Harriot's notes on Ralegh's speech before
his execution.

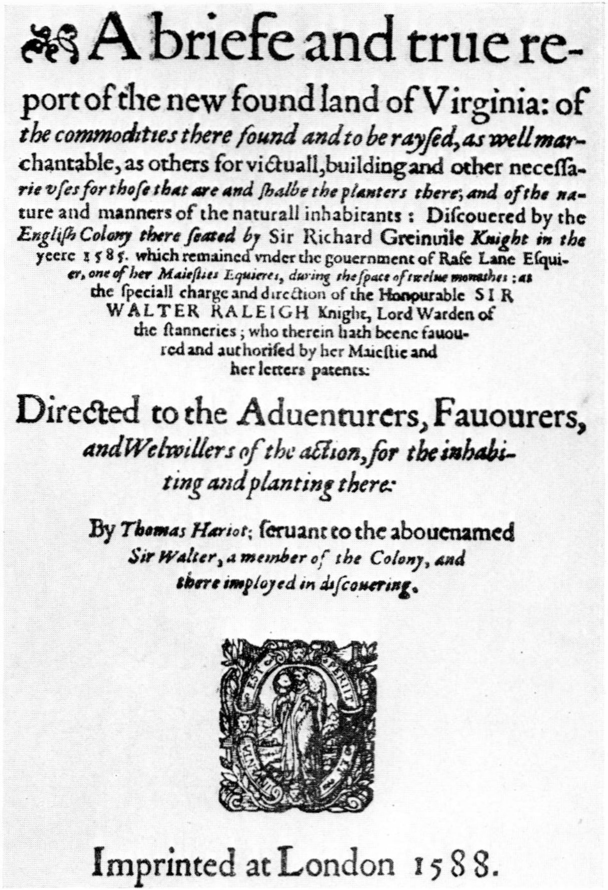

8.) came back by constreynt.
9.) My L. of Arundell
10.) Company vsed ill in the voyadge.
11.) Spotting of his face & conter=
     fetting sickness.
12.) The E. of Essex.

Lastly, he desired the company
to ioyne with him in prayer, &c.

A close analysis of this outline with the known copies of Ralegh's speech, particularly the detailed account of Archbishop Sancroft, shows that Harriot's outline is probably the most accurate yet encountered. The order of items here, with the traditional paragraphs rearranged, is more logical and progressive than the published accounts. It is, therefore, highly probable that this is an accurate rendering of the Ralegh speech, written, as the final statement shows, during or just after the event.

The scene forms a point of transition between two philosophical worlds. Ralegh, seen in historical perspective, represents the last of the great Elizabethans and the passing of an age. Harriot, his contemporary, may be seen as the first modern mathematical experimental scientist, reflecting the dawn of the modern period.

Just when and how Harriot met Ralegh cannot now be determined. It is barely possible that they met in Oxford, Thomas Harriot's hometown, but the difference in their ages renders this unlikely. Though there is no evidence that he was ever graduated from the University, Ralegh is generally credited with having studied at Oriel College for some time between 1568 and 1572.[1] Harriot, born in Oxford in 1560, matriculated at St. Mary's Hall (an independent academic establishment, adjacent to and later affiliated with Oriel) in 1577, and graduated as a Bachelor of Arts in February, 1579/80. It has been suggested that a common tutor brought the two men together,[2] but it is much more likely that their joint interest in navigation and exploration brought them to the attention of mutual friends: Richard Hakluyt of Christ Church who was lecturing on geography during Harriot's college years, and Lawrence Keymis of Balliol who gave up his fellowship to join the London circle.[3] It is likely that Harriot moved to London immediately after his graduation, and was in the household of Ralegh, as Quinn surmises,[4] by late 1582 or early 1583 at the latest.

It is certain, however, that Harriot was working with Ralegh in making plans for the Virginia voyages by 1584. The late E. G. R. Taylor's study of Harriot's manuscripts has shown that Harriot's lost *Arcticon* was made in preparation for the Amadas–Barlow expedition of 1584.[5] Quinn surmises that Harriot may have been a member of that voyage as John White claims to have been (see Chapter 3). On their return in September of that year, Harriot began or continued to work with the two natives brought back from the voyage, Manteo and Wanchese, both to teach them English and to study their language, and perhaps to interrogate them about the new world, its resources, and its inhabitants in preparation for the colonizing venture of 1585[6]. But Harriot's role in Ralegh's household was largely that of scientist, mathematical tutor, and navigational expert. In the Preface to the 1587 edition of *De Orbe Novo Petri Martyris Anglerii Mediolanensis*, dedicated to Ralegh, Richard Hakluyt in praising Ralegh casts some light on Harriot as well. Translated, his comment reads:

... By your experience in navigation you clearly saw that our highest glory as an insular kingdom would be built up to its greatest splendor on the firm foundation of the mathematical sciences, and so *for a long time* (italics mine) you have nourished in your household, with a most liberal salary, a young man well trained in those studies, Thomas Harriot; so that under his guidance you might in spare hours learn those noble sciences and your collaborating sea captains, who are many, might very profitably unite theory with practice, not without almost incredible results.[7]

All of this evidence together makes it almost certain that Harriot was close to Ralegh during these jubilant years of his rise to wealth and prominence: his selection as escort to the Duke of Anjou in 1583; his receipt of royal benefices— the gift of the royal guest mansion, Durham House; the All Souls leases, vintner's licenses, wool cloth monopoly, his knighthood in 1585, and his grant of colonization patents to replace those of his half-brother, Sir Humphrey Gilbert.

As trust between Ralegh and Harriot grew, Ralegh gave his young friend more responsible assignments. In the second expedition to the new world, Ralegh made Harriot his personal emissary. As Quinn described his duties:

Hariot's task when he sailed with Grenville in April 1585 was to take astronomical observations at sea and to act as a consultant on navigation. Once the North American mainland was reached, he was to take on responsibility for studying the Indians and also for supervising the mapping of the new territories, noting natural phenomena such as comets and storms, and above all making a survey, with any assistance he could obtain, of the economic resources of the region—metals, minerals, timber, wild or cultivated plants, and all living creatures likely to affect or be useful to man.[8]

The story of the 1585–86 colonial venture has been told countless times, and need not be repeated here. Accounts occurred in Holinshed and in Hakluyt, which were rehearsed and repeated until they are part of the tradition of the age. Harriot discharged, at least in part, his duty to Ralegh by publishing his own brief account of the project, under the comprehensive title of (see Plate 2):

A briefe and true report of the new found land of Virginia: of *the commodities there found and to be raysed, as well mar*chantable, as others for victuall, building and other necessa*rie vses for those that are and shalbe the planters there*; *and of the na*ture and manners of the naturall inhabitants: Discouered by the *English Colony there seated by* Sir Richard Greinuile *Knight in the* yeare 1585. which remained vnder the gouernment of Rafe Lane, Esqui*er one of her Maiesties Equieres, during the space of twelue monethes*: *at* the speciall charge and direction of the Honourable SIR WALTER RALEIGH Knight, Lord Warden of the stanneries; who therein hath been fauoured and authorised by her Maiestie and her letters patents: Directed to the Aduenturers, Fauourers, *and Welwillers of the action, for the inhabiting and planting there*: By *Thomas Hariot*: seruant to the abouenamed *Sir Walter, a member of the Colony, and there imployed in discouering.* Imprinted at London 1588.

This work, called by Randolph G. Adams 'The first original English book describing the first English colony in America', and by Quinn 'the most delectable of Americana', has kept Harriot's memory alive among British and American historians, even though his major mathematical and scientific works have been generally lost or unappreciated until modern days.

The original purpose of Harriot's volume is difficult to determine. Its title page appears to indicate that it was a propaganda tract designed to attract support for colonization in the new world. It seems also to have served, in the peculiar timing of its preparation and publication as an apologist tract to counteract the evil rumors surrounding Ralegh's colonizing ventures.[9] In any event, the work attracted immediate attention as a first-hand account of the exciting new continent. It was republished in 1590 in Frankfort in Latin, English, French, and German, this time illustrated by the drawings of John White, for which Harriot wrote simple captions. Richard Hakluyt printed the text in his *Principall navigations* in 1589 and again in 1600, and in many later editions. This one work gave the young Harriot a wide reputation as one of the leading authorities on America and the American Indian.

Harriot was in all probability the first Englishman to learn the Algonquian language or at least to attempt its systematic study. According to John Aubrey, 'Dr. Pell tells me that he finds amongst his papers (which are now, 1684, in Dr. Busby's hands), an alphabet that he contrived for the American language, like Devills.'[10] These particular papers have never been found, but it is known that Busby did collect Indian language materials. At the second Thomas Harriot Seminar at Oxford in December, 1968, Quinn pointed out the need for a special study of Harriot's linguistic and cryptographic work. He also called attention to the fact that outside the 76 Indian words in the Harriot–White volume, only one phrase of Algonquian remains in Harriot's hand among his manuscripts now located. On the back of one sheet appears the phrase: 'Kecow hit tamen. What is your name.'[11]

Harriot's interest in navigational instruments and scientific experimentation is also first expressed in his *Report*. His scientific observations on this expedition really make him America's first practising scientist. As he tells the story:

Most thinges they (the Indians) sawe with vs, as Mathematicall instruments, sea compasses, the vertue of the loadstone in drawing yron, a perspectiue glasse whereby was shewed manie strange sightes, burning glasses, wilde-fire woorkes, gunnes, bookes, writing and reading, spring clocks that seeme to goe of themselues, and

manie other thinges that wee had, were so straunge vnto them, and so farre exceeded
their capacities to comprehend the reason and meanes how they should be made and
done, that they thought they were rather the works of gods then of men, or at the
leastwise they had bin giuen and taught vs of the gods.[12]

Such an early reference to a perspective glass is intriguing, though it is impossible to determine just what the term means. It may refer to a concave mirror
structure, or it may actually have meant a simple telescope or 'spy glass'
carried on the voyage for navigational purposes, as E. G. R. Taylor casually
assumes.[13] There can be no doubt that, on these crossings, Harriot took the
first formal observations of the variation of the 'sea compasses' which as-
tounded the natives. It is entirely probable that he also at this time made his
corrections on the parallax in the use of the cross staff,[14] and perhaps even
experimented with his version of the back staff.[15] It is probable, too, that the
'spring clock'—very new at this time—was being used for the computation of
longitude. Inaccuracy of this timepiece may have led Harriot to be critical of
other navigational mathematicians who attempted longitude determination
by this means.[16]

At the close of the *Briefe and True Report*, Harriot indicated that he planned
a more detailed publication 'in a discourse by itself in maner of a Chronicle'
which he had already completed. This volume was designed to go into detail
on 'the nature and manners of the inhabitants of *Virginia*: The number with
the particularities of the voyages thither made; and of the actions of such that
haue bene by Sir Water [*sic*] Raleigh therein and there imployed . . .' Many
searches have been made for this invaluable Chronicle, but no trace has ever
been found, nor is it likely to be found at this late date. Why it was never
published in an age avidly seeking news of the new world cannot be determined. Probably it was because Ralegh's interests (and consequently Harriot's)
were shifting to other romantic and hopefully profitable ventures.

During the year that Harriot was carrying out his scientific, navigational,
and observational duties in the new world, Ralegh was turning elsewhere to
fill his dreams of empire. Having received his patent for the exploration of
America, he returned to Ireland—another land of savages in the eyes of the
English—where he had earned his reputation as a ruthless warrior in the late
70's and early 80's. During the winter of 1585–86, Ralegh and Grenville considered the possibility of colonizing Munster, where the Catholic uprising had
been brutally suppressed and the land desolated between 1579 and 1583.
Using his new found power in court to back his desires, Ralegh emerged with
an illegally large grant of three and a half seignories, approximating 40,000
acres, in the vicinity of the counties of Waterford and Cork, extending along
the Blackwater River from Lismore Castle to the estuary at Youghal.[17] In
June of 1586, while the Roanoke colonists were anxiously awaiting the relief
ships from England, Ralegh was already listed as being settled in Youghal[18]
where tradition has it that he lived in the house called Myrtle Grove and was

elected mayor of the town.[19] During the fall and winter of 1586–87, an official survey of the property was undertaken, a slow and arduous task as described by the surveyors:

... which hath been exceeding difficult and painful, by reason that the land having been long waste are generally overgrown with deep grass, and in most places with heath, brambles, and furze, whereby and by the extremity of rain and foul weather, that hitherto we have found, we have been greatly hindred in our proceeding.[20]

Whether Harriot returned from Virginia to join Ralegh in Youghal immediately cannot be determined. It is probable, however, that he spent much time in London where excitement about the new world and the possibility of a Spanish invasion of England were intermingled. There are among Harriot's papers in the British Museum a large number of notes and jottings which appear to be notes for lecturing to novice seamen.[21] These have frequently been assumed to be preparation for the Spanish invasion, but they may easily have been part of the preparation for the Virginia voyages of 1584, 1585, or 1587. There is no doubt, however, that Harriot did become one of Ralegh's Irish colonists, since the census taken on 12 May 1589, 'A note or abstract of all such freeholders, fee farmers, lessees for years, copyholders, and cottagers, as are inhabiting upon the lands and possessions of Sir Walter Raleigh, Knight' lists 'Upon the Abbeyhouse of Mollanna, Thomas Harriott, gent. and his family.'[22] The census phrase, 'and his family', is intriguing. No evidence exists that Harriot ever married, and his will lists only one relative—a cousin who lived in Newbury and who could not have been in Ireland. Probably the phrase merely indicates a household with servants adequate to run an establishment as large as the Abbey, since no other property holders are listed for these estates. Possibly the family may have been fictitious, since Ralegh was attempting to show vast colonial efforts in peopling his estates, and may have padded the figures.

The Abbey of Molana, latterly an Augustinian priory, was founded in 501 by St. Mael-Anfaidh (or Saint Molanfide, hence the name Molana) on the island of Dair-Inis in the Blackwater River, about two and a half miles north of Youghal.[23] The abbey was in constant use from the date of its founding until its final dissolution, as a follow-up of the reformation movement which was later in Ireland than in England. Originally allocated to the Bishopric of Lismore, it was on February 3, 1585/6, by a warrant of privy seal, granted to Sir Walter Ralegh, who thus became the first lay owner of the property. It is probable that he in turn assigned it to Thomas Harriot as partial payment for his services in Virginia. A petition to King James in 1604 from William Floyer, Gent.,[24] indicates that Harriot held title to Molana until about 1597, at which time he sold the property to 'your Majesties orator for 200ˡⁱ'. The petition alleges that Harriot entered and seized the property, though there is no indication how long he occupied it.

The ruined remains of the Abbey, now connected to the main shore of the Blackwater by a causeway, lie in full view of Ballynatray House, former home of the Holroyd-Smyths. The ruins are extensive, and well-enough preserved that it is possible to determine the organization of the establishment.[25] Beside the church, of considerable interest as an original Irish choirless church, the sacristy, chapter rooms, refectory, kitchens, and gate house show potential for having housed at least a dozen of Ralegh's colonists. It is difficult to see, however, how they could have supported themselves on the island alone. Though active fish weirs from times before Harriot's day still exist and catch fish, the island itself is small, overgrown with oak trees, and to this day reflects the undergrowth and lack of fertility deplored by the original surveyors. What Harriot did in Youghal, therefore, remains a matter for conjecture. There remains no evidence that he propagated trees or plants brought from Virginia. The location is probably too far from Youghal for him to have served in Ralegh's affairs, as might be anticipated, and the name of Ralegh's deputy for these years is known. Perhaps a more complete search of the town records might reveal additional evidence, but at the moment we can only be sure that Harriot did serve a term as colonist here following his return from Virginia. We know also that Lane returned to Ireland to reassume his military duties in 1592, and that John White returned as a planter in Munster in 1593,[26] but it is highly unlikely that Harriot remained in Youghal this long.

Like many of Ralegh's promising ventures, the Irish colonial project ended in tragedy and loss. Following the violent uprisings of the Irish in October, 1598, which at Kilcolman caused the tragedy and ultimate death of Ralegh's friend Edmund Spenser, 'all the English of the seignory of Sir Walter Ralegh ... ran away'.[27] In December, 1602, Ralegh sold all his Irish property 'at a ridiculously low figure' to Richard Boyle, later known as the 'Great Earl of Cork'[28] and father of the famous chemist. Title was granted in full at Ralegh's attainder.[29] But by this time, Ralegh's colonial ambitions were but a futile memory.

During the late years of the 1580's, Ralegh (and consequently Harriot) developed his closest personal friendship with Henry Percy, Ninth Earl of Northumberland. Northumberland, though always suspect for his religious views, had practically abandoned his northern estates in the 1570's to reside in Petworth and in Syon House, in Isleworth, near London near to the Queen and the court.[30] Having traveled extensively on the continent in his youth, Northumberland was known as a free thinking, scientifically oriented, contemplative scholar. He had been a great contributor to the development of the sea power in preparation for the Armada.[31] Among his household accounts still extant at Alnwick Castle are many records of his growing friendship with Ralegh:

Jan. 27, 1587: 'To Sir Walter Rawley his man that brought your L^P a sherte of maile . . . 20s.[32]

'To the man that brought S*ir* Walter Rawley's Pich^r (picture or pitcher?) ... 20s[33]

Mar. 14, 1587: 'To S*ir* Walter Raley's Surgion for letting his L^P bloud the 14th of Marche 1586 ... To S*ir* Walter Rawley a stroe (straw) coloured veluet saddle 4^l 3^s . . . to S*ir* Walter Rawleys man that brought his L^P a bed of Cedar or Cypress 10^s [34]

'to S*ir* Walter Rawley in parte of payment of 800^li for a Jewell of Diamonds the 17 of ffebruary 1586 ... 200^li ... to S*ir* Walter Raw- leye in part of payment of 800^li for the pryce of a Jewell 11th of maij 1587 ... 200^li ... [35]

'... lost in play to S*ir* Walter Rawley ... 10^li [36]

'Paid by the same Accomptant as in the pryce of Newyeares gyfts given by his L^P viz to her ma^tie: as in the pryce of an imbrodered Kirtle given to her ma^tie: 18^li ... to m^ris Throckmorton 15 yeardes of velvet 13^li 12^s 6^d [37]

These were probably the years of Ralegh's greatest affluence and influence. He was in favor in court: he was receiving large incomes from his patents and monopolies. But as the Elizabethans loved to point out, this was the pride that preceded the fall.

In the early years of the 1590's, gossip began to swirl around the heads of the Ralegh–Northumberland circle of friends. In November, 1591, the Jesuit Robert Parsons licensed for publication his *Elizabethae, Angliae Reginae ... edictum promulgatis. . . cum responsione* which brought forward the charge that Sir Walter Ralegh was operating a school of atheism in London. This Latin work, published in 1592, was followed by a number of English versions, the most widely circulated bearing the title *An Advertisement written to a Secretarie of my L. Treasurers of Ingland.* This work carried the same charge:

Of Sir Walter Rawleys Schoole of Atheisme by the waye, and of the Coniurer that is M*aster* thereof, and of the diligence vsed to get young gentlemen to this Schoole, where in both Moyses and our Sauior; the olde, and the new Testamente are iested at, and the schollers taught amonge other thinges, to spell God backwarde.[38]

These charges, widely circulated, became part of the rallying cry in the search of atheism which swept England at about this time. They are central to the investigations surrounding the orthodoxy of Kyd and Marlowe, in the late spring of 1593. Richard Cholmeley then testified that 'Marloe tolde him that hee hath read the Atheist lecture to Sr Walter Raleighe & others.'[39] A spy re- ported that Cholmeley was attempting to seduce folk to atheism with such horrible and damnable speeches as that 'Jhesus Christe was a bastarde St Mary a whore & the Angell Gabriell a Bawde to the holy ghoste . . . that Moyses was a Jugler & Aaron a Cosener. . . .' Notes on the margin of this report tie in the Ralegh circle by listing the names of 'hariet' and 'borage'.[40] The testimony of Richard Baines, too, brought the Ralegh group and Harriot in particular into the Marlowe investigation. In May, 1593, testimony of Baines, 'A note containing the opinion of one Christopher Morly concerning his damnable Judgment of Religion, and scorn of Gods word,' contained as its first two items:

> (1) That the Indians and many authors of antiquity have assuredly written of above 16 thousand yeares agone wher Adam is proved to have lived within 6 thowsand yeares.
> (2) He affirmeth that Moyses was but a Iugler, & and that one Heriots being Sir W. Raleighs man can do more then he. . . .[41]

Another reference to the Ralegh group may be read into the thirteenth charge:

That all that love not Tobacco & Boies were fooles.[42]

In the 1590's tobacco was certainly associated with Ralegh and Northumberland.

When these investigations turned to Thomas Kyd, he protested innocence, and brought character witnesses to bear:

For more assurance that I was not of that vile opinion, lett it but please yor L^p to enquire of such as he covers^d wthall, that is (as I am geven to vnderstand) wth Harriot, Warner, Royden, and some stationers in Paules churchyard . . .[43]

The constant references to Harriot would imply that he must have been called to question at this time, but no evidence exists to this effect. There can be no question, however, but that the free thinking and free speech of Ralegh, Northumberland, and Harriot were subjects of considerable speculation in court circles. And it is just at this time that Ralegh fell from the protection of the Queen, from whom all his power derived.

Ralegh had become involved with Elizabeth Throckmorton, one of Elizabeth's ladies in waiting. Her pregnancy was a court scandal. She and Ralegh were secretly married, and Elizabeth was furious. Ralegh was imprisoned, lost his place at court, and began to lose his wealth. Attacks on his religious views and morals became more open.

These rumors culminated in an inquest at Cerne Abbas in Dorset in March, 1594.[44] A special commission was named to look into the 'impious opinions concerning God & Prouidence &c' of 'Sr Walter Rawleigh, Mr Carewe Rawley, & one Heryott of Sr Walter Rawleigh's House. . . .'[45] This was evidently a fishing expedition for evidence of atheism, but the interrogatories appear to present only hearsay evidence. John Jessop, Minister at Gillingham,

. . . hath harde that one Herryot of Sr Walter Rawleigh his howse hath brought the godhedd in question, and the whole course of the scriptures, but of whome he soe harde it he doth not remember. . . .[46]

Nicholas Jefferys, Parson of Wyke Regis,

. . . sayeth he hath harde that one Herriott Attendant ouer Sr Walter Rawleigh hath ben convented before the Lords of the Counsell for denyinge the resurreccon of the bodye.[47]

Thomas Norman, another minister from Melcombe, testified 'that he harde of one Herryott of Sr Walter Rawleigh his house to be suspected of Atheisme'.[48] Apparently no legal or ecclesiastical action followed these investigations, but the publicity and the danger must have had a profound impact on those charged. The danger of retaining documents which might be interpreted as unorthodox was obvious, and it is extremely likely that all concerned saw to it that all letters or documents which might be construed as evidence were destroyed. Future searches of the houses of both Ralegh and Harriot showed almost no letters or papers of a personal nature.[49]

During this time of Ralegh's decline from favour, Harriot began to look to Northumberland as a new patron. New evidence reveals that Harriot was living as a member of Northumberland's household as early as the autumn of 1591.[50] First record of his being granted a regular pension, however, comes at the time of the ninth Earl's gartering on St. George's Day, 1593. On this occasion, for which 'one Peele a poet' was paid sixty pounds by Walter Warner for composing a memorial poem for the occasion, an additional payment 'to Mr Heriot . . . 80*li*'[51] was listed without comment or reason among the Gifts and Rewards. Two years later, Northumberland records show Harriot serving as the Earl's auditor, collecting rents in northern England, and acting as his intermediary in various suits of law.[52]

But during these same years, Harriot was still active in the household of Ralegh. He was assisting in obtaining financing for Ralegh's first Guiana voyage, was obviously responsible for maintaining Ralegh's accounts, and was in personal attendance to Ralegh on the night he prepared to sail.[53]

A will made by Sir Walter Ralegh on 10 July 1597, has been recently found in the Estate Office of Mr. Simon Wingfield-Digby which shows the high esteem in which Ralegh still held Harriot, though by now Harriot was a full pensioner of Northumberland. Besides property grants to his wife, Elizabeth, and his son, Walter, Ralegh made monetary annuity grants: 100 pounds annually to his half brother Adrian Gilbert, 500 pounds annually to wife Elizabeth, another 500 pounds annually to son Walter, and 100 pounds to 'Thomas Harryott of London Gent.' Two additional grants were made to Harriot:[54]

Moreover I geve to the said Thomas Harryott all my bookes & the furniture in his owne Chamber and in my bedchamber in Durham House Togeather with all such blacke suites of apparell as I haue in the same house.

and the very intriguing

. . . I will that my Reputed Daughter begotten on the bodye of Alice Goold now in Ireland shall haue the soome of ffyue hundreth Markes That Thomas Harryott shall haue twoe hundred poundes Allsoe Lawrence Keymishe one hundred poundes.

Overseers of this will were Ralegh's

... trustye & faithfull frindes Arthur Throkemorton of Pawlersburye in the Countye of Northampton knight George Carewe of London knight Alexander Brett of Whitechurche in the Countye of Dorset esquire & Thomas Harryott of London gent.

Harriot's place in the affection of Ralegh appears to be undiminished. Indeed, there is much evidence to show that Harriot continued to be responsible for Ralegh's accounts while he was in the Tower,[55] and he may even have been acting as his accountant and steward to the time of his death.[56] In Northumberland's household, however, Harriot gradually dropped his role of accountant and servitor and became a member of the household, an intellectual companion, and an associate free to follow his interest in mathematics and experimental sciences.[57]

The death of Elizabeth saw Ralegh and Northumberland taking very different tacks in their political negotiations. Northumberland was one of the Lords of the Council who signed in the Palace at Whitehall on 28 March 1603 the document which proclaimed James as King of England.[58] In May, as his Majesty rode into England, Northumberland rode on his right hand, with the Earl of Nottingham on his left.[59] And during the progress which accompanied the new King's tour of his new kingdom, the royal entourage was housed at Syon House on 8 June, at great expense still recorded in the Northumberland household books of the period.[60] Out of this entertainment came the grant of Syon to Northumberland to replace the lease which he had held from Elizabeth.[61] This new ownership gave greater stability to the Syon residence of Harriot, whose domicile adjacent to the main house was known as Mr. Harriot's house for the rest of his life.[62]

Though Ralegh, too, attempted to ingratiate himself early with James, he met with constant rebuffs. James looked on Essex as his partisan, and Ralegh, as a result, was suspect. Again, Ralegh's avowed desire for an increased intensity of the war with Spain turned the peace-minded James against him. It is possible that, in his anger and despair, Ralegh may have engaged in some plotting against the new monarch, but in the complication of conspiracies and of plots and counterplots surrounding these first months of the Stuart reign, Ralegh was questioned at Windsor, subjected to investigation by the Privy Council, and committed to the Tower on 19 July 1603.[63]

Eight days later, a special commission was sent to the Tower to examine the prisoners. Hearing of their presence, and in despair at proving his loyalty to the King and his innocence of plotting against him, Ralegh attempted a clumsy suicide. In his attempt, the knife glanced off a rib, inflicting a great wound, but having no serious effect. Ralegh's secretary, Edward Hancock, who attempted suicide at the same time, was successful, and did kill himself.[64] Among the friends and medical assistants Ralegh called for at this time was Thomas Harriot.

Ralegh's formal trial for treason was held in Winchester on 17 November 1603.[65] This trial was 'conducted with such outrageous unfairness as to shock the opinion of the time'.[66] Clearly, Ralegh's reputation, more than his reputed actions, was on trial. Lord Chief Justice Popham summed up for the final sentence in one account:

To conclude other things there goes of you which are very atheisticall and prophane precepts said to be S^r Wa: Ra: if not yours you shall do well to protest against them. If yours then renounce them and aske God forgivenesse for them as you do hope for another life and lett not Heriott nor any such Doctor persuade you there is no Eternity. . . .[67]

In another official record, Popham was even more vicious:

. . . you haue been taxed by the world wth the defense of moste heathenishe and blasphemous opinions wch I lyst not repeate because Christian eares cannot endure to heare them nor the authers and mayntainers of them suffered to liue in any Christian common wealth. Yow know what men say of *Hereiat* You should doe well before yow goe out of the world to geue satisffaction heerin, and not to die wth those imputations in yow. Lett not any devill persuade yow to thincke ther is no eternytie in hell fire.[68]

From the first, the judgment was never in doubt. It was 'Guilty of high Treason', and the penalty was the traditional one for treason—drawing and quartering. But in Ralegh's case, as in many such cases under James, execution was delayed and Ralegh was committed to the Tower to live at the pleasure of the King. His conviction, however, denied him all rights to hold property or offices, and he was, in the eyes of the law, a dead man from that day forth.

In the Tower, however, discipline was somewhat lax. On 4 December 1603, a secretary to Lord Cecil wrote to Sir Benjamin Titchbourne that the King had received Ralegh's letter requesting 'Heriot's coming about his Accompts' 'which grace his M^{tie} intends to afford him'.[69] Harriot, though now fully pensioned by Northumberland and in residence at Syon House, Isleworth, was still serving Ralegh in his imprisonment.

Some of James' fear and distrust of Ralegh rubbed off on his friends. Northumberland, though still a member of the Council, was not an intimate of the court. The tinge of suspicion of his possible leanings toward Catholicism, his free thought in matters philosophical, his wide-ranging interest in the new science and the occult—all of these made him an object of James' suspicion. The fiasco of the Gunpowder Plot in November, 1605, was the final blow which destroyed Northumberland's political aspirations.

Distressed by the severe laws against Catholicism passed by James' urgings, a group of English Catholics had planned a series of violent uprisings in revolt. The actions were to begin by a most dramatic gesture—the blowing up of the houses of parliament on 5 November 1605, while King James was opening the session. It was hoped thus that the whole English government could be swept away to leave the country wide open for further disruption.

Among the central conspirators was Thomas Percy, a distant cousin of the Ninth Earl, and his agent for his northern estates. Perhaps to warn his cousin that he should miss the opening of parliament, Thomas Percy dined at Syon House on the evening of 4 November. Present at the dinner were Northumberland, Captain Whitlock, Thomas Harriot, and Sir William Lower, member of parliament for Carmarthenshire, Wales. During the dinner, Thomas Percy was called into the courtyard to speak to a messenger from London.[70] The messenger was none other than Guy Fawkes, with whom Thomas Percy returned to London, to the house he had rented adjacent to the houses of parliament and in which the gunpowder had been stored.

The conspiratorial group was too large. Some informer sent a letter to Lord Monteagle, urging him to absent himself from opening day. James got the message, the plot was uncovered, Fawkes was captured, and Thomas Percy, with Catesby and the others, fled. Three days later they were tracked down; Thomas Percy, Catesby, and two others were killed outright.

That Northumberland, Whitlock, Harriot, and Lower were innocent of the plot is without doubt, but the occasion of their dining with Thomas Percy gave the King a pretext to arrest Northumberland and imprison him, near Ralegh, in the Tower. Following a summary trial in the Star Chamber, Northumberland was fined £30,000—the largest fine ever exacted in England—and since he could not immediately pay he was imprisoned for life. On 9 November Ralegh was questioned about his possible implication in the plot. Asked about his conversations with Whitlock, he wrote:

I have not had any other affair with Cap. Whitlock, then familiar & ordinarie discourse . . . I haue sumetime spoked to him to finde the Earle of Northumberland's disposition towards me, from whom I never receiv'd other than a drie & friendless awnswere. . . .[71]

Interrogatories still remain in the Gunpowder Book at the Public Record Office for the testimony of Northumberland,[72] Nathaniel Torporley,[73] and Sir William Lower.[74] Dudley Carleton and Thomas Harriot were also questioned,[75] and it is interesting to note that the questions to be asked of them were written in the hand of James himself. The superstitious James appears to have been more concerned over the possible casting of his horoscope than by political plots against his life. James' questions for Harriot were:

l herriote wolde be asked quhat purpose he hath haerde his lorde use anent my natiuitie or fortune
ll if euer his lorde desyred him to caste it, or tell him my fortune.
lll if euer his lorde seemed to be discontented of the state.
lv if euer he harde him talke, or aske him of my childrens fortunes.
v if euer his lorde desyred to knowe quat should be his own fortune & ende.
vl & if he did caste milorde, & his sonnes natiuities by his owin commande & knowledge.[76]

Harriot's answers to these questions do not survive, but there is evidence that he was imprisoned in the Gatehouse prison, his house at Syon was searched, and he was left to languish in jail. On 16 December 1605, he addressed a letter to 'The Lordes of his Ma^{tyes} most honorable privy councell' which is probably the most personal record of the man which is left.

Right honorable my very good Lordes:

The present misery I feele being truly innocent in hart and thought presseth me to be an humble suter to your lordships for fauorable respect. All that know me can witnes that I was alwayes of honest conversation and life. I was neuer any busy medler in matters of state. I was neuer ambitions for preferments. But contented with a priuate life for the loue of learning that I might study freely. Wherein my labours & endeuours, if I may speak it without praesumption, haue ben paynfull & great. And I hoped & do yet hope by the grace of God & your Lordships fauour that the effectes shall so shew themselues shortly, to the good liking & allowance of the state and common weale. But now this misery of close imprisonment happening vnto me at the time of my sickness, which was more then three weeks old before; being great windenes in my stomack & fumings into my head rising from my spleen, besides other infirmityes, as my Doctor knoweth & some effectes my keeper can witnes. This I say without your honours fauour wilbe my vtter vndoing, not only in respect of great charges, greater then I am able to endure; but also of being in place where I am not likely to recouer health. Therefore the innocency of my hart feeling this misery of close imprisonment with sicknes & many wantes, besides the desire of proceeding in my studyes, maketh me an humble suter to your honours for liberty in what measure your wisedomes shall think fit. So shall I with faythfull acknowledgement spend the rest of my time so, that your honours shall not think any lawfull fauour ill bestowed. And I shall as my bounden duty is continue my dayly prayers to almighty god for the preseruation of his Ma^{ty} and Royall progeny, and for the encrease of all honor and happiness to your honors.

Your honors humble petitioner:
a poore prisoner in the gatehouse

December 16. 1605.   Tho: Harriots[77]

No reply to this touching request remains, but it is likely that Harriot's release came quickly. In early 1606 his notes show that he was back in his laboratory, working on the refraction of light through diverse media.

On 26 July 1608, Sir Francis Bacon was casting around for experimentally inclined persons who might be induced to work on his 'Great Instauration'. Only a handful came to mind, and first among these were the political prisoners in the Tower, Sir Walter Ralegh, the Earl of Northumberland, through whom Bacon felt he might reach their friend, Thomas Harriot. These men, Bacon noted, were 'themselves ... already inclined to experiments'.[78]

What happened in the Tower during the years that Ralegh and Northumberland were resident there has been a matter of romantic speculation since that time. Dr. Alexander Read, who attended Harriot in his last illness, began the story. In his surgical lectures before the Fellows of the Physicians of London in 1634, he spoke of the death of Mr. Harriot.

... whom at one time, together with Mr. *Hughes*, who wrote of the Globes, Mr. *Warner*, and Mr. *Turperley*, the Noble Earle of *Northumberland*, the fauourer of all good learning and Mecaenas of learned men, maintained while he was in the Tower, for their worth and various literature.[79]

John Aubrey picked up the gossip. His manuscript notes carry on the tale:

When (Henry Percy, ninth) earle of Northumberland, and Sir Walter Ralegh were both prisoners in the Tower, they grew acquainted, and Sir Walter Raleigh recommended Mr. Hariot to him, and the earle settled an annuity of two hundred pounds a yeare on him for his life, which he enjoyed, But to (Robert) Hues (who wrote *De Usu Globorum*) and to Mr. Warner he gave an annuity but of sixty pounds per annum. These 3 were usually called *the earle of Northumberland's three Magi*. They had a table at the earles chardge, and the earle himselfe had them to converse with, singly or together.[80]

A marginal note ascribes this story to Dr. John Pell as of 31 March 1680. Anthony à Wood carried Aubrey's story in his *Athenae Oxonienses*:

... So that when the said earl was committed prisoner to the Tower of London in 1606 (sic), to remain there during life, our author, Hues, and Warner, were his constant companions, and were usually called the earl of Northumberland's three *magi*. They had a table at the earl's charge, and the earl himself did constantly converse with them, either singly or all together, as Sir Walter, then in the Tower did.[81]

This tale has become part of the folklore of the time, and has been repeated in almost all accounts of the Tower years.

At the same time, stories have grown about Harriot and Ralegh in the Tower, and of Harriot's association with Ralegh's *History of the World*. The general estimate of Harriot's contribution was expressed by Oldys in his *Life of Ralegh* in 1736:

In all parts of chronology, geography, and other branches of mathematical science, he wanted not the opinions of the learned *Hariot*, and the earl of *Northumberland's* three *Magi*, long his neighbors in the Tower. .... [82]

a statement which has generally been repeated without question by most later commentators.

Though the study of the contemporary evidence—the household accounts of the Northumberlands, the public records, the Harriot manuscripts—has not been completed to date, it would appear that all of these stories are greatly exaggerated. True, Harriot was pensioned by Northumberland, probably from 1593 until his death, at £80 a year until 1614 and at 100 pounds thereafter. Walter Warner was a servant in Northumberland's household for many years, pensioned finally at 40 pounds annually in 1607, and Hues became a pensioner in 1615, at the same 40 pound rate granted Walter Warner. But there is no evidence that the three were ever together in the Tower. Warner and Harriot kept residence at Syon House (there is some evidence that Warner had a room at Petworth as well), commuting to the Tower for special assignments. Hues' name does not appear among any records I have seen except those very few listings already recorded of his pension late in the Tower years.[83] The idea that Harriot, or Warner, could have served as tutor to the children in the Tower cannot be seriously considered when one looks at the very occasional visits recorded for them in London, and the very large number of records of their presence in Syon.

A search of the Harriot papers currently found gives little evidence of large-scale assistance to Ralegh's *History of the World*. Pierre Lefranc has made a fairly thorough investigation of Harriot's papers, and he reports 'The only documents significant in this matter seem to be some pages of notes and calculations relative to certain problems of chronology, and the mention of different works which Ralegh used.'[84] There is no evidence that the new world of science which Harriot was exploring—the nature of space viewed through the first telescopes, the 'Venus horned like the moon' which proved the error of Ptolemaic astronomy, the explanation of refraction in spherical bodies which explained the rainbow for the first time—made any impact on the activities, the writing, or even the reading of the Tower occupants. Nor is there evidence that Harriot was deeply involved in the preparation for Ralegh's second Guiana voyage as he had been in the first.

As I have said, closer analysis of all the evidence needs to be undertaken before a final position on the matter is assumed. But I should be inclined to defend the thesis that these early years of the seventeenth century saw the change in world view which marked the modern age from the past. Ralegh was still the Elizabethan—looking backward into history, romantically dreaming of El Dorado and cities of gold, and planning chivalric deeds. Harriot was seeking truth in the present—looking to the present and the future, observing closely the phenomena of nature and trying with extreme facility to determine nature's mathematical laws. By the time of Ralegh's execution, Harriot and Ralegh were living in totally different philosophical worlds.

Thomas Harriot himself shortly contemplated death. The cancer of the nose which had plagued his last years[85] finally struck him down, perhaps suddenly, as he visited at the home of Thomas Buckner, a mercer dwelling in St. Christopher Parish, London[86]—an old friend who had been with Harriot in the New World in 1585–6.[87] Here, 'being troubled in my bodie wth infirmitie. But of perfect minde & memorie . . .'[88] Harriot left detailed instruction for the disposition of his effects. After making grants of telescopes, maps, and scientific apparatus to his patrons and scientific friends, testimonial grants of money to servants and relatives, arranging for literary executors to review and publish his mathematical and scientific papers, and arranging for the payment of all his debts, Harriot's thoughts turned to the past and to his association with Sir Walter Ralegh. Just before formally closing the will, an additional item was added:

ITEM. whereas I haue diuerse waste papers (of which some are in a Canvas bagge) of my Accompts to Sr Walter Rawley for all wch I haue discharges or acquitances lying in some boxes or other—my desire is that they may bee all burnte. Alsoe there is an other Canvas bagge of papers concerning Irishe Accompts (the persons whom they concerne are dead many yeares since in the raigne of queene Elizabeth) which I desire alsoe maye burnte as likewise many Idle papers and Cancelled deedes wch are good for no use.[89]

The will is dated 'the nine and twentieth daie of June, in the yeare of our Lord God 1621.' Three days later, Harriot died.[90] On 3 July he was buried in the Chancel of St. Christopher-le-Stocks. The church registers, 1558–1653, still preserved in the Guildhall, London, carry the following notation:

Buryalls 1621.

. . . 5. Mr Thomas Hariots Sojorner

at Mr Buckners was bu-   July.

ried in the Quire—   3.

the Chancell   July 3, 1621.   1621[91]

Modern historians may lament the burning of the Ralegh accounts and the Irish papers which could throw new light on a very dark corner of Ralegh and Harriot's association. But like Camelot, the glory was gone, and only the memory was to remain.

NOTES

1. In the list of members at Oriel in 1572, *Registrum Orielense, an Account of the Members of Oriel College, Oxford,* London, Oxford University Press, 1893, I, 42, is listed: (Rawley, W.) 'Son of Walter Raleigh, Esq., and Katharine his wife daughter of Sir Philip Champernowne, of Modbury, Devon, Knight.' Wood, *Athenae,* ed. Bliss, II 235, suggests that Ralegh entered Oriel as a commoner in 1568. There is, however, some evidence that he was in France during these years.

2. See C. S. Emden, *Oriel Papers,* 1948, pp. 18–19.

3. Christopher Hill, *Intellectual Origins of the English Revolution.* Oxford, Clarendon Press, 1965, p. 305.

4. David B. Quinn, *The Roanoke Voyages,* 1584–90, Cambridge, Hakluyt Society, I, 1955, p. 36.

5. E. G. R. Taylor, 'Harriot's Instructions for Raleigh's Voyage to Guiana, 1595.' *Journal of the Institute of Navigation,* V (1952), p. 345.

6. Quinn, *op. cit.,* pp. 37–43.

7. Sig. A iiij^v.

8. Quinn, *op. cit.,* p. 37.

9. *Ibid.,* II, 548. Quinn holds that the work was probably written in May or September 1587, designed as publicity for the 1587 voyage, but was delayed in publication.

10. MS Aubr. 6, fol. 35.

11. Additional MSS 6788, 417^v.

12. 1588 edition, E 4^r.

13. It is so considered in her *The Geometrical Seaman.* Institute of Navigation, 1962, p. 87. This seems to me unlikely, since this would place the date for telescopic compound lens systems nearly a quarter of a century before generally assumed for them. Harriot's observation of the moon with a 6 power glass on 26 July 1609 is, I feel, his first telescopic observation.

14. *Ibid.,* p. 40.

15. A rough illustration of Harriot's back-staff, later perfected by Captain John Davis, is found in the Petworth MSS, *Doctrine of Nauticall Triangles Compendious,* Sheet 21. See Quinn and Shirley, 'A Contemporary List of Hariot References,' *Renaissance Quarterly,*

XXII, 1 (Spring 1969), p. 9–26 for evidence that Harriot gave Davis the idea for developing this instrument.

16. Quinn and Shirley, *op. cit.*, p. 13. Quinn, *Roanoke Voyages,* I, p. 53. Harriot's astronomical observations refer frequently to times recorded by his clock and his watch, and make frequent corrections for their inaccuracies.

17. David B. Quinn, *The Elizabethans and the Irish*, Cornell University Press for the Folger Library, 1966, pp. 112–16.

18. *Calendar of State Papers, Ireland*, 1586–88, CXXIV, Item 80, p. 77.

19. Lord Killanin and N. V. Duignan, *Shell Guide to Ireland*, Second edition, 1967, 'Youghal,' p. 462–65.

20. Account of the Commission, *Calendar of State Papers, Ireland, 1586–88,* CXXVI, Item 52, p. 168.

21. Additional MSS 6788.

22. *Calendar of State Papers,* Ireland, 1588–92, CXLIV, Item 28, pp. 170–71.

23. Rev. Samuel Hayman, *Notes and Records of the Ancient Religious Foundations at Youghal, County Cork, and its Vicinity*, Youghal, MDCCCLV, p. 11.

24. Hatfield House MSS, *196*.131.

25. For a detailed account of the ruins, see Patrick Power, *Waterford and Lismore: a Compendious History of the United Dioceses*, Dublin and Cork, Cork University Press, 1937, p. 214–15. I am personally grateful, too, for Mr. Holroyd-Smyth's kindness in showing me the whole settlement in October, 1968.

26. Quinn, *Elizabethans and the Irish*, pp. 115–16.

27. *Ibid.*, p. 116.

28. Rev. Patrick Power, *A Short History of County Waterford*, The Waterford News, Ltd., 1933, p. 45. *Shell Guide to Ireland*, p. 463.

29. *Calendar of Patent Rolls, Ireland, James I*, XXI, pp. 41–2.

30. M. E. James, *Estate Accounts of the Earls of Northumberland, 1562–1637*, Publications of the Surtees Society, CLXIII, London, Bernard Quaritch, 1955, p. xxii.

31. *Syon House: the Story of a Great House*, Syon House Estate, 1950, p. 13.

32. Alnwick Household Accounts, Andrewe Yong, Pursebearer, 'Rewards.'

33. *Ibid.*, Thomas Wycliffe, Coferer, 'Rewards.'

34. *Ibid.*, Thomas Wycliffe, Coferer, 'Rewards.'

35. *Ibid.*, Thomas Wycliffe, Coferer, 'Payment of Debts.'

36. *Ibid.*, Thomas Wycliffe, Coferer, 'Money to his L\u1d56 hands.'

37. *Ibid.*, Thomas Power, Pursebearer, 'Newyeares gyfts.'

38. *An Advertisement . . . 1592*, 'The Extract and Abbreviation of the Booke of Iohn Philopatris Against her Maiesties Proclamation,' Sig. B 1ᵛ, p. 18. For a detailed account of all these charges, see Pierre Lefranc, *Sir Walter Raleigh, Ecrivain*, Paris, Librairie Armand Colin, 1968, pp. 356–93.

39. Harleian MSS 6848: 190 (old 175). Item # 7.

40. Harleian MSS 6848: 191 (old 176)ᵛ.

41. Harleian MSS 6848: 185ʳ. Items 1 7 2.

42. Ibid., 185ᵛ Item 13.

43. Harleian MSS 6849, 218 .

44. Lefranc, *op. cit.*, p. 379–93, gives a full account of this.

45. Harleian MSS 7042: 206ʳ.

46. Harleian MSS 6849; 184ʳ.

47. *Ibid.*, 185ʳ.

48. Ibid., 186ʳ.

49. Searches made in 1603 and 1605 in connection with treason investigations. Hatfield House MSS: 113:43—Sir Thomas Smith to the Earl of Salisbury. This reads in part as follows: '. . . I haue made as diligent search of Mʳ Herriotts Lodging and studie at Sion as the time would permitt; . . . *Letters* there are few, and almost none at all; and such as are, carrie an olde date; scarcely one written of late . . . '

50. Syon MSS (Alnwick Castle), X. II. 12. 4. 'Brevinge Booke—September xxj, 1591.'

51. Alnwick Household Accounts. Henry Forest . . . foreign payments, 'Among expenses attending the Earl at the Gartering: . . . "Gifts and Rewards." '

52. William Wycliffe . . . Receiver General. 1596–97.

53. J. W. Shirley, 'Sir Walter Raleigh's Guiana Finances,' *Huntington Library Quarterly*, XIII (1949–50), pp. 55–69. See particularly p. 62.

54. For an account of the will in detail, see A. M. C. Latham, 'Sir Walter Ralegh's will', *Review of English Studies*, XXII, 86 (May, 1971), p. 129–136.

55. Hatfield House MSS, XV: 305 (102.48.) 4 December 1603.

56. See account of Harriot's will following.

57. Harriot's manuscripts show experiments which indicate almost total freedom of his time for his intellectual pursuits. For example, his observations of sunspots and the Jovial planets cover hundreds of observations over several years.

58. John Nichols, *The Progresses, Processions, and Magnificent Festivities of King James the First*, London, 1828, I, page 38, note 1.

59. *Ibid.*, pp. 138–9.

60. Alnwick Household Accounts, 1603–4. See the accounts of Giles Greene, Steward; Christopher Ingram, Clerk of Works; Henrye Taylor, Clerk of Kytchen; William Lucas, Apparel; Robert Delavale, Gentleman of the Horse; and Edmunde Metcalfe, Clarke of his Lo: Kytchen.

61. Nichols, *op. cit.*, p. 165, note 3.

62. In 1606–7 Mr. Ingram, Chief of Works at Syon House, lists expenses 'for makinge a brick wall betweene the towre of her la: lodgings and mr. heryotts house'. Again, in the accounts for 1621 after Harriot's death, Mr. Christopher Ingram, in accounts separated from the Alnwick accounts and now at Petworth (MSS # 429) lists among repairs 'Bricklayers, repayring the tiles and slates in sondrie places of the house, new tyling the house where Mr harriot dwelt . . . ' The past tense shows this came after 2 July 1621.

63. *Encyclopaedia Britannica,* eleventh edition, 'Raleigh,' XXII, p. 870.

64. Pierre Lefranc, Manuscript dissertation, *Sir Walter Ralegh, a Biography*, I, 476–7; *Sir Walter Ralegh, Ecrivan*, p. 669.

65. Harleian MSS 39, 265–312. This almost verbatim report of Ralegh's trial must have been written after 1621, since it is written in the blank spaces of later documents. It is, however, the most complete account, and the one usually cited.

66. *Encyclopaedia Britannica, loc. cit.*

67. Harleian MSS 39, 312^r.

68. Public Record Office: State Papers 14/4/83.

69. Hatfield House MSS: XV:305 (*102*.48.)

70. Testimony of Sir William Lower; PRO Gunpowder Book, SP 14/216 (137).

71. Additional MSS 6178: 22^r (old 469^r).

72. First Interrogatory—13 November—SP 14/216: 112–13; Second Interrogatory—30 November—SP 14/216: 125.

73. 27 November—SP 14/216: 122.

74. 2 December—SP 14/216: 137.

75. Hatfield House MSS: XVII: 530 (*134*.86.).

76. *Ibid.*

77. Hatfield House MSS: XVII:554 (*114*.41.).

78. Spedding, Ellis, and Heath, *The Works of Francis Bacon*, 1868, XI, p. 63.

79. Alexander Read, *The Chirurgicall Lectures of Tumors and Vlcers*, London, 1635, p. 307.

80. Andrew Clark, ed., *Brief Lives*, Oxford, Clarendon Press, 1898, pp. 258–6.

81. Anthony à Wood, *Athenae Oxonienses*, 1815, II, p. 300.

82. Oldys, 'Life of Ralegh', prefixed to the Eleventh edition of *The History of the World*, London, 1736, p. clxxxiv.

83. Details of these records are to be found in my 'Scientific Experiments of Sir Walter Ralegh, the Wizard Earl, and the *Three Magi* in the Tower; 1603–17,' *Ambix.*, IV (1949), 52-66.

84. *Sir Walter Ralegh, Ecrivain*, p. 266. Translation mine.

85. In addition to the account given by Dr. Alexander Read, some letters of Harriot remain to and from his doctors concerning his illness. See, for example, Additional MSS 6789, 446^v, dating from 1616.

86. Harriot was still maintaining residence at Syon House, and obviously hoped to repair

there before death. His will gives double instructions for his burial; one set if he dies in London; a second if he dies in Isleworth. It is probable that his fatal illness struck him during one of his visits to the Tower.

87. The list of names of the colonists who spent the winter in America, given by Richard Hakluyt in his *Principall Navigations*, 1589, lists 'Thomas Bookener' who is obviously this same man. This list is reproduced in Quinn's *Roanoke Voyages*, 1584–90, I, pp. 194–7.

88. Harriot's will, in many ways a most revealing document, has been printed several times since it was discovered in 1885 by Henry Stevens. It was first printed in *Thomas Hariot and his Associates*, London 1900, in an appendix. For the most complete study of the will, see Dr. R. C. H. Tanner, 'The Study of Thomas Harriot's Manuscripts, I. Harriot's Will,' *History of Science*, VI, 1967, pp. 1–16, where it is again printed in full.

89. From the certified copy of the Archdeaconry Court of London, now housed in the Guildhall Library in London.

90. Testimony for this date is the epitaph from St. Christopher's Church cited in John Stow's *Survey of London*, Second Edition, 1633. The Church and the memorial were completely destroyed in the Great Fire of 1666. The memorial was replaced in the Bank of England, site of the former church, on the 350th anniversary of Harriot's death, as a result of the activities of the Editorial Board.

91. Guildhall MSS 4421/1.

3

THOMAS HARRIOT AND THE NEW WORLD

DAVID BEERS QUINN

University of Liverpool

THOMAS HARRIOT lived from 1560 to 1621: during at least half that period the New World, the Americas, north and south, the tropical river valleys of Amazon and Orinoco, the sounds and islands and rivers of the first Virginia (which comprised those parts of North Carolina and Virginia which lay between the Neuse River and the James River), fur- and fish-rich Canada, the northern passages to the west of Greenland, the routes across the Atlantic to America north and south, were in his mind. His active concerns with the Americas can be traced from 1584 to 1613 and his interest almost certainly extended some way on either side of these dates. Between 1584 and 1590 he was himself involved in American activities, including temporary residence in North America, not merely as an adviser but as a participant. Otherwise he stayed in the background, giving technical advice and assistance in the solution of problems which lay ahead of the actual participants, or making some response to the discoveries, or problems connected with the discoveries, of others. Some of his activities we can follow in detail; others can only be glimpsed; in still other cases we are forced to speculate on what precise part he played and trust that time, study, and possibly the discovery of new materials may allow such speculations to be confirmed or fruitfully altered so that gradually a full and balanced picture of his place in New World exploration and its popularization can be more fully and accurately assessed.

When Harriot graduated at Oxford in 1580 he was equipped with a rather stereotyped scientific knowledge in mathematics and astronomy. How far he had begun to specialize in mathematics and its applications we are wholly unable to say, except to indicate that his basic intellectual equipment was mathematical though he had a scholar's interest and capacity in a wide range of other areas of knowledge. From St Mary's Hall he presumably took himself to London; it is not unlikely that he entered the household of some gentleman or merchant who had need of a tutor for his children. One might speculate on the possibility that wherever he settled it was in the company of men who were interested not in theory but in practice, in the problems of applying mathematics to such questions as navigation at sea, in the expansion of trade, and in the extension of knowledge about the world outside Europe. Such matters were being discussed in London in the years 1580 to 1583 and at the end of them Harriot emerges as a man who is vitally concerned with them. Drake's return in 1580 had revealed to many that the world could be encompassed by Englishmen and not by Portuguese and Spaniards alone. Interest in instrumental navigation among merchants, gentlemen, and scholars was beginning to produce English books on the subject.

In 1582 the younger Richard Hakluyt was urging the establishment of a lectureship in London where those interested could be trained: Drake at one point offered to endow it. Later it was financed by the elder Thomas Smith, customer of London, and his son Thomas, who was to head so many companies concerned with the overseas world. English sailing-masters were efficient in the use of older rule-of-thumb methods of navigation, but these were not enough for exploration of new and extensive oceans and coastlines. Nor was it sufficient any longer for a gentleman to be a competent commander of men at sea: he needed himself to know enough of the theory of navigation to understand what the specialist seamen were doing, to conduct effective discussions with them when he wished his view of what should be done to be effective; to be able to plan ahead flexibly where ships could safely, or possibly with safety, go. Drake had shown how vitally important such training and capacity was to a wide ranging expedition. A young man-about-town, a close friend of the younger Thomas Smith, Maurice Browne, who had spent a few months at sea at the Azores, came back to London to study maps and navigation. 'I will apply my tyme', he wrote on 6 July 1582,[1] 'to the studdy of Cosmography, and the art of Navigatione'. He was planning to do so with his friend John Thynne: 'we will device to have somme convenient tyme . . . to have an excellent fellowe who dwelleth here at London to read Cosmography and to instruct us and to make us learned in the art of Navigation, that with the more easines we may come to the full knowlege thereof by experience'. We have no evidence that the 'excellent fellowe' mentioned by Browne was Thomas Harriot but it could well have been.

Maurice Browne was to seek his experience at sea in command of one of the ships of Sir Humphrey Gilbert's American expedition of 1583 and, ironically, was to die of the results of defective seamanship when the *Delight* went down at Sable Island later that year. But he was not the only one of his kind who felt the need to learn what should be done at sea.

Walter Ralegh had taken part as captain of the *Falcon* in Gilbert's earlier voyage in 1578–9 and had drifted rather aimlessly in the Atlantic to the Canaries and farther south, instead of sailing on to America. It may have been then that he learned to regret that he did not know enough to direct his Portuguese pilot, Simon Fernandes, to set an effective trans-Atlantic course. Ralegh too was involved in 1583 in Gilbert's final venture. About the beginning of May 1583 Maurice Browne reported that Ralegh had bought a new ship from Henry Oughtred at Southampton and had equipped it for sixty men, and that it was to be the flagship of the expedition.[2] When Ralegh bought and renamed his ship the *Bark Ralegh* he may have thought of going in her himself; he may even have begun to think of equipping himself with sufficient navigational knowledge to command her effectively. But he had now climbed into the inner circle of courtiers; it would be risking his future if he asked to leave too soon on a dangerous voyage, and in any case the Queen would not allow him to go. *Bark Ralegh* sailed with the fleet on 13 June without him, but two days later her captain turned back and she returned to Plymouth, the men forcing her captain, Michael Butler, an old companion in arms of Ralegh, to do so because they were afraid to take the risk of crossing the ocean in a ship in whose equipment they did not have confidence. By the end of September one ship alone had come back from American waters to report the loss of the *Delight* and probably of the *Swallow* with Gilbert on board as well.[3] But Ralegh had his ship; if he was to use her, he must, he felt, learn how to do so.

This is where Harriot came in; he was certainly the 'excellent fellowe' Ralegh employed to teach him cosmography and navigation as he had perhaps taught Maurice Browne before. Whether Ralegh was installed by the Queen in spacious apartments in Durham House in the Strand before the end of the year is not clear. But it was then that the idea took hold of Ralegh that he should take on Gilbert's task of exploring and exploiting, if he could, eastern North America; though he convinced himself he must train not only himself but also his probable associates and such sailing masters as were still flexible enough in mind to learn the new language of the sea. Over the winter of 1583-4, probably latterly at Durham House, Harriot held his classes for Ralegh and for his friends and dependents, to instruct them how to follow a course by the use of instruments and charts, and also how to make charts themselves at sea. His textbook, the *Arcticon*, we know by name but it has not survived.[4] Authority for the transfer of Gilbert's rights of exploration and settlement to Ralegh was given on 16 March, but already his preparations for a reconnaissance were well advanced and his two ships, under the command of Philip Amadas and Arthur Barlowe, put to sea on 27 April. Besides the captains, we are given in Barlowe's account of the voyage the names of eight other members, but John White the artist, when he claimed that his 1590 voyage was his fifth to Virginia,[5] was clearly informing us that he too had been on the 1584 voyage. We might well ask, since White and Harriot were to be close partners in the newly named Virginia in the next year, whether they did not serve an apprenticeship together on the 1584 voyage; in other words whether Harriot's practical experience of America did not begin in 1584 rather than in 1585.

This is not a matter on which we have any direct evidence, but there are some indications in the surviving materials which make it not improbable, though it must be stressed that his presence on the first Virginia voyage of 1584 is a conjecture rather than an established fact. It is at least probable that Arthur Barlowe and Philip Amadas (or one of them) had been Harriot's pupils before he set sail; Amadas was to sail again in 1585 as 'admiral of Virginia' and was something of an authority on maritime affairs. Hitherto it has been supposed that Harriot became involved with North America directly only after the return of the ships to England in September; that it was then he learnt to understand something of what the two Indians brought home had to say and was able to teach them some English. The narrative of Arthur Barlowe, as we have it in the form in which it was first published in 1589,[6] was almost certainly prepared for circulation as promotional material for the 1585 venture as early as November or the beginning of December 1584. It contains geographical information which would seem to have required some linguistic bridge to be established before it could become intelligible. Since the Indians brought back were reported on 18 October to be still unable to make themselves understood in English, but were referred to in mid-December as sources of information on the new land discovered by Amadas and Barlowe, it is clear that remarkable advances in contact with them were made during a very short period, so short as to raise serious doubts on whether it was possible in the time available. Nonetheless it was Harriot who was credited with making the bridge; it was he who by July 1585 had a working knowledge of Carolina Algonquian; and who was sent out then to take special note of everything concerning the Indians which was relevant to the English plans for settlement. It might seem much more possible for Harriot to have done what he did if he had indeed been able to go on the 1584 reconnaissance. This would have given him some practical knowledge of the problems of navigation on which he had been theorizing for some time; it would have given him six weeks of fairly intensive contact with the Indians in which to get some inkling of their language and of the topography of their tribal arrangements; he would, too, have had some weeks on the ship going back to England to begin the communication of English to the two Indians, Manteo and Wanchese, who were being taken with the ship; there would then be a good possibility that, with his rapid capacity for learning new techniques, he had himself established some command over the language by the time of their return in the middle of September 1584. Even if the Indians were not able to make themselves understood by the middle of October, their English was probably sufficient, and Harriot's Algonquian adequate, for a good deal of information to be incorporated rapidly in the version of Barlowe's narrative which, it is suggested, was circulated, and for the statement in the bill put before the House of Commons on 14 December to confirm Ralegh's American rights to be justified on the basis that by 'some of the people borne in those parties brought home into this our Realme of England . . . singuler great comodities of that Lande are revealed & made knowen vnto vs'.[7] Thus, though there is no direct evidence that Harriot was in Virginia in 1584, if we accept him as the main (or sole) linguistic link between the Algonquian-speaking Indians brought to England and the English public, his employment on the 1584 voyage would appear to be a necessary concomitant.

The role which Harriot was designed to play, alongside John White, in the 1585 colonizing voyage also becomes more intelligible if we concede that their partnership was not new, and that each had had an opportunity in 1584 to make sufficient contact with the land, the products, and the people of the Carolina Outer Banks in 1584 to have some influence on the shaping of the tasks that were set them in 1585 so as to make them manageable in scope. We need not assume that White was and remained wholly ignorant of Algonquian (his naming of many of his drawings with the appropriate Indian words show he was not), but it is clear that Harriot was the main instrument in bridging the linguistic gap between the Amerindian language and English. Harriot was well enough informed as to be able to discuss the indigenous religion with the priests, to note the occurrence of dialectal differences from place to place and to admit that he and his associates lacked 'perfect vtterance in their language' (which did not exclude on his part fluency and academic understanding).[8] He developed a system of orthography for the recording of the sound values which could not be expressed by letters of the English alphabet,[9] and he knew some phrases of the language in 1602 (and possibly taught something of it to even later voyagers).[10]

On the 1585 voyage Harriot, especially if he had already been out in 1584, would be able to test the problems of relating celestial observations at sea to the rather crude dead reckoning which was all that was normally available for recording the route and longitudinal distance run, and of estimating the effects of winds and currents on the course. Whether in fact he developed any instrumental novelties in the course of his voyages we cannot tell, though he was very much interested in practical applications and made some later on.[11] No doubt he tried to reckon longitude with the aid of the eclipse of the sun on 19 April 1585 on the outward voyage though it is doubtful whether he saw very much of it and its partial nature in any event would have rendered it of little value for this purpose.[12] Once the ships arrived at the site of the colony Harriot and White had to begin their survey. They had the seemingly impossible task of mapping as much as they could of the land they explored. One small surviving sketch shows how rough the first attempts were,[13] even though such sketches were much better than nothing. But a good deal of work was done with the plane table and other surveying instruments so that accurate directions were established and maintained. This work was probably begun on 11 July, when the two men formed part of the boat expedition across Pamlico Sound from Wococon to the Pamlico River and other swamp-enclosed inlets which marked the mainland shores.

Since we have no examples of their journals or notebooks we cannot tell

precisely how they carried out their tasks from day to day. It would seem from
the map which emerged at the end of the year-long survey that they worked up
and down the Carolina Outer Banks by boat, and checked the whole of the
coastline from Wococon (approximately the modern island of Ocracoke)
north to Cape Henry and westwards up the Roanoke and Chowan Rivers,
into the numerous bays and river channels of the north shore of Albemarle
Sound, and, farther north in Virginia proper, examined the southern shore of
Chesapeake Bay as far as the site of modern Portsmouth and perhaps made an
excursion across the James to Kecoughtan.[14] We would conclude therefore,
that Harriot accompanied Lane up the Chowan and Roanoke Rivers and that
he and White made a number of smaller and more localized excursions to the
sites of the numerous villages included on their map. It would also follow that
both were members of the party which spent some time during the winter of
1585–6 in the vicinity of modern Norfolk and at no great distance from Chesapeake Bay.[15] Harriot would thus make contact with Chesapeake and possibly
Powhatan Indians in the north, and with Chawanoac, Moratuc, Weapemeoc,
Roanoke, Croatoan, Secotan, Neuse, and possibly other Algonquian-speaking
peoples further south. It is thus possible to see that he would have had ample
evidence of such variations as dialectal differences and also of culture traits
of other sorts.

It is evident that the surviving drawings of Indians by John White belong
largely to the Secotan, Pomeioc, and Roanoke village complexes.[16] It is
probable, indeed almost certain, that he made drawings of much more distant
groups. Indeed it is not at all unlikely that the original notebooks which White
and Harriot made between them consisted of detailed descriptions of each
Indian village which was examined, with notes of unusual customs and details
of ceremonial objects and of cultivation variations, amongst other things, and
that the notes were united each day with the sketches which White drew.[17] If
this was so it is clear that the failure of these records to survive has robbed us
of a unique ethnographic record which, had it been fully published, would
have set an entirely new standard in the description of a non-European
people.

As it is we have a summary only of Harriot's general report, one prepared
for popular consumption, a selection of the drawings which White worked up
for preservation and later copying on his return to England, and a series of
rather limited notes by Harriot on the small selection of the John White
Indian drawings chosen for engraving.[18] We have something from Harriot on
plants, those of medicinal value and those cultivated by the Indians, but very
little either from him or from White on the wild flora.[19] We have rather more
from both Harriot and White on the animals, fish, and birds found on their
travels (not all on the mainland but some from the Caribbean and from the
sea voyage as well);[20] we have some rather generalized matter on climate,
vegetation, soil, mineral resources, and such like from Harriot.[21] Here, in

addition to notes and drawings, specimens were no doubt collected, though whether these were confined to mineral specimens or included dried plants and skins as well cannot be specifically established. Some botanical specimens and seeds were, we know, brought home, and it is probable that Harriot was responsible for many of them.[22] It might seem also that by continued activity Harriot and White had carried through the greater part of their task (so far as it could be done by sampling a territory of some 5000 square miles) by the time Drake arrived off the Carolina Outer Banks in June 1586. When it was finally decided to take them off, much of their work was ruined. According to Lane,[23] in their haste to get the settlers off Roanoke Island, 'all our Cardes (i.e. maps), Bookes and writings, were by the Saylors cast ouer boord'. This is clearly an exaggeration. Harriot certainly saved some of his notes, possibly the major part of them, and White many, if by no means all, of his drawings, but the effect was to leave them only with a sample of a sample, together with what they could piece together from memory. It was this which led Harriot to stress that further inquiry would be necessary before a complete picture of the natural resources of the area could be published. Writing about the fauna of the area, he said 'after wee are better furnished and stored vpon further discouery, with their strange beastes, fishe, trees, plants and hearbes they shalbe also published'.[24] It is highly probable that while the primary purpose of the survey was to inform Ralegh and his associates of the major features of Virginia as a basis for colonial development there, from an early stage in the process of their survey, Harriot and White had in mind the preparation from their collections of a systematic illustrated survey, covering both natural resources and ethnography. With its illustrations and maps this would make a full picture of part of America available on a scale and with a thoroughness not hitherto attempted in print. (It will be remembered that Oviedo's full text did not appear until 1851 and that the records of the Francisco Hernandes survey of Mexico in the decade before the Roanoke voyages were never published directly from the drawings and texts at all.)[25]

In July 1586, when he landed at Plymouth, Harriot's active association with the New World ended so far as his participation in its exploration and direct study was concerned—indeed he is never known again to have left England for parts more distant than Ireland and may rarely for many years have stirred from London and its near surroundings. He had had enough of voyaging and of distant lands. But he was to sit down over the next few years after 1586 to extract all that he could out of his own knowledge and that of others so that as much as possible could be salvaged from the survey and from the other knowledge obtained by participants in the 1584 and later voyages, so that alongside the descriptive record a detailed dossier on which a narrative could be based could at last be assembled. His and Ralegh's reasoning was to the effect that the discovery and settlement of Virginia was an enterprise which would make the fame both of England and of its promoter Sir Walter Ralegh, so that any and every record must be kept of its progress as well as the descriptive and scientific data which had emerged, with whatever gaps and deficiencies, from the Harriot–White survey.

We can see Harriot in action later in 1586. Alongside the Reverend Richard Hakluyt, home from Paris and his embassy chaplaincy there for a time, he interrogated Nicholas Bourgoignon, a Frenchman liberated at San Agustín by Drake and brought eventually to England along with the Roanoke colonists. The surviving version of the interrogation is concerned largely with what the Spaniards had discovered about the interior of what is now South Carolina through their occupation for some years after 1566 of the fort and colony of Santa Elena on Port Royal Sound. This was published by Hakluyt in 1600.[26] But Hakluyt was able to publish as early as 1589 the Barlowe report to which reference has already been made, a narrative of the 1585 Virginia voyage and a report by Ralph Lane on the colony of 1585–6,[27] all of which appear, with a high degree of probability, to have derived from the archive which Harriot was assembling on the enterprises, and which he passed on to Hakluyt, with, no doubt, the active approval of Ralegh. (Hakluyt did not get a narrative of the 1586 venture and it is probable that he derived the narratives of the expeditions of 1587 and 1588, as he did that of the last in 1590, directly from John White.) For some months after his return we can imagine Harriot busily interviewing those who had been on each of the preceding enterprises, obtaining their unvarnished narratives and their opinions on the ventures, and storing them away towards the major chronicle which he was engaged in compiling as his material reached some degree of finality. In my opinion Harriot was able during the first eight months after his return from Virginia not only to collect but to write up in draft his material on the history of the enterprises of 1584 to 1586. When he said at the end of his *A briefe and true report of the new found land of Virginia*, published in 1588, 'I haue ready in a discourse by it self in maner of a Chronicle according to the course of times and when time shall bee thought conuenient shall be also published' he was writing I believe, not of February 1588 (new style) but of February 1587.[28]

We must, I think, place the writing of *A briefe and true report* not in 1587–8 but in 1586–7. The pamphlet speaks of Ralegh's work in sponsoring voyages of discovery, settlement and supply in 1584, 1585, 1586 'and now of late this last yeere of 1587'[29] and I would suggest that the last phrase is wholly an addition made near the time the finished work was sent for publication in 'February. 1588' (as the text concludes). It goes on to report that of the voyages already made, the 1584 expedition stayed only six weeks and that the main discoveries were made in the 1585–6 colony when the colonists stayed 'a whole yeare'. He says 'the others after were onlie for supply and transportation, nothing more being discouered then had been before'. It seems most unlikely that had he been writing the pamphlet in 1588 he would have expressed himself thus and ignored altogether the colony which had gone out with John

White in May 1587 and from which John White had returned in search of additional supplies in November 1587.[30]

I would suggest that the tract was prepared originally to support the following up of the 1585–6 colony by a new venture in 1587 and that it was intended to be published about January or February 1587, but that for some reason this was not done. It may be remembered that on 7 January 1587, Ralegh handed over the settlement of the City of Ralegh in Virginia to a corporate body, headed by John White, to found the colony, some of whose members were to go and others to remain in England.[31] The city was to be established on the southern shores of Chesapeake Bay and the grant did not comprise more than a small section of the territory included within the terms of Ralegh's grant of 1584. We do not know to what extent Ralegh himself contributed to the financing of this corporate enterprise, or indeed whether he did so at all at this stage. But it must be realized that the promotion of this colony was from January onwards in the hands of the company and not of Ralegh himself. Clearly Harriot wrote his tract for 'the Aduenturers [that is investors in], Fauourers, and Welwillers of the enterprise for the inhabiting and planting in Virginia.'[32] as he said in the opening paragraph in the published version. It was designed to counteract the unfavourable reports circulated by some members of the first colony who returned in 1586 and to present a conspectus of the natural resources of the country, so that intending settlers would gain some insight into local conditions there and receive some guidance while preparing to invest or settle in America. He also wished it to be regarded as an advertisement for the illustrated survey he and White planned to produce. For some reason it would appear that this tract did not commend itself to the promoters of the venture, and its publication in 1587 was not carried out. It may be that White and his associates thought the picture painted by Harriot was not sufficiently glowing, but it is more likely that it was ready rather too late to do any good. If it was completed late in February 1587 it would not be available until well into March and by that time, it is not unlikely, White hoped to be at sea with a body of at least 150 settlers bound for the foundation of the City of Ralegh: that they did not leave in the end until May was probably fortuitous.[33]

By the beginning of 1588 the situation had changed once more. White had come back in November 1587, urgently demanding assistance from Ralegh (and anyone else with whom he could make contact) for the colony.[34] Ralegh undertook to despatch a pinnace, but if it was prepared in the month or six weeks after 20 November it did not sail, probably because weather conditions made it impossible for its men to put to sea. Ralegh, however, decided to make a further great effort to revive the whole Virginia venture, as well as to relieve the City of Ralegh colonists, and to get a formidable squadron to sea as early as possible in 1588. The embargo on overseas voyages imposed by the privy council on 9 October 1587 meant that special permission would be needed for such an expedition, but it would seem that Ralegh, and Sir Richard Grenville who had undertaken to lead the expedition for him, had reason to believe that they would get an exemption for their squadron, as it could be argued that the establishment of a firmly-based American colony would be a valuable gambit in the war with Spain. The seven or eight vessels preparing at Bideford may have been held up by uncertainties about this during February 1588, but it was expected to get them to sea in late March or early April.[35] It was in these circumstances that Harriot's pamphlet, held over, it is believed, in 1587, was hurriedly put into print with no further changes than redating it to February 1588 and a few verbal alterations, and appeared towards the end of the month or at the beginning of March. Its purpose at this point would be somewhat different from that which had previously been intended. Its principal object would now be to establish the fact that Sir Walter Ralegh was still vitally concerned with the Virginia ventures. The title-page stressed that it was Ralegh who had sent out the 1585 colony and that the author, Thomas Harriot, was 'seruant to the abouenamed Sir Walter', while the association was reinforced by printing on the back of the title-page Ralegh's armorial achievement.[36] Harriot's stress on the advantages of Virginia still carried weight but, it is suggested, it was Ralegh's revived interest or, we should probably say, continued interest which it might now seem most important to stress. The publication may indeed have been part of the campaign, now seen to be necessary, to convince members of the court and of the privy council that the Virginia enterprise was an important objective of state policy and worthy of exemption from the embargo. Yet the attempt to get a licence failed in the end: Grenville was forbidden on 31 March to engage in the voyage and on 9 April was told to bring his ships to join Drake at Plymouth: he was allowed only to detach two small pinnaces to carry White and some stores to Virginia, though they were later forced to put back to England, badly damaged by pirates, and so were unable to carry out their task.[37]

The countermanding of the 1588 expedition altered again the perspective inside which Harriot worked. It would seem probable that his tract attracted a good deal of favourable attention on its publication, because it subsequently proved so popular. It was important because it was the first broad assessment of the potential resources of North America as seen by an educated Englishman who had been there. Its constant use as a standard of reference for so many years indicates how substantial a gap it filled. At the same time it can scarcely have seemed to Harriot himself much more than a stop-gap. In 1586-7 it is highly probable that he was working out with John White some plan for the publication of at least a part of the graphic materials collected in Virginia, and it seems likely that before White set out in 1587 he had completed a number of finished drawings from his earlier sketches, possibly including the greater part of the fine set which survives in the British Museum, while Harriot was involved in putting his notes in order to provide a text—a learned

Latin text no doubt—with which they could be engraved and published. Ralegh was in close touch at this time with another American reporter and artist in the person of Jacques Le Moyne, who was busy preparing for Ralegh a set of his drawings, first made in Florida in 1564–5, with appropriate texts added to them, for another illustrated monograph.[38] It is probable that these collections were proceeding for the time being as ones which would remain in manuscript until such time as it should seem desirable or possible to publish them. The interim report (*A briefe and true report*), intended originally for use in the particular circumstances of 1587, was to be as far as Harriot was to get, for the time being, with publication.

Later in 1588, probably during the early summer, Richard Hakluyt came home for good from Paris, full of his desire to get his volume of English voyages into print as soon as possible.[39] It is clear that he wished to stress particularly the significance of North America as an objective of English interest. It was, then, as has already been indicated, that Harriot was able to give him a selection of the materials he had gathered for the voyages of 1584–6. All these were edited, or we might say tampered with, to some extent before they were finally published and it is likely that Harriot carried out for Ralegh such re-shaping as he considered desirable, and which was intended to show him up in the most favourable light, while still concealing certain information from the Spaniards and possibly other English rivals or critics. The 1587/1588 narratives which Hakluyt printed, we think, as he got them from White, are much franker and fuller.[40] To them Hakluyt was able to add as his book, *The principall navigations*, went to press, the agreement by which Hakluyt, with a number of London merchants undertook at the opening of 1589 to underwrite further Virginia voyages.[41] He also reprinted Harriot's tract.[42]

Hakluyt had been closely associated with the plans for building up illustrated records of American voyages, as he showed in his remarks on Le Moyne published in 1587.[43] and it was most probably through him that Theodor de Bry, the Frankfurt publisher, had come into contact with Ralegh, Harriot, and Le Moyne when he was in England in 1587 to discuss the possibility of some such publication as Harriot had in mind. It does not seem that agreement was reached at this point. Le Moyne does not appear to have been attracted by whatever plan De Bry put forward. But the latter on a further visit in 1588 to England returned to his project: by this time Le Moyne was dead and his widow did not sustain his objections. Hakluyt too, was in England; Ralegh was reconciled that for some time the war would prevent the revival on any scale of the Virginia ventures; *The principall navigations* came out shortly afterwards and attracted much attention in England, and it appears to have impressed De Bry very favourably. An agreement for De Bry to publish both an illustrated Le Moyne volume and an illustrated White–Harriot volume was worked out, with Hakluyt's active assistance, and so the project for a multilingual, American voyage series was born.[44]

America, part i, as we know it, took shape in 1589. It represented an enormous boost for Harriot in that his *Briefe and true report* was to come out in Latin, French, and German as well as, for the third time, in English. (He long afterwards noted the multilingual appearance of this edition with pride.)[45] He was also asked to supply notes for the illustrations which De Bry selected from amongst White's drawings for engraving. Though Harriot wrote the notes in Latin it is likely that he did them in a hurry and it is likely that De Bry changed them about somewhat as he made his final selection of drawings from which to engrave the plates once he got back to his Frankfurt workshop. (The crude versions of the captions in English were attributed by De Bry to Hakluyt, but some are so garbled it would seem that De Bry himself may have been responsible for them—the Latin versions, if altered, were in the careful hands of Charles de l'Ecluse who undertook the translation of the *Briefe and true report* into Latin.)[46] The note which appeared under White's drawing of the arrival of the Englishmen[47] is more appropriate to the 1584 than the 1585 entry, and it is possible that it should be taken as some slight evidence that Harriot was a member of this enterprise. What is quite clear is that in whatever version we read them these notes are rather elementary in character and it is hard to see in them much evidence of the intellectual detachment shown in the *Briefe and true report*, though they do include some useful points on Indian culture traits and help appreciably to make the illustrations intelligible which, after all, was their main function. Several possible reasons for their simplicity suggest themselves. One may well be that though Harriot was pleased to have his tract brought out in a multilingual edition, he regarded the whole project as very much an essay in vulgarization. Instead of a whole gallery of natural history specimens and a systematic body of material on the Indians, his rather elementary tract (as he would have considered it) and a few pretty pictures of Indian life were to replace the series of folio volumes which it appears he had in mind in 1587. The notes may be seen therefore as the popularized remnants of an unwritten, or at least incomplete, ethnographical treatise, filling out the brief but cogent section on the Indians in his published tract. It may be remembered that Harriot was, or became, a perfectionist, letting nothing of his, or scarcely anything, emerge in print during his lifetime. Another factor in the slight appearance of the notes, or perhaps it would be more accurate and less misleading to call them captions, is that Harriot's interest in Virginia may have been fading as he became more absorbed in mathematical problems. No clear sequence in his scientific activities is yet evident, but we know that his scientific interests were growing as his ethnographical ones were receding. Perhaps the captions then reflect his writing at a point when he had ceased to care very much about such matters as the peculiarities in the dress and social customs of the American Indians he had left behind in 1586, though it would be interesting to know whether he met and conversed with the Indian brought back by Grenville from his 1586 voyage, who was christened on 27 March 1588, and died in April of the following year.[48] A decline in his ethnographical interests is more probable than a comparable decline in his interest in the Algonquian language he had learnt between 1584 and 1586; this was still a living thing for him as late as 1602 and perhaps later. His only other 'Virginia' writing at this period, or perhaps of this period, is a brief note for a paper, which he may never have written, contrasting the character of a trading corporation with the closely similar, but by no means identical, chartered colonization venture:[49] it would have been of great interest to have had this topic developed by his hand. We can say, however, that between 1584 and 1589 the affairs of North America were a major preoccupation, though it is unlikely that thereafter they formed more than an occasional interlude for him in the midst of a sea of scientific enterprises and speculations.

Up to 1590 we have a reasonable range of documentary material on which to base a study of Harriot's concern with the Americas. Thereafter, from 1590 to 1621, our information is very scrappy and incomplete. That Harriot retained and perhaps developed his interests in some respects is undoubted, but it is premature to attempt any detailed analysis. In regard to Ralegh's Guiana enterprises which preoccupied him from 1593 onwards it is clear that he depended on Harriot to an appreciable degree. Harriot worked out detailed instructions for the navigation of Ralegh's ships from England to the north coast of South America.[50] He was given responsibility, when Ralegh went to sea in 1595, for administering a complex scheme regarding the financing of the voyage which was called in question in the courts many years later.[51] He worked on the maps brought back by Ralegh and was engaged on preparing one for Sir Robert Cecil[52]—though whether he completed it we do not know. While Ralegh was on the Cadiz voyage in 1596 he had the task of trying to prevent leakage of information and maps on Guiana through members of Lawrence Keymis' expedition.[53] He was, moreover, highly praised for his intelligence and by implication for his intellectual contributions to the Guiana venture in a poem prefixed to Keymis' published account of the 1596 venture.[54] How these disparate facts add up is not wholly clear. We appear to see Harriot taking a greater share in such proceedings as a business and technical consultant and less as a personally-involved participant. Harriot the business manager—or at least adviser—takes the place of Harriot the field-worker and explorer.

He is increasingly concerned with maps and in the years before 1600 is found in close association with Richard Hakluyt in the collection and interpretation of cartographic materials and, possibly, in map construction, but once more our evidence is partial, and it is difficult to draw from it specific conclusions, as for example, on what part he may have had in the compilation of data (or other more specific involvement) in the Wright–Molyneux world map of 1599.[55]

During the period 1593 to 1605, Harriot's links with Ralegh became less exclusive. He was in close contact with Henry Percy, earl of Northumberland, as early as 1591 and became his pensioner in 1598. By 1601 he had settled at Northumberland's house at Syon,[56] though his status as an associate of Ralegh's—rather than a dependent—is strongly emphasized in the Ralegh will of 1597.[57] He may have continued his residence in Durham House until 1602 or after.[58] Thus when, from 1600 onwards, Ralegh again involved himself actively in Virginia voyages, Harriot's expertise was called on. We have shown him to have been involved in drawing up lists of supplies and trade goods for Samuel Mace's trading and exploring voyage to the Carolina Outer Banks in 1602 and he even designed copper gorgets to be disposed of profitably to the Indians. He revived his interest in the Algonquian language he had learnt in 1584-6 and may have provided the explorers with a wordlist.[59] He went on later in 1602 to help Ralegh in tracking down sassafras brought from what is now Massachusetts by Bartholomew Gosnold and Bartholomew Gilbert in apparent defiance of Ralegh's chartered monopoly of trade with North America.[60] It is highly probable that this revived association with North America would have been maintained and developed had Ralegh not fallen and lost his charter, and almost his life, in 1603.

We cannot tell how far Northumberland shared Ralegh's and Harriot's concern with North America before 1603, but it is likely that he took at least a benevolent interest in their plans and may have been prepared to invest in them. We have no evidence, however, that between 1603 and 1605 Harriot enlisted Northumberland to carry out any of the American projects which Ralegh—in the Tower—was unable to continue.

After 1605 when Northumberland joined Ralegh in the Tower and when Harriot became their principal mutual link with the outside world, it might seem that Northumberland's interest in North America was somewhat more closely engaged. But Harriot for all his expertise on Virginia is not known to have been consulted in the long series of discussions from which the Virginia Company charter emerged in April 1606: he was, during the crucial months, peripherally suspected of involvement in the Gunpowder Plot, was arrested, and retired after his release to obscurity at Syon. At the same time it is probably significant of his continuing interest and influence that George Percy, Northumberland's brother, sailed with Christopher Newport in December 1606 and became an important member of the struggling Jamestown colony until his return in 1612. Like Harriot, George Percy was a pensioner of the Earl and during his absence his pension was largely paid out under Harriot's supervision to provide him with necessities and an occasional luxury in Virginia.[61] He may well have given Percy, before he left England, some instruction in Algonquian, and a word list, as there appear to be indications that Percy could converse, at least to the extent of a few words, with the Powhatan Indians of the James River—whose language was very close to that of the

Indians of the Carolina Outer Banks in 1607.[62] We can reasonably assume also that he provided Percy with a copy of *A briefe and true report* which would instruct him in the natural history and ethnology of the region, perhaps in De Bry's edition with its engravings from the White drawings. It may be—though the indications are in no way specific—that it was Harriot who encouraged Percy to keep a journal, and it is probable that he read the version which it would appear Newport brought home in 1608. There are a few reasonably specific traces of Harriot's influence in the Northumberland household accounts which cover payments on behalf of George Percy or which arose from his presence in Virginia.[63] Thus, one of the entries in the accounts of 8 February 1608–3 February 1609 clearly exhibits Harriot's hand. In January 1609 Christopher Newport returned once more after 'crowning' Powhatan as 'king' or 'sub-king' of Virginia under James I. He had with him one of Powhatan's sons (we do not know his name). This young man was duly brought to Syon. Here he would have found Harriot still able to understand (we think) some of his own language and speak it. Harriot advised that no expensive gift be made to him but that he would be satisfied with copper decorations only, so that there duly appeared in the accounts a payment of three shillings 'for 2 Rings and other peeces of copper giuene to the Virginia prince'. Similarly, we can identify as probably chosen by Harriot, amongst the goods sent to George Percy in July 1608, 'for blewe beades' six shillings and 'for Read copp*er*' nineteen shillings and sixpence, objects Harriot had long ago found the Indians anxious to have. In return we have Percy sending over attractive, if not valuable, stones, some of which were in 1609 set into a ring, probably under Harriot's supervision. When Percy returned in 1612 the two men are likely to have reinforced each other's knowledge and understanding of the North American scene.

It may well have been through Harriot that Richard Hakluyt obtained a copy of Percy's 1607–8 journal which in due course was passed to Samuel Purchas who printed a selection from it in 1625.[64] Percy's later journal, 1608–12, formed the basis of his 'True Relation' which he completed about 1625, after Harriot's death.[65] We may see George Percy, though still rather dimly from the existing evidence, as a significant continuing link between Harriot and the early settlement of Virginia in which he had been so important a precursor.[66]

We know Harriot to have been consulted only once by the Virginia Company. This was in February 1609 when the revision of the Virginia Company charter was under discussion and some widening of the scope of English economic activity was being considered. It appears highly likely that he was cross-questioned about a wide range of North American topics as probably also was his old associate Richard Hakluyt. We know only, through Hakluyt,[67] that he gave evidence of what he believed to have been Indian practices in obtaining alluvial copper on the Roanoke River during his stay in North

America over twenty years before. We have no other evidence of his involvement with Virginia, but as late as 1622 the Virginia Company purchased a copy of his 1588 tract, perhaps either to send out to Jamestown or to add to their own reference collection.[68]

Harriot's name as an American pioneer appeared prominently in John Smith's *Map of Virginia* (1612) and in his *General historie* (1624), and also in William Strachey's 'Historie of travell in Virginia Britania' which circulated in manuscript from 1612 onwards.[69] Purchas likewise, in successive editions of his *Pilgrimage* (1613, 1614, 1617, 1625) and in his *Pilgrimes* (1625),[70] refers to him with respect. De Bry and his successors kept his name alive on the continent as an authority on America by the repeated reissue of the Latin edition of *America* part i. As early as 1597, as Harriot was to note about 1602,[71] Cornelis van Wytfliet took over some of the Harriot material in De Bry, making due acknowledgement to Harriot. A full tracing of his European reputation in this area still remains to be made.

Harriot as a young man in his twenties made a major contribution to European knowledge and understanding of eastern North America. He not only did significant pioneer work as an observer and student in the year he spent in what are now North Carolina and Virginia, but he became a popular authority on the natural history and ethnography of the region, so that his name and reputation in the literature of the subject endured. His active associations with North America after 1590 were slighter and indirect but up to perhaps 1613 at least they had some thread of continuity. As late as 1613, he was in correspondence with Sir Thomas Aylesbury about the implications of recent Northwest Passage voyages which had led to the penetration of Hudson Bay. And he continued to purchase books about the overseas world into which he had penetrated.[72] Yet, if Harriot's retreat from exploration, geography, and ethnography to the mathematical sciences was not complete, his later life saw his New World interests recede, and become largely a memory for him, an aspect only of his widely ranging intellectual activity, a facet only of his enduring fame.

NOTES

1. D. B. Quinn and N. M. Cheshire, *The new found land of Stephen Parmenius,* Toronto, 1972. pp. 39, 191.

2. *Ibid.*, pp. 203–4.

3. D. B. Quinn, *The voyages and colonising enterprises of Sir Humphrey Gilbert*, 2 vols., Hakluyt Society, 1940, II: 420, 446.

4. British Museum, Additional MSS 6788, f. 487. See E. G. R. Taylor. 'Hariot's instructions for Ralegh's voyage to Guiana, 1595,' *Journal of the Institute of Navigation*, V (1952): 345; 'The doctrine of nauticall triangles compendious', *Ibid.*, VI (1953): 131.

5. P. H. Hulton and D. B. Quinn, *The American drawings of John White*. 2 vols., London and Chapel Hill, 1964. I: 13–14.

6. D. B. Quinn, *The Roanoke voyages*, 2 vols., Hakluyt Society, 1955. I: 15–17; 91–115.

7. *Ibid.*, I: 127.

8. *Ibid.*, I: 375.

9. *Ibid.*, I: 389.

10. D. B. Quinn, 'Thomas Hariot and the Virginia voyages of 1602,' *William and Mary Quarterly*, XXVIII, no. 2 (April 1970); 273–4.

11. See especially E. G. R. Taylor in *Journal of the Institute of Navigation*, VI: 134–7; also D. B. Quinn and J. W. Shirley, 'A contemporary list of Hariot references,' *Renaissance Quarterly*, XXII (1969): 13–17; 26.

12. Quinn, *Roanoke voyages*, I: 53; 380–1.

13. *Ibid.*, I: 215–17.

14. Hulton and Quinn, *American drawings of John White*, I: 136–7; II: pl. 59.

15. *Ibid.*, I: 15, Quinn, *Roanoke voyages*, I: 244–6.

16. See the catalogue in Hulton and Quinn, I: 84–113.

17. Quinn, *Roanoke voyages*, i: 47–55.

18. Theodor de Bry, *America*, part i, Frankfurt, 1590. See also Quinn, *Roanoke voyages*, I: 413–44.

19. Two specimens only of the mainland flora were separately drawn and described (Hulton and Quinn, I: 113–15; II: pl. 49, 50); though others appear in their natural setting without description, notably in II: pl. 42 (I: 102–4).

20. *A briefe and true report*, 1588, sig. B1–D4^v; Quinn, *Roanoke voyages*, I: 325–66; Hulton and Quinn, *American drawings, passim.*

21. *A briefe and true report*, Sig. B2, B3^{r-v}, D4–E1^v, F2^v–3^v; Quinn, *Roanoke voyages*, I: 327–8, 331–4, 363, 366–7, 382–5.

22. *Ibid.*, I: 54–5, 329 n., 339 n., 340 n., 347 n., 348 n., 353–4 n.

23. *Ibid.*, I: 293.

24. *A briefe and true report*, Sig. D3; Quinn, *Roanoke voyages*, I: 359.

25. See Hulton and Quinn, *American drawings*, I: 31–3.

26. *Principal navigations*, III (1600): 361–2; Quinn, *Roanoke voyages*, II: 763–6.

27. *Principall navigations*, (1589), pp. 728–47.

28. Sig. F4^v; Quinn, *Roanoke voyages*, I: 387.

29. Sig. A3; Quinn, *Roanoke voyages*, I: 320.

30. *Ibid.*, I: 538.

31. *Ibid.*, II: 497–502.

32. *A briefe and true report*, Sig. A1 (Title page), A3; Quinn, *Roanoke voyages*, I: 318; 320.

33. *Ibid.*, II: 498–500.

34. *Ibid.*, II: 505, 532–8, 553–4.

35. *Ibid.*, II: 554–5.

36. *A briefe and true report*, Sig. A1–2, F4^v; Quinn, *Roanoke voyages*, I: 317–19, 387.

37. *Ibid.*, II: 555–6, 562–9.

38. Epistle by the translator, Richard Hakluyt, to Sir Walter Ralegh, René de Laudonnière, *A notable historie containing foure voyages made by certayne French captaynes vnto Florida*, London, 1587, Sig. [] 2^v; Quinn, *Roanoke voyages*, II: 546–7.

39. D. B. Quinn and R. A. Skelton, eds., Richard Hakluyt, *The principall navigations*, (1589), 2 vols. Hakluyt Society, 1965, I: xiv–xix.

40. *Principall navigations* (1589), pp. 764–73.

41. *Ibid.*, pp. 815–19.

42. *Ibid.*, pp. 748–64.

43. See note 38, *supra*.

44. Hulton and Quinn, *American drawings*, I: 25–7.

45. Quinn and Shirley, *op. cit.*, XXII, 26.

46. Preliminaries to T. de Bry, *America*, pt. i (1590), Latin.

47. *America*, pt. i, pl. 2; See Hulton and Quinn, I: 84–5; II: pl. 123(a); Quinn, *Roanoke voyages*, I: 413–15.

48. *Ibid.*, I: 495.

49. British Museum, Additional MSS 6798, f. 523^r.

50. E. G. R. Taylor, 'Hariot's instructions,' *loc.cit.*, pp. 345–51.

51. J. W. Shirley, 'Sir Walter Ralegh's Guiana finances,' *Huntington Library Quarterly*, XIII (1949), pp. 55–69.

52. Historical Manuscripts Commission, *Cecil*, VI: 256–7; Edward Edwards, *Life of Sir Walter Ralegh*, 2 vols., London, 1868, II: 420–3.

53. Historical Manuscripts Commission, *Cecil*, VI: 256–7, 300, 321.

54. Lawrence Keymis, *A relation of the second voyage to Guiana* (1596); reprinted by Hakluyt, *Principal navigations*, III (1600): 672.

55. A study of Hakluyt's maps by the late R. A. Skelton, including the one referred to, has been contributed to *The Hakluyt handbook*, ed. D. B. Quinn, Hakluyt Society, Second Series, 144–5, 1974.

56. J. W. Shirley, 'The scientific experiments of Sir Walter Ralegh, the Wizard Earl, and the three Magi in the Tower,' *Ambix*, IV (1949): 59.

57. A. M. C. Latham, 'Sir Walter Ralegh's will,' *Review of English Studies*, XXII (1971): 129–56.

58. That Harriot maintained both establishments is indicated by British Museum, Additional MSS 6786, f. 554^v, where Harriot computes the distance from observations taken at Syon House to Durham House, and the reverse.

59. Quinn, 'Hariot and the Virginia voyages,' *loc. cit.*, 268–75.

60. *Ibid.*, pp. 275–9.

61. J. W. Shirley, 'George Percy at Jamestown,' *Virginia Magazine of History and Biography*, LVII (1949), pp. 227–43.

62. George Percy, 'Discourse of the plantation of the southerne colonie in Virginia,' P. L. Barbour, *The Jamestown voyages, 1607–9*, 2 vols., Hakluyt Society, 1969, '. . . we knew little what they meant' (not nothing of what they meant), p. 136; 'one of the chiefest . . . with a bold vttering of his speech, demanded of vs our being there, willing vs to bee gone,' p. 138; 'two Sauages . . . came as Messengers from the Wirowance of Paspihae; telling vs that their Werowance was comming and would be merry with vs with a fat Deare', pp. 138–9; 'they told vs the rest were gone a hunting with the Werowance', p. 139; 'this Werowance made answere againe very wisely of a Sauage, Why should you bee offended with them as long as they hurt you not, nor take any thing away by force, they take but a little waste ground, which doth you nor any of vs any good', p. 141.

These references carry Percy beyond the interpretation of signs to the understanding of words. There had, however, been Indians, probably from this area, brought to London in 1603, who might have, alternatively to Harriot, perhaps, established a linguistic bridge. See D. B. Quinn, ' "Virginians" in the Thames in 1603,' *Terrae Incognitae*, II (1970): 7–14.

63. The Syon and Alnwick accounts of the Earl of Northumberland (Historical Manuscripts Commission, *Sixth Report*, pp. 221–9, 300–19; G. R. Batho, *The household papers of Henry Percy, ninth earl of Northumberland*, Camden Series, 1962; and the extracts in Shirley, *Ambix*, V: 57–9; Shirley, *Virginia Magazine*, LVII: 235–42) make up a mine of information. The items cited are in the last item, pp. 234–6, and in the Hist. MSS Comm., *Sixth Report*, p. 229.

64. *Pilgrimes*, IV (1625): 1685–90; D. B. Quinn, *Observations gathered out of 'A discourse'*, Charlottesville, 1967; Barbour, *Jamestown voyages*, I: 129–47.

65. 'A true relation,' *Tyler's Historical and Genealogical Magazine*, III (1922): 259–82. The manuscript is in the Elkins collection in Philadelphia Public Library.

66. P. L. Barbour, 'The Honorable George Percy, premier chronicler of the first Virginia voyage,' *Early American Literature*, VI (1971): 7–17.

67. Gentleman of Elvas, *Virginia richly valued*, 1609. Dedication by Richard Hakluyt, the translator, Sig. A3^r. See Quinn, *Roanoke voyages*, I: 388.

68. D. B. Quinn, 'A list of books purchased for the Virginia Company,' *The Virginia Magazine of History and Biography*, LXXVI (1969): 348–9, 359.

69. John Smith, *Works*, ed. E. Arber, 2 vols. Edinburgh, 1910. I: 55, 189, 234, 310–11, 315, 317, 319, 325; II: 685, 703, 964; William Strachey, *The historie of travell into Virginia Britania*, ed. L. B. Wright and V. Freund, Hakluyt Society, 1953, pp. 21–2, 49, 142, 144–5. The Bodleian Library, MS Ashmole 1758, copy of Strachey contains the De Bry plates from *America*, pt. i, with the Harriot captions.

70. *Pilgrimes*, IV (1625): 1645–6.

71. Quinn and Shirley, *op. cit.*, pp. 12, 26.

72. He noted the purchase of a number of books on American affairs, e.g. Antonio de Herrera's *Historia general*, Madrid, 1601 'Herera Spanish, 2 vol.'—British Museum, Additional MSS 6784, f. 39, in or a little after 1602.

4

HARRIOT'S EARLIER WORK ON MATHEMATICAL NAVIGATION: THEORY AND PRACTICE

JON V. PEPPER

Polytechnic of the South Bank
(now at North East London Polytechnic)

1. INTRODUCTION

THIS paper deals mainly with Harriot's early work in mathematical navigation and its background. I have already described elsewhere[1] Harriot's later full solution of the mercator problem, for which he created new mathematics of a very high order, but, apart from a brief paper which appeared some years ago,[2] and accounts deriving from it, the earlier work has not been discussed in detail before, certainly not from a mathematical point of view. The stages of Harriot's work on navigation appear to be three. First, in the early fifteen-eighties, he solved the problem of reconciling sun and pole star observations for determining latitude, introduced the idea of using solar amplitude to determine magnetic variation, and, as well as improving methods and devices for observation of solar or stellar altitudes, he recalculated tables for the sun's declination on the basis of his own astronomical observations. Secondly, probably about the same time and certainly by about 1594, he produced a practical numerical solution of the mercator problem, most probably by the addition of secants, as Dee[3] may have done earlier, and as Wright[4] also did about the same time. Thirdly, between 1594 and 1614, no doubt with considerable breaks in his efforts, he produced his great tables of meridional parts calculated (in effect) as logarithmic tangents. The first two stages applied traditional mathematics ingeniously, but the third stage had to call into existence a whole new range of mathematical techniques, such as the conformality of stereographic projections, the rectification and quadrature of the logarithmic or equiangular spiral, the exponential series, and the derivation and use of interpolation formulae.[5]

This paper restricts itself to an account of the first two stages. First, it may be as well to give a brief summary of the navigational problems which faced the seaman in an ocean crossing towards the end of the sixteenth century. Until English seamen turned their attention from navigating in or near home waters, they had no need for a very developed science of navigation. In home waters they were in soundings, and the depth and material of the sea bottom were useful in making more precise any rough estimate there was of the ship's position. This was particularly useful when the ship first came into soundings in the western approaches, at about the one hundred fathom line. The cumulative experience of seamen enabled an art of pilotage to be developed[6] and handbooks or rutters were later put into print. But the longer voyages required more, and the basic problems, then as now, were to know where the ship was, and in what direction it should be sailed. It was desirable to be able to determine latitude, longitude,[7] a suitable sea-chart, the effects of tides, winds and currents, the use and correction of magnetic compass readings, and apply this knowledge.

In principle, the latitude could be got directly from the meridian altitude[8]

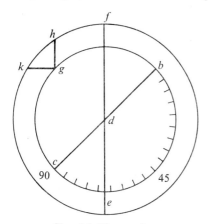

Fig. 4.1. The sea ring.

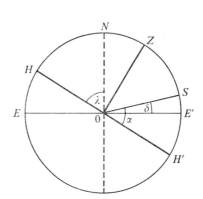

Fig. 4.2. Latitude from meridian altitude.

of the sun or a star. The instrument commonly used for this observation was the cross-staff; both Davis[9] and Harriot devised instruments of their own. Other instruments were the sea astrolabe and the sea ring, the latter first described by Nuñez[10] (see Fig. 4.1) and in many ways preferable to the astrolabe, as it had no moving parts, and could have a graduation double that of an astrolabe of the same size. For a celestial body of known declination, the meridian altitude, however obtained, gives the latitude easily. There are various different cases, but the following is the general method. In Fig. 4.2, HH' is the horizon, N the North Pole, Z the zenith, and S the sun or star. $H\hat{O}N = \lambda$ is the latitude or *altitude of the pole*, as the older name has it. EE is the equator and $S\hat{O}E'$ the declination of the body, δ. The diagram is for a North latitude of about 50 degrees. The meridian altitude, α, is $S\hat{O}H'$, and as $H\hat{O}E = 90° - \lambda$, we have $\alpha = 90° - \lambda + \delta$. Hence (in this particular case), the latitude is $90° - (\alpha - \delta)$. It is not the arithmetic in each case that makes this difficult, but the consideration of the different cases arising from the different latitudes and declinations. The Renaissance seaman was rather infrequently a mathematician of any pretensions, and the difficulties must not be underestimated.

A second method for latitude was to observe the pole star. The altitude of the North Pole was easily seen to be equal to the latitude. Unfortunately, the Pole Star is not exactly above the North Pole. Various more or less incorrect figures for its distance from the pole were current in the 16th century. A complication was that the polar distance was gradually decreasing. By the end of the century it was rather less than 3° 0', but the value of 3°30' used early in the century had been too large, even then, and Martin Cortes (often referred to in English books as Martin Curtis, thus making him appear to be an Englishman[11]), did not improve matters by taking a value of 4°09' about 1550. This he had from 'the Astronomers' (probably John Werner) who, he tells us, are to be preferred to the opinions of mariners.

The Pole Star, *Polaris*, circles about the pole, and so its altitude may be greater or less than that of the pole. Sailors were taught to know the position of Polaris relative to the pole by observing the position of another star of the Little Bear, *Kocab* or *Ursa Minoris β*, which they called the Greater Guard, and the position of a third star, the Lesser Guard. The table given in Bourne's Regiment[12] is typical of those based on *an allowance* (as it was called) of $3\frac{1}{2}$ degrees between the pole and *Polaris*. The position of *Kocab* relative to *Polaris* determined what difference of altitude there was between the pole and Polaris, or so it was thought. Equal and opposite allowances were made on opposite positions of the Guards. This introduced further errors, and it was due to the accumulation of errors that meridian altitude and pole star methods did not always agree.[13] Pole Star observations became rather discredited as the century progressed.

No direct solution of the longitude problem was obtained until the 18th century. Indeed it was this problem that led to the founding of the observatories at Greenwich (1675) and Paris (1672); and to the later Board of Longitude in England (1714) and the solutions of Tobias Mayer (lunar distances) and John Harrison (the chronometer).[14]

The 16th-century approach to longitude was of necessity different, and involved both the question of the best sea-chart and the use of the compass. Longitude was usually estimated by dead-reckoning. It was necessary to know the *way* of a ship. The good sea-master was one who knew this.[15] Roughly, it was two knots in a light wind, 4 knots in a good wind, and 6 knots in 'a bit of a blow'. With these low speeds, the question of currents was extremely important. For example, the current off Alderney can be six to eight knots, and the ship finding itself there on the wrong tide is not in a happy position.

If a place to be sailed to was on a known latitude, the sailor first took his ship to that latitude, then sailed east or west along the small circle.[16] His *way* then told him how long he might have to sail before the landfall.

Ships were not steered to the modern precision. A *point* of the compass was $11\frac{1}{4}$ degrees and half a point was as much as could be expected in the best conditions. Sailing closer to the wind than eight points was hardly possible. Sailors used tables of 'Raysing or laying a degree of latitude' to know how far to sail on a given *rhumb* (or one of the eight points in a quarter of the compass) to increase or decrease their latitude by one degree.[17] This instance, taken with their *way*, gave how many days' sail were necessary. In the open ocean, winds may blow for days without changing, and the difficulties associated with headlands, or approaching England round Ushant were replaced by other problems. The tables just mentioned were surprisingly accurate, mainly, I imagine, because of the coincidence that the correct formula happens to be the same as that obtained by assuming a plane approximation for the surface of the globe.[18]

Currents and tides in the open ocean are difficult to estimate, although their long-term effects were often important. The use of the compass, however, raised many difficult problems. These had been neglected by earlier writers such as Cortes, Bourne and Pedro Medina.[19] It was necessary to know the allowance for the variation, otherwise erroneous and dangerous courses would be set. Borough's methods[20] were fine for good mathematicians on land, but easier methods were needed for use at sea. It was thought by many,[21] and hoped by Harriot, as we shall see, that knowledge of the variation would lead gradually to determination of the longitude. There is a certain unreality about this now, not because of the change in variation, not convincingly established until later,[22] but because of the very great accuracy that would have been needed to get worthwhile and safe results. The regular change of variation over the North Atlantic was misleading. Variation in high latitudes was extreme and compass behaviour unreliable, as the Arctic explorers found.[23]

2. HARRIOT'S INSTRUCTIONS OF 1595

The papers I shall now consider are located at British Museum Add MS 6788, folios 205–20, 423, 468–91; and MS Add 6789, folios 534–7. They form six complete chapters, taken with associated tables, and a few isolated or incomplete fragments, and are in the form of very rough drafts, with many corrections.[24]

The papers were put together by Harriot for assisting the navigators of Sir Walter Ralegh's voyage to Guiana of 1595. Harriot refers to Captains Douglas and Whiddon, who were employed on this voyage (Add 6788, folios 485, 486). As for the date we read (Add 6788, folio 471) in an illustrative example, 'this yeare 1595 the 6 of May', and the date for another example (folio 475) is 18 March 1595. At Add 6789, folio 535 there is 'the 10 of February next the yeare 1595'.

Harriot is providing a resumé of (part of) his *Arcticon*, a text now unfortunately lost. At folio 486 he says 'how this . . . may be knowne and reformed I have demonstrated & taught 11 yeares past in my booke called Arcticon'. At folio 487 (referring to *Dip*), he has 'By truth of demonstration which I have vttered in my *Arcticon*, which here for brevity sake I omit', and at folio 484* he says that

The mathematicall demonstrations[25] perticulerly to discover the errors of it, are not fit to be vttered in this manner of writing, in my *Arcticon* they are at large.

Nothing more is known of the *Arcticon*; it would seem to have been more a manuscript treatise than teaching notes, for in the latter it would not have been necessary to provide proofs for the practical navigators.

The heading of the complete Chapters are as follows:[26]

1. Some Remembrances of taking the altitude of the Sonne by Astrolabe & Sea Ring.   (folio 485)

2. Of taking of altitudes of the Sonne or any starre by the crosse staffe with more exactenes then hath ben vsed heretofore.   (folios 486–9)

3. How to find the declination of the Sonne for any time of the yeare & any place; by a speciall table called the Sonnes Regiment newly made according to late observations.   (folios 468–72)

4. How to finde the elevation of the pole, by the Meridian altitude of the Sonne, & his declination.   (folios 473–5)

5. Of taking the altitude or eleuation of the North pole by the north starre & a new rule of the guardes made and calculated according to praecise & later observations.   (folios 476, 481–4, 423)

6. Of the manner to observe the variation of the compasse, or of the wires of the same, by the Sonnes rising or setting.   (Add 6789, folios 534–7)

There are the following tables or diagrams:

  (i) Surplus of the Horizon   (folio 488)

  (ii) Eleuation of the pole from meridian altitude of the Sonne. (folio 474)

  (iii) A figure shewing when the guardes are in rule   (folio 423)

  (iv) Allowances of the pole starre   (folio 423)

  (v) Regiment of the Sonne   (folios 205–10 v)

  (vi) Amplitudes of the Sonne   (folios 211v–20 v)

There is also, at folio 490, about a dozen lines of doggerel, which I quote here, although not to put forward any literary claims for their author.

THREE SEA MARRIADGES

Three new Marriadges here are made
one of the staffe & sea Astrolabe.
Of the sonne & starre is an other
which now agree like sister & brother.
And charde & compasse which now at bate,
will now agree like & master & mate.
If you vse them well in this your iourny
They will be the Kinge of Spaynes Atarny
To bringe you to siluer & Indian Gold
which will keepe you in age from hunger & cold
God speed you well & send you fayre wether
And that agayne we may meet to gether.

The first six lines refer to all the chapters in turn, except the third. Ralegh & Harriot were to meet again very many times, but the 'siluer & Indian Gold' were to have a different effect on Ralegh from that pathetically referred to here.[27]

The Instructions—Chapter 1[28]
In this chapter it is explained how to make allowances for the movement of a ship when observing the altitude of the sun with a sea astrolabe. Seamen much prefer the astrolabe to the staff for high altitudes of the sun. Unfortunately

when the sea is rough it is very hard to make any observations by it also; because of his agitation & unquiet hanging. [Add. 6788, f. 485.]

The recommended method is that if the sun does not shine through both holes of the sights simultaneously, then

When you finde the leght of the syghtes to moue as much over as under: then your Index standeth as precisely as if the Astrolabe had hong quietly; & sheweth the true altitude of the center of the Sonne. [*ibid.*]

The astrolabe may also be turned around, and an average of the two readings taken if they do not agree. However the Sea Ring is to be preferred to the Astrolabe. It

is of late yeares in great vse with the Portingalles & Spaniardes, the making where of & use they had about 40 yeares past of a country man of there owne a learned Mathematician called Petrus Nonius who also hath written much of the arte of Navigating as well in Latin as in Spanish . . . for ease and speed it much excelleth it as also for exactnes. [*ibid.*]

(Nuñez is mentioned later in the *Instructions* for the impractibility of his recommendations for Pole Star observations.) At the end of the Chapter Harriot says that these instruments prepared for 'your servant Cap. Whidden'[29] were lighter than they ought to be, but that [*ibid.*, r. & v.]

By reason of your speedy setting forth it cannot now be remidied; but is to be used as conveniently as it may. & the inconvenience I will show you shall be remidyd by the staffe in the next chapter.

The Instructions—Chapter 2

Harriot starts by saying that in the use of the cross staff 'seamasters com*m*itt greater errors then sometime they are aware of' [Add. 6788, folio 486.]. There are two main sources of error:

(i) the surplus of the horizon (the modern *dip*)
(ii) the parallaxis of the staff,

in addition to refraction, and (for the sun, but not for a star) the parallaxis of altitude. The latter two he dismisses with

but because in your voyadge they amount not ether one or both to 3 minutes when most, I leaue them for another place & time to be vttered.

The astrolabe and sea ring measure the zenith distance, whereas the cross-staff measures the altitude from the horizon. These two angles are not exactly complementary, because of

(i) the height of eye above the surface of the earth, assumed a sphere, and
(ii) the refraction of the air.

If only (i) is taken into account a rather larger correction is obtained than if both are allowed for (Fig. 4.3).

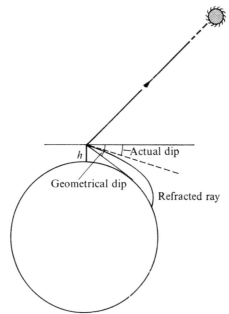

FIG. 4.3. The surplus of the horizon.

The seaman of the time knew that there was some discrepancy, but was unable to explain it. Harriot says

The seamen vse comonly to leaue the horizon open in observing, which in deed were good if they knew how much, but because of the vncertayne coniecture they may make greater error then is fit to be permitted. They haue the practice by tradition from one to another. The reason thereof they yeld none in there writinges, nether being demanded Do they answere any otherwise then that not doing so, the altitude would not be true, nor agree with the Astrolabe. Which without doubt haue ben found by comparing the staff & the Astrolabe together. [Add. 6788, f. 487.]

In his *Arcticon* he had proved that the eye saw more than half the heavens. Even so, it was best *not* to leave a gap at the horizon, but to take what he calls the *Apparent Altitude* and to correct this by using his table of *surplus* which is at folio 488 (See Table 1).

TABLE 1. *Surplus of the horizon*

Hight of the ey aboue the water in pases	Surplus of the Horizon in minutes
1	3′
2	4′
3	5′
4	5′
5	6′
6	6′
7	7′
8	7′
9	8′
10	8′

He says 'as when the ey is one pase that is 5 foot from the levell of the water, then the abatement is 3′'. His values are slightly high by modern ideas, but he is explicit about the magnitude of his pace, which in medieval times had been not 5 feet, but 5 cubits. He does not mention what hypothesis he used about refraction, but his figures do take this into account in some way. His extensive papers on optics in BM Add 6788–6789 await a full report on their contents, which might answer this question. The modern values of the *Nautical Almanac* are given (approximately) by 'dip in minutes is square root of the height of eye in feet'.

The so-called *parallaxis of the staffe* was due to the fact that whereas the graduations on the staff assumed that the centre of the eye was at the end of the staff, this was not the case. Attempts had been made to allow for this by choosing a certain place at which to rest the end of the staff during observation. We read the common practiser thinketh there is little error in setting of it close under that ey they behold withall: some on the vtmost corner of that ey: some on the cheeke bone: & some on one side of the bridge of the nose. [Add. 6788, f. 486.]

These may, for some eyes, prove true; but not in general, and this also had led to discrepancies with astrolabe observations. Harriot recommended 'the best place to set the end of your staffe is the vtmost corner of the seat of that ey which you mind to behold withall'. He had observed the distance error 'by a staffe I haue for the purpose', probably one with two cross-pieces, and had found the same quantity for Whiddon, Douglas, '& many mens eyes else, as in yours & mine'. He calls this the *excentricity of the staffe,* and has it marked on the staff; whence it is used for correcting the observed altitude. It is possible to determine something about what this excentricity was in magnitude, although he says no more about this. The resultant parallaxis of the staff comes into three examples, two at folio 475 and one at folio 484, as in Table 2.

TABLE 2. *Excentricity of the staff*

Apparent altitude	Parallaxis	x
39° 47½′	0° 47½′	·034
16° 07½′	0° 09½′	·036
21° 15′	0° 16′	·036

The x in the third column of Table 2 is the ratio of the excentricity to half the length of the cross-piece, and has been obtained by simple trigonometry (Fig. 4.4). The results are satisfactorily consistent, and show an excentricity of about 1″ with an instrument of average size.

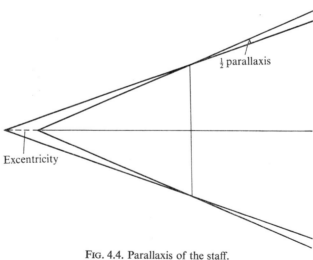

FIG. 4.4. Parallaxis of the staff.

In observations of the sun, its semidiameter, quoted as 16′, must be taken into account. As the use of this instrument involves looking directly towards the sun, Harriot recommends that the elevation of the upper limb be observed, and 16′ subtracted, which is contrary to the modern practice with the sextant, when the lower limb is usually used. The sun should be covered by the instrument during the observation by 'the orderly mouing of your body & hand answerable to the surge of the sea, & then bring him downe by litle & litle till you se only the edge of the sonne.' [Add. 6788, folio 489.]. This will avoid 'offending the ey'. There can be little doubt that the cross-staff was both a difficult and a dangerous instrument to use.

The Instructions—Chapter 3
This chapter, on the declination of the sun, starts with an historical introduction. He says that sailors used one or other of two sorts of Regiment. One sort was based on the Alfonsine tables of 1252 (first printed towards the end of the 15th century), and the other sort on the theory of 'certayne notable mathematicians & especially of one Nicholaus Copernicus of Cracow in poland'. The former was still popular with Spaniards and Portuguese, because of its origins. Although it had led to obvious errors in the determination of latitudes, which had not always agreed, even in the same place at different times, these sailors had blamed the discrepancies on the instruments used rather than the tables.

The latter tables were the Prutenic, made by Erasmus Reinhold, *Prutenicae Tabulae Coelestium Motuum* (Tubingae, 1551). Declination tables were usually, Harriot says, made from Stading's version of these tables, *Ephemerides* (Coloniae Agrippinae, various dates from about 1554). He adds that these should be better tables, but

it falleth out they are worse; our owne men find faults as also sometimes the Spaniardes but know not where the fault is, nether is it to be tried, found, or decerned by there manner of experiments. [Add. 6788, f. 468.]

He goes on to refer to Tycho Brahe (1546–1601) at Hua*e*na (Hveen), and the Landgrave of Hesse (whose astronomer was Christopher Rothmann); their work (that of Tycho since 1577) had shown that 'Copernicus his tables, the prutenickes, & all ephimerides made out of them' were half a degree or more out in the sun's place, and the Alfonsine tables about a quarter of a degree. This leads, he says, to an error of about 12′ (6′ from the Alfonsines) in the sun's Regiment. This comes from the result (Fig. 4.5) that the sine of the declination equals the sine of the obliquity times the sine of the longitude. The declination is changing most rapidly when the longitude is zero, and the consequent error is $\sin^{-1}(\sin \varepsilon \sin 30')$. If ε is $23°\ 31'$ (Harriot's value), then this error is $\sin^{-1} 0 \cdot 00348$, and $\sin 12' = 0 \cdot 00349$. These errors are most serious near the equinoxes, since for most of the year the declination changes more slowly.

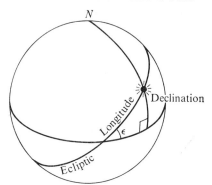

FIG. 4.5. The sun's annual motion.

Harriot's value of the obliquity of the ecliptic just mentioned had been obtained during 1590–93 'by myne owne experiment with an instrument of 12 foote long upon Duresme house leades'. (This includes a reference to Ralegh's residence, Durham House, in the Strand.) The value is 2′ less than that of the Alfonsine tables, and 3′ more than Copernicus' result. He adds that the errors of these earlier tables are clear to all who have found that eclipses occur an hour or more before or after their predicted times. In fact, the obliquity in the early 1590's was probably about 23° 29½′.[30]

Harriot particularly points out that a table of declinations applies to only one meridian, and that for use elsewhere an appropriate allowance must be made. He provides differences in his tables for this purpose (it also enables the tables to be checked for errors); his tables are calculated for the meridian of the West of England. Corrections are not necessary within 7½ degrees of longitude (or 150 leagues of the equinoctial, he adds, showing the use of the result of 20 leagues to a degree, more accurate than the 17½ leagues commonly used by Spanish sailors), and so it serves 'without any allowance' for the narrow seas, the coasts of Ireland, France, Spain, Portugal, and all places north or south of them. For other places he gives an example of the calculation:

Suppose the 18 of March 1595 you were from the west of England to the westard 900 leagues & that there you were disirouse to have the true declination of the sonne for that place at noone. [Add. 6788, f. 470.][31]

The tables give 2° 56′. 900 leagues is 3 hours. The difference in the table is 24, the change of declination in 24 hours, so that for 3 hours it is 3′. So the true declination is 2° 59′ (at the local noon, that is). It is quite adequate, he says, to use the 'common' (that is, dead) reckoning for this. If you are to the East of England, as suppose on a voyage to the East Indies, then the correction is subtracted.

After giving another worked example, the case of times near the equinox is considered. At the equinoxes the sun moves about 24′ in declination in one day, that is in every hour 1 minute. The example of 13 September 1595 is considered. At the West of England at noon the declination is 7′N, and so 7 hours after noon or 7 hours to the West the declination is zero. But in the South Seas, about 10 hours to the West of England, the sun has 3 minutes of declination to the South. This paradox is due, of course, to the use of Local Time. The chapter is concluded with a similar example in which the mariner is east of England 'the nexte yeare 1596 being leape yeare and the 10 of march which then is the day after the aequinocitium' [Add. 6788 folio 472.]; this trouble then occurs on the day after the equinox.

In order to construct declination tables, it is necessary to have a method of obtaining the longitude of the sun, so that the result sine of the declination equals the sine of the obliquity times the sine of the longitude may be used. For this we need to have a theory of the sun's (or earth's) motion; and then, if this is of the usual type, the eccentricity of the orbit e; the obliquity ε; the direction of the apse line, and for tables to cover a sequence of years, the rate of advance of this line; and the length of the year, T.

In Fig. 4.6, in which all the letters are the conventional ones,
$$\psi = \theta - \varphi$$
that is, the direction of the sun, ψ, is obtainable from the mean motion, θ, and the equation of centre, φ. φ has a maximum value ($= \sin^{-1} e$) when $\psi = \frac{1}{2}\pi$. Copernicus in his *Commentariolus*[32] has this as 2° 10′, corresponding to $e = 0.03781$, but in the *de revolutionibus*[33] he has $e = 0.0323$ ($= 1/31$), so that $\varphi_{max} = 1° 51′$. What value Harriot used is not known.[34]

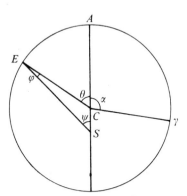

FIG. 4.6. Longitude of the sun.

The Instructions—Chapter 4
This chapter is quite straightforward, and shows how to obtain the latitude from a single meridian altitude of the sun. It is necessary to know the declination, which is found from the tables, as explained in his previous chapter; but there are different cases to be considered according to the name (North or South) of the sun's declination, and the relative position of the zenith to

TABLE 3. *Schema for meridian altitude observations*

When you have the meridian altitude of the sonne you are to consider whether the sonne also hath.

Declination

Northerly & if your zenith in respect of the sonne be

More northerly and the meridian altitude in respect of other altitudes [out] of the Meridian be

1. *Greatest.* Subtracte the declination from the meridian altitude & you have the hight of the aequinoctiall. deduct that out of 90 deg. & the remayne is your distance from the aequinoctiall northward, or elevation of the north pole.
2. *Least.* Subtracte the altitude from the declination, you have the hight of the aequinoctiall. And that from 9ō, you have the elevation of the North pole.
3. *Aequall* or aequall with the declination you ar vnder the North pole.

More southerly Adde the declination to the Meridian altitude & if the summe be in respecte of 9ō be

4. *Greater.* Subtracte 9ō out of that some, and the remayne is the elevation of the north pole.
5. *Lesse.* It is then the hight of the aequinoctiall. Deduct it out of 9ō. & the remayne is the elevation of the south pole.
6. *Aequall.* Then you are vnder the aequinoctiall.

Southerly & if you(r) zenith in respecte of the sonne be

More southerly and the meridian altitude in respect of other altitudes out of the meridian be

7. *Greatest.* Subtracte the declination from the Meridian altitude & you have the hight of the aequinoctiall. deducte that out of 9ō, & you have the elevation of the south pole.
8. *Least.* Subtracte the altitude from the declination, you have the hight of the aequinoctiall. & that from 9ō. you have the elevation of the south pole.
9. *Aequall.* or aequall with the declination: you are vnder the south pole.

More northerly Adde the declination to the Meridian altitude & if the summe be in respecte of 9ō be

10. *Greater.* Subtracte 9ō out of that somme, & the remayne is the elevation of the south pole.
11. *Lesse.* It is then the hight of the aequinoctiall, deducte it out of 9ō & the remayne is the elevation of the north pole.
12. *Aequall* then you are vnder the aequinoctiall.

No Declination

Then the Meridian altitude is the hight of the aequinoctiall. deduct that out of 9ō & you have the elevation of the pole, that is to say of that pole which the Zenith hath respect unto fromwardes the sonne.

the sun. At folio 474 a table is given (see Table 3) that shows in detail the steps to be taken in the calculation in each case. Harriot claimed that this was not only clearer, but also more accurate, than many of the rules then in use. The rules are all correct and are illustrated in Fig. 4.7.[35] Of course, the meridian zenith distance (M.Z.D.), rather than the altitude, would considerably simplify the problem, the modern rule being to take the declination and the M.Z.D., add them if they have the same name, subtract if different, and take the name of the greater to give the latitude.

Two examples are given, of which the second is quoted here:[36]

> An other president of the 11 rule.
> The declination being southerly and zenith more
> Northerly then the sonne.

Anno. 1595. February 10. not a hundred leagues to the westwardes of England & therefore within the limit of the regiment.

Apparent Meridian altitude of the hyer edge of the sonne by the lesser staffe	3̄2·15′
parallaxis of the staffe. 0̄·19′ ⎫	
surplus of the horizon. 0̄· 5′ ⎬ to be abated	0̄·40′
semidiameter of the sonne 0̄·16′ ⎭	
Therefore the true Meridian altitude of the sonne as by the Astrolabe or Ring	3̄1·35′
The true declination of the sonne southerly to be added	1̄0·58′
The summe is the elevation of the aequinoctiall because by the rule it is less than 90̄.	4̄2·33′
Subtracte it out of 90 degrees	
Then the Elevation of the North pole is	4̄7·27′

In conclusion it may be mentioned that the latitude may also be obtained from the meridian altitude of a star of known declination. This declination will usually be known with greater accuracy, and is more or less constant over long periods, and so its use has advantages. But although Wright mentions it in his *Certaine Errors in Nauigation &c* (London, 1599), Pp2, Pp4, and gives the necessary tables, Harriot ignores the method in the papers under consideration.

The Instructions—Chapter 5
This is a long chapter on obtaining the latitude from the altitude of the pole star, and breaks new ground in its contribution to improving the existing methods. Harriot begins by pointing out that the old rule, whereby the elevation of the North Pole was obtained by an allowance of 3½ degrees on a Northeast guard (i.e. by adding 3½ degrees to the observed altitude of *Polaris* when the leading guard *Kocab* and the lesser guard form a vertical line to the Northeast of *Polaris*), was admitted by Spanish and Portuguese sailors to be false. This was the rule given in William Bourne's *Regiment for the sea*, but Harriot does not refer to Bourne in this connection. He does, however, say[37]

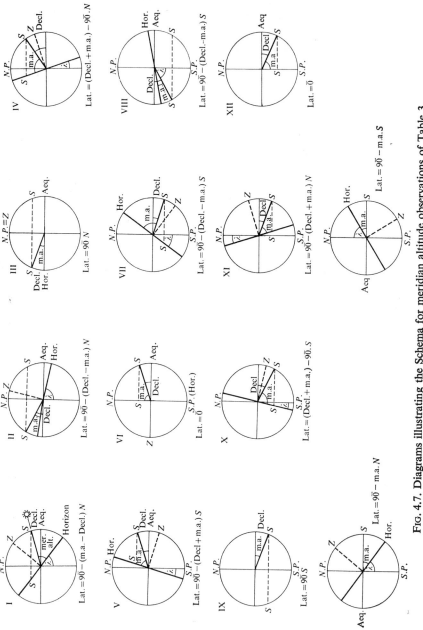

FIG. 4.7. Diagrams illustrating the Schema for meridian altitude observations of Table 3.

that 'these 15 yeares past . . . Rodrigo Samerano one of the King of Spaynes cosmographers', had taken the smaller and better figure of 3° 8' and reduced, in proportion, the values for other positions of the guards. But this had been found to lead to latitude values differing from those obtained from the meridian altitude of the sun by as much as a degree or more.

Harriot had obtained this information, he says, on his own voyage to the Indies, Virginia and homeward. Martin Cortes' rule (which had appeared in Richard Eden's translation of 1561, *op. cit.*) where the allowance on the North East guard was 4° 09' was much worse; it was correct only at least 60 years earlier than it was made. He explains that the distance of *Polaris* from the pole is gradually decreasing, and will continue until it is only half a degree; it will then move out to 48 degrees distance 'if the world do last so long'.

He quotes Ptolemy's *Geography* (Bk. 1, Ch. 7) as saying that Hipparchos had found the distance to be 12° 24' in 130 B.C.; and that he (Harriot) has found that this distance decreases by about 24' in the time which the stars take to move one degree in longitude. If the rate of change of longitude, due to precession, is about 50″ per annum, then this time is about 72 years. This is the value given in G. Rheticus' *Narratio Prima* of 1539[38] and is roughly correct. Gemma Frisius is quoted, *de catholico astrolabio* (Antwerp, 1556), as having obtained the distance of rather less than 3° 8' at Louvain in 1547. In 1591–2 Harriot had observed the value to be just over 2° 56' and he predicts that in 1598 it will be 2° 55'. He remarks that this agrees with his idea that the distance decreases 24' in 100 years. But this does not agree with the previous figures. In the 1697 years from Hipparchos to Gemma Frisius the distance had decreased by 556', a rate of nearly 33' a century or 24' in 72 years. It seems that the '100 yeares' is a slip. He suggests that Frisius should have got the value 3° 0' in 1547, and that Zamorano's rule was obtained from the already incorrect result of Frisius, without an allowance for the passage of time.

If the allowances on the Northeast guard had been wrong, as they had, those on other positions had been even more wrong. Harriot attacks Cortes for having (Book 3, Chapter 10) set out the false view that the allowances on contrary positions of the guards were equal and opposite. He omits any proofs (as he is not writing a treatise), and goes on to define what he means by the various positions of the guards, and how they may be accurately observed. Verticality is to be checked against a plumb line, but horizontality is not so critical. He then gives (folio 423, separated from the main part of the chapter) a table of allowances (Table 4). He intended to compare these with those of about 1490 and Zamorano's of 1580, but these are not included in the manuscript.

The use of the table is explained, and it is stated that the results obtained from it will be correct to within at least 8'. If this is not thought to be good enough, the table is to be entered again, using the first differences. This can be avoided by following his recommendation to make the observation on a

North, South, or Northeast guard (which is clear from the table). He completes his chapter with the following example:

TABLE 4. *The allowances of the Pole Star*

A table of the pole starres allowances vpon any rule of the guardes, & for diverse elevations.

Altitude of the pole	E	W	NE	SW	N	S	NW	SE
10	1·27'	1·19'	2·50	2·46	2·33	2·34	1·0'	0·48'
	3	3	2	2	0	0	5	5
20	1·30'	1·16'	2·52	2·44	2·33	2·34	1·5'	0·43'
	4	4	1	3	0	0	6	9
30	1·34'	1·12	2·53	2·41	2·33	2·34	1·11'	0·36'
	5	6	1	5	0	0	8	9
40	1·39'	1·6	2·54	2·36	2·33	2·34	1·19'	0·27'
	6	7	1	8	1	1	10	11
50	1·45'	0·59	2·55	2·28	2·32	2·35	1·29'	0·16'
	7	8	1	12	0	0	12	14
60	1·52'	0·51	2·54	2·16	2·32	2·35	1·41'	0·2'

An other example or praesident vpon an East guard.

Apparent altitude of the starre by the lesse staffe close from the Horizon	$\bar{4}2{\cdot}30'$
Paralaxis of the staffe $\bar{0}{\cdot}32'$ Surplus of the Horizon. $\bar{0}{\cdot}5'$ } to be abated	$0{\cdot}37'$
Therefore the true altitude of the starre	$4\bar{1}{\cdot}53'$
The allowance agaynst $4\bar{0}$ because it is next, vnder an East Guard to be added }	$\bar{1}{\cdot}39'$
Therefore the altitude of the pole nere	$4\bar{3}{\cdot}32'$

By that altitude of the pole seeke a praecise allowance

Agaynst $4\bar{0}$ you haue the same allowance as before	$\bar{1}{\cdot}39'$

The difference from the next vnderneath is 6 minutes which multiply by the odd $\bar{3}$. & 32' or 4 degrees because the minutes are more then half a Degree

& that summe wilbe 24. which hath 2 tennes & therefore 2 minutes are to be added to the allowance aboue.	$0{\cdot}2'$
Therefore the true allowance is	$\bar{1}{\cdot}41'$

which added as by the title to the true altitude of the starre

Then the precise altitude of the pole is	$4\bar{3}{\cdot}34'$

It may be wondered if the construction and use of the instruments used was sufficient to bear the precision of this method.

Perhaps it should be said that the construction of the pole star tables is not in principle a difficult matter. Consider the case of a South Guard (Fig. 4.8).

The correction is *PZ−PN*, and so it is necessary to know Harriot's values for *NK* and the R.A.s of the stars, which he does not state at this place, although as with the declination tables they may be elsewhere. Edward Wright in his *Certaine Errors* of 1599 says that he (Wright) had not yet had the leisure

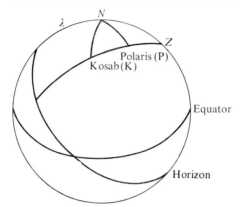

FIG. 4.8. Allowance of the Pole Star.

to provide an accurate theory for obtaining the latitude from the pole star. In the 1610 edition he produces tables on the lines of Harriot's, but much more involved. For example, he has corrections not only for every degree of latitude (pages 113–22), but also entries to seconds of arc, which is rather overdoing things. His (1599) values of the star positions are given at sig. p 4:

	Distance from the pole		R.A.	
	D.	M.	h.	m.
The foremost guard	14	11	14	54
The hindmost guard	16	42	15	54

The Instructions—Chapter 6

The sailor who wished to find the compass variation by a single observation of the sun, and who was sufficient of a mathematician, could use the method given in Chapter 5 of William Borough's *Variation of the Cumpas*, which was annexed to Robert Norman's *Newe Attractive* (London, 1581). This required observations of the sun's altitude and azimuth at any time when it was visible, perferably not too near to noon when the sun's altitude changes slowly relative to the azimuth. The observed azimuth is then compared with that calculated by Borough's method, which is equivalent to the use of the formula

$$\cos \text{Az.} = (\sin \varepsilon \sin \lambda + \sin \delta)/\cos \lambda \cos \varepsilon,$$

where ε is the altitude, λ the latitude, and δ the declination. It is possible to reduce this to a graphical method, as Wright does in his book, but it is doubtful if such constructions could be done very accurately in the difficult conditions found at sea. Ralph Handson gives an arithmetical solution in his *Nauticall Questions*, attached to Pitiscus' *Trigonometry* (London, 1614), a translation from Pitiscus. Such solutions required a knowledge of the latitude, not always well known. This requirement could be dispensed with

T.H.—6

if two observations were available, preferably one in the early morning and the other in the late afternoon, and Borough shows how this calculation can then be effected.

Harriot simplified the problem considerably, although at the cost of some flexibility. After describing the two types of compass card available, he directs the navigator to observe the apparent direction of sunrise or sunset and to compare it with the theoretical value, the so-called *amplitude*, for the latitude of the ship, which is to be obtained from the tables he provides. These amplitude tables are of double entry, for latitudes from 1 to 54 degrees at one degree intervals, and for declinations from 1 to 24 degrees, again at a one degree interval. First differences are also given. The following example (folio 535) is worked:

Suppose you be to the Southwestwardes of the Lysard & in the hight of 48 degrees the 10 of February next this yeare 1595. And that you find the sonne to rise 7 degrees to the Southwardes of the East by such a compasse as hath the wires due north. [Add. 6789, f. 535.]

First the declination is obtained. At noon it is 10° 58', so, from the first difference, 21', it was about 11° 3' at sunrise (larger, as the declination is decreasing in February). The 3' is neglected. The amplitude table is entered for latitude 48 degrees and declination 11 degrees, and the amplitude found to be 16° 33' (folio 213 and folio 218v) South. Hence the variation is about 9½ degrees East. If the compass has its wires placed to allow for variation, then this too must be accounted for.

There is a partial condemnation of the method sometimes used where the azimuth of *Polaris* was observed on a North East guard. This he says, will only be accurate for latitudes near to 40 or 50 degrees; and there are great uncertainties when the star's altitude is large. However, for low altitudes, the method can give a rough idea of the variation, and is better than a single high altitude observation, or than a double observation, as had been described by Borough.

The chapter finishes with two remarks. Firstly, Harriot says of the variation

Besides the benefit that it hath in shewing your true course, it will hereafter be a means to observe the longitude sufficiently exacte; & therefore I weshe it the more to be regarded.

Stevin's *Havenvinding* of 1599 was based on this idea, but it came to nothing, as already mentioned. Secondly, Harriot mentions that the amplitude tables can be used in conjunction with the moon, or indeed any star whose declination is known. Of course, the method of amplitudes is still in use at sea. Tables are given in *Reed's Almanac* or any other seaman's almanac, but nowadays, when the variation is read off the chart, the amplitude is used to determine the *deviation*, or residual compass error, due to iron, engines and electrical devices, things that were absent from the ships of Harriot's day.

Harriot's theory of the construction of his amplitude tables appears at Leconfield 241, vi.b, folio 18, where there is the following analogy:

For the Variation of the compasse by the east or west amplitude of the Sunnes risinge or satting.

I	II	III	IIII
The sine of the elevation of ye aequinoctiall	Sine totall 10000	Sine of the declination of the sonne if: vltra aequinoctialum citra aequinoctialum	Sine of the risinge or setting amplitude: versus polum depressum polum versus elevatum

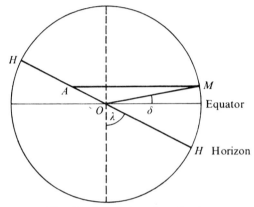

FIG. 4.9. Calculation of amplitudes.

This is easily verified as follows by reference to Fig. 4.9, which is an orthogonal projection on the solsticial colure; OA is the sine of the amplitude φ, and hence

$$\sin \varphi = \sec \lambda \sin \delta.$$

The table is then constructed by elementary, but tedious, arithmetic, followed by searching in a table of sines.[39]

The fragmentary unnumbered chapter is an abandoned draft. It begins

In the arte of Navigation it is praesupposed that all plottes & seachartes have the costes, Islandes portes & other shewes of places in them described duly situated proportionably & ansuerable to those places they represent as well for true course & distance as forme & magnitude [Add. 6788, f. 491.]

but peters out after one page, the only definite remark being that in deciding the course between places, the compass variation must be allowed for. It is in such a chapter that one would expect to find a discussion of the mercator chart, but there is no hint of this.

An entirely cancelled sheet, inserted as folio 484* in 1952, after having been identified among the papers at Petworth and presented by the owner, is part of an earlier draft of Chapter 5. It refers to Nonius (Pedro Nuñez) who had shown the inexactness of Cortes' rule of the Pole Star; and to Thomas Digges who had [40] mentioned that even if the rule were correct for a given latitude, it would be wrong for all others. Harriot says that Nuñez's rules are 'to curious' for the mariner and not so serviceable as Nuñez thought. The extract is continued at folio 490, where it is said that Nuñez himself would have realized this had he tried to use them at sea.

Finally, attention is drawn to folio 478, which is a graduated circular card, graduated in degrees from 0 to 360. On it are marked with ink dots the trace of seven spiral lines which are those of the stereographic projection of the seven rhumb lines on the equatorial plane. This is indicated, approximately, in Fig. 4.10. Folio 479 illustrates a compass rose.

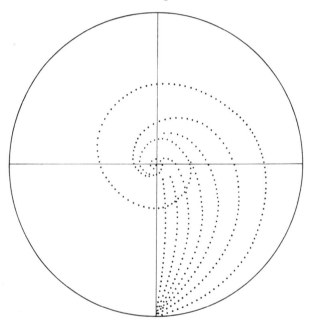

FIG. 4.10. Stereographic projection of the rhumb lines.

In summarizing the *Instructions*, it may be said that they introduce valuable theoretical innovations as well as sound practical sense on observational techniques. The amplitude tables appear to be original and are of course accurate; they form a major contribution to the seaman's art. The Pole Star tables are based on sound principles, something not done before. In the absence of a full and certain knowledge of the observational parameters on which they are based, it is difficult to be sure about their accuracy, but one can have every confidence in Harriot's astronomical care and mathematical competence in calculating them. A similar remark applies to his new regiment of the Sun. The latitude algorithm is unnecessarily involved, but is stated clearly and in quite a practicable form. Taken as a whole, the *Instructions* are a great improvement on the practice current until (and indeed, after) their time, and give a very clear foretaste of the calibre and the later much wider attainments of the able young man of about 23 who produced them.

3. THE DOCTRINE OF NAUTICALL TRIANGLES COMPENDIOUS

Harriot's incomplete manuscript, to which he gave the name *The Doctrine of Nauticall Triangles Compendious*, is to be found among the Leconfield papers.[41] While recognizing its importance, one should not however, overinterpret it— it does not by any means go all the way to providing a full basis for the mer-parts tables of 1614 mentioned above, and this may very well explain its incompleteness—equally, one should not underestimate it, as Rigaud did in the early nineteenth century.[42]

It is a reasonable conjecture that the manuscript dates from 1594. It consists of 11 double folio sheets, folded and stitched to form a booklet. The stitching is modern. The title appears on the front page, and the pages are numbered 1–40 from the next page. The last 3 pages are unnumbered, but not blank, although 16 of the numbered pages are entirely blank, and a few nearly so. The first unnumbered page at the end has some astronomical observations of 19 October 1594 under the heading 'Mr Dee'. The next page contains a book-list, which mentions works that came out between about 1586 and 1602.[43]

TABLE 5. *Raising or laying a degree of latitude*

The Quantity of the segment of euery Rumbe betweene two paralleles of a degree in distance: that is to say how many leagues do rayse or lay a degree of latitude vpon any poynte of the compasse

I	II		Secantes		
			III	IIII	
10,000,000	3600"	1:$\overline{1}\overline{1}$•15'	10,195,910.	3670"$\frac{53}{100}$	$\overline{1}$·1'·10"
	or	2:$\overline{2}\overline{2}$·30'	10,823,920.	3896 $\frac{6}{10}$	$\overline{1}$·4'·56"
	1 degree	3:$\overline{3}\overline{3}$·45'	12,026,897.	4329 $\frac{8}{10}$	$\overline{1}$·12'·9"
		4:$\overline{4}\overline{5}$· 0'	14,142,135.	5091 $\frac{2}{10}$	$\overline{1}$·24'·51"
		5:$\overline{5}\overline{6}$·15'	17,999,525.	6479 $\frac{7}{10}$	$\overline{1}$·47'·59"
		6:$\overline{6}\overline{7}$·30'	26,131,259.	9407 $\frac{2}{10}$	$\overline{2}$·36'·47"
		7:$\overline{7}\overline{8}$·45'	51,259,321.	18,453 $\frac{2}{10}$	$\overline{5}$·7'·33"
		$\overline{9}\overline{0}$· 0'			

On page 1 of the manuscript there is a table for raising or laying a degree of latitude. This is based on the correct result that the distance equals the difference of latitude times the secant of the course, which Harriot considers on page 4. The distance is given, first in seconds of arc, in column 4. The result is illustrated in Fig. 4.12(a) below.[44] The main part of the work begins at page 2, where Harriot defines the nautical triangle (on a sphere) to be bounded by a rhumb line, a meridian line, and a line of latitude. Thus only one side is a great circle: the latitude line is (usually) a small circle, and the rhumb is not a circle at all but a 'helicall line'. In order to be able to solve such a triangle, which always has a right angle, it is necessary to know two sides or one side and an angle.

At paragraph 4 of page 2 the error of the plane chart, that is its understatement of the latitude line or difference of longitude, is pointed out. The other two lines (paragraph 5) do not have their length changed, they are only 'extended', and the angle between the rhumb and the meridian is not altered. This last is the result used on page 1 for the table above, as he says at paragraph 6 that

so many leagues of any rumbe as do rayse or lay a degree in one latitude; the same number do rayse or lay a degree of the pole in an other latitude.

Not everyone believed this, for

This conclusion is holden also of the common seamasters although erroneously accordinge to Martin Coygnet; but the difference which he findeth by calculation vpon groundes wrongly assumed is so small, that if it were true, need not to be regarded.[45] [p. 4, para. 6.]

Difficulties do not arise until the difference of longitude (*d*.long.) is sought or used (paragraph 7); except for this the plane chart may be used with accuracy. To find the *d*.long. exactly

the meridian & the helicall line must be assumed in a certayne rate greater; the quantity how much in euery segment apphereth by my nauticall canon, or compendiously vpon my staffe; the reason whereof shalbe demonstrated in my Nauticall Doctrine. The meridian for common vse Mercator hath sufficiently enlarged. [p. 4, para. 8].

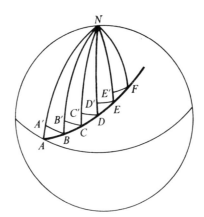

FIG. 4.11. Nautical triangles on the globe.

It thus appears that at the date of the manuscript, while Harriot was actively employed in navigational work, he had some sort of table of meridional parts. So had Wright, and from him Blundeville (*His Exercises* (London, 1594)). Wright's tables are probably of about 1590, and were obtained by addition of secants, as he explains in the 1610 edition of his *Certaine Errors*. They were not exact, although good enough for most practical purposes. Harriot had put his scale on a staff, perhaps rather as Edmund Gunter did later.[46] Whether or not he ever wrote out the full *Nauticall doctrine*, as promised in the last extract, and as foreseen by Hues, is not known.[47]

In Fig. 4.11, *ABCDE* . . . is a rhumb line or course of constant bearing, say a. $A'B, B'C, C'D$, &c., are parts of latitude lines (small circles). We may choose $A, B, C, \ldots$ so that AB, BC, CD, &c., are each equal to d, say. Now imagine that the triangles $AA'B, BB'C, \ldots$, are small enough for the following equations to apply (as they will in the limit):

$$AA' = BB' = CC' = \ldots = d \cos a,$$
and
$$A'B = B'C = C'D = \ldots = d \sin a.$$

Now AA', BB', &c. are direct measures of latitude, so that the total difference of latitude (*d*.lat.) is $\cos a \Sigma d$. This result is the basis of modern *traverse tables*[48] and may explain the table of cosines at BM Add 6789, 7–16, entitled *Canon Triangulorum Nauticorum*. But $A'B, B'C$, &c. do *not* measure *d*.long. They are the so-called *departures*, or distance from the meridian, and are related to the *d*.long by the simple equation

$$d.\text{long.} = \text{departure times sec latitude.}$$

The equivalent of this result appears at page 16 of the manuscript. Thus the statement

$$d.\text{long} = \sin a \, (\Sigma d \sec \lambda)$$

where λ is the latitude, is an approximation, whose accuracy can be improved by choosing a smaller d, and hence adding the secants at a closer interval of latitude, subject only of course to the existence of sufficienctly subtabulated tables. Wright (1599) used 1'. Harriot, by the time of this manuscript, had done the same, and was also part of the way to his highly accurate tables of 1614. The integral calculus shows, of course, that

$$\lim \Sigma \sec \lambda = \ln \tan (\tfrac{1}{4}\pi + \tfrac{1}{2}\lambda),$$

and I have shown elsewhere how near Harriot was to this result.[49] A consideration of the few detailed calculations that appear in this manuscript is omitted here so that we can now turn to the solution of the nautical triangle.

From the results above it follows that

$$d.\text{long.} = \tan a \, (d.\text{lat. } \Sigma \sec \lambda)$$

or that

$$d.\text{long.} = \tan a \, (\text{meridional part for latitude } \lambda).$$

Further, the meridional part (mer-part) is exactly equal to the *d*.long. on the rhumb of 45 degrees, a result of which Harriot makes excellent use in his later construction of 1614, and which he states more explicitly at page 3 here:

A Theoreme.

The difference of longitude, of the extremes of any segment of the Rombe of 45g: is the nomber of aequall degrees aequinoctiall or meridian that is aequall to the vnequall degrees of the difference of latitude of the sayd extremes. Be it that the extremes be both out of the aequinoctiall or one in the same: or both being out on one side of the aequinoctiall only, or one on the one side & the other on the other.

This is followed by three *consectaries* which repeat this for special cases. At page 6 the six cases for determining two of the elements of the nautical triangle in terms of the other two are listed, as in Table 6.

TABLE 6. *Cases of the nautical triangle.*[50]

The propositions praemised beinge sufficient to expresse the nature of the nauticall triangle; The methode for practice I order thus:

The rectangle beinge alwayes geuen I say also muste be knowne the:

1. Meridian segment & Angle of derection	And then the thing sought is	1. The line of distance 2. The difference of longitude
2. Meridian segment & distance	The thing sought	2. Difference of longitude 1. Angle of direction
3. Meridian segment & Diff: of longitude	The thinge sought	1. Angle of direction 2. Distance
4. Angle of direction & distance	The thing sought	1. Merid: segment 2. Difference of long.
5. Angle of direction & diff. of longitude	The thing sought	1. Merid. segment 2. Distance
6. Distance & Diff: of longitude	The thing sought	2. Merid: segment 1. Angle of direction

This list is complete, and the solutions are given at pages 8 and 10 of the manuscript. Harriot's 'vnequall degrees of the Meridian' are the mer-parts. The solutions of the various cases are given in Table 7 here.

TABLE 7. *Solutions of the nautical triangle*[51]

The proportionall terms of the first order.

I	II	III	IIII
1. Whole sine 10,000	Degrees of ye segm: of ye meridian	Secant of ye angle of direction	Degrees of distance.
2. Whole sine 10,000	Aequall degrees awnswerable to the vnequall of the Meridian	Tangent of the angle of direction	Degrees of longitude or arke of a parallel

The second order

I	II	III	IIII
1. Degrees of the segment of ye meridian	Whole sine 10,000	Degrees of distance	secant of the angle of direction
⁵²2. Degrees of the segment of ye Meridian	A*equall* Degrees awnswerable to ye vna*equall* of the Merid.	Degrees of distance	Degrees awnswerable to the supposed vnequall of distance

for the second parte of this order the spediest way to find the thing sought is by the second sorte of termes of the first order: thus:

I	II	III	IIII
2. Whole sine 10,000	Aequall degrees answerable to ye vna*equall* of the Meridian	Tangent of the angle of direction.	Degrees of long: or arcke of a parallell.

The third order.

1. Aequall degrees awnswerable to ye vnequall of ye meridian	Whole sine 10,000	Degrees of diffe: of longitude	Tangent of ye angle of direction

2. The second parte hath the termes of the first parte of the first order.

The fourth order.

I	II	III	IIII
1. Whole sine 10,000	Degrees of distance	Sine of ye complement of ye angle of direction	Segment or degrees of the meridian.

2. The termes of the 2 of the first order.

The fifth order.

I	II	III	IIII
1. Whole sine 10,000	Degrees of longitude	Tangent of the complement of ye angle of direction	a*equall* degrees answerable to the vna*equall* of the segment of the Meridian.

2. The first of the 1 order.

The solutions are equivalent to the following equations, which may be verified by reference to Fig. 4.12.

I.1 distance = d.lat. sec Co.
I.2 d.long = d.m.p. tan Co.
II.1 sec Co = distance/d.lat.
II.2 d.long = d.m.p. tan Co.
     (where the Course has already been found by II.1. Harriot also gives d.lat./d.m.p. = distance/distance in d.m.p., but has cancelled this.)
III.1 tan Co. = d.long./d.m.p.
III.2 This is stated to be as I.1.
IV.1 d.lat. = distance. cos Co.
IV.2 This is as I.2 (when the distance has been turned into d.lat. and hence d.m.p. by I.1.)

V.1 d.m.p. $= d$.long. cot Co.
V.2   This is as I.1 (turn d.long into departure, if latitude known).
No results are given for the 6th order.

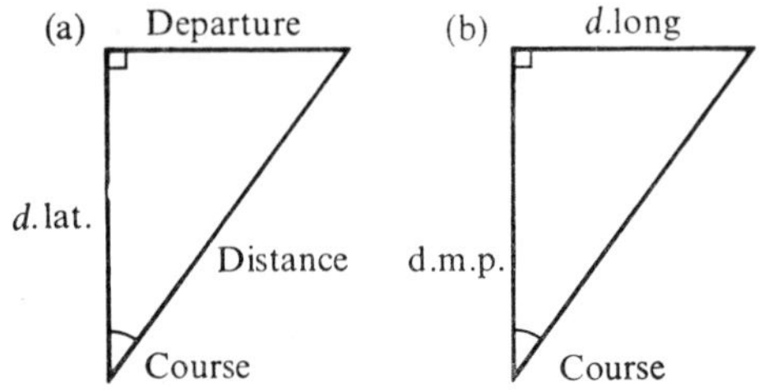

FIG. 4.12. Solution of the nautical triangle:
(a) plane triangle;
(b) nautical triangle extended *in plano*.

Consideration of pages 13, 14, 19, and 21 of the manuscript is omitted here.[53] The relation between d.long. and departure is given at page 16. There is an unclear (and probably incorrect) rule on page 17 for interpolating for a mid-point value using constant second differences:

To take the parte proportionall in sines or tangentes where the differences are vnaequall & the differences of differences aequall.
for halfes thus.
devide the difference in two aequall partes; also the[54] difference of differences; & half that adde to the one half of the difference; and the other half to the other, then have you two halfes as of differences proportionall.

This looks like (in modern notation)

$$f_{\frac{1}{2}} = f_0 + \tfrac{1}{2}\Delta_0 + \tfrac{1}{4}\Delta_0{}^2,$$

whereas the correct result has $-\tfrac{1}{8}\Delta_0{}^2$ for its last term. Nor is it clear where the sine or tangent function comes in, although this type of thing is mentioned in the extensive papers on triangular numbers at BM Add MS 6782, folios 107–253.

The construction of an approximate table of mer-parts by the addition of secants is considered rather incompletely on pages 25, 26, 37, 39, 40, and 41. It begins at page 37 with:

1. The degrees of the meridian augmented in the same proportion towards the pole; as the degrees of euery parallel of a degree distance do decrease, that is to say by what rate the degrees of euery parallell are lesse then the degrees of the aequinoctiall; by such a rate the degrees of the meridian vnder euery such parallell beinge greater; I say euery such degree of the meridian is only of an exacte quantyty to measure that parallell by which he was proportionated, that is to say that parallell which termina-teth that end of the degree next to the pole.

This appears to mean that the augmented meridian line is increasing at any latitude at the same rate as the degrees (and hence the radii) of small circles of latitude decrease, or that the increase is proportional to the secant of the latitude, since $r_\lambda = r_0 \cos \lambda$; but that this rate is (obviously) changing so that the addition must be proportioned to the corresponding latitude. (The word 'proportionated' is interesting in view of scaling difficulties in the solution on the lines begun at pages 13 and 14). The interval indicated is 1 degree. This is illustrated in the diagram, Fig. 4.13, which is taken from William Barlow's

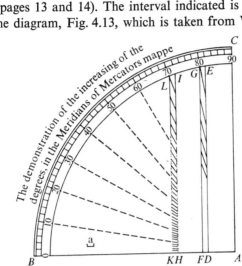

FIG. 4.13. The augmentation of the meridian line.

The Navigators Supply (London, 1597), opp. sig. K, which Barlow says he had from a friend, who may well have been Harriot. The next comment is

2. And for the measuringe of any parallell vnder the sayd terme; the sayd degree is of to great a quantity. [p. 37.]

That is, the quantities are increasing. Paragraph 3 considers the addition of secants at intervals of 1′. Here the x of Fig. 4.13 must be replaced by $x/60$. In paragraph 4 we read that the meridian line formed by adding at one degree intervals is greater than that obtained with a 1′ interval by an amount 'the totall of all the differences of euery such minute from the 60′ of the sayd degree. by the 4.' This '4' is paragraph 4 of page 35 where it is stated that if u_i is a monotonic increasing sequence, then (in modern notation)

$$nu_n - \sum_{i=1}^{n} u_i = \sum_{i=1}^{n} (u_n - u_i),$$

which in this case gives

$$60 \sec (\lambda+1)^0 - \sum_{i=1}^{60} \sec (\lambda^0 + i')$$

$$= \sum_{i=1}^{60} \sec (\lambda+1)^0 - \sec (\lambda^0 + i'),$$

but it is not clear where this leads to.

On pages 39 and 40 there is an inconclusive discussion of the relationship between the addition of secants and the enlarged meridian line. The former total is always larger than the latter, whatever the interval of addition. A starting value for $1°$ of $1 \cdot 0001523$ is given ($= \sec 1°$). Harriot asks how to find a meridian line that would be too small, so that 'a line aequall or within those limites we desire' may be found, and refers us to page 25, where we read:

Proposition to find a lesse line &c. mentioned on the 40 page, numb, 2.

1. A line made by the addition of minutes according to the doctrine of the 37 page; euery minute is to greate to measure any parallell vnder the pole ende; but aequall & iuste to measure that parallell that passeth by the pole of that minute; & therefore to little to measure any parallel neer the pole, then the pole end of that minute.

There are no other propositions. All that the above says is that (see Fig. 4.14) AB is too large to measure the increase in mer-part from $(n-1)'$ to n', just

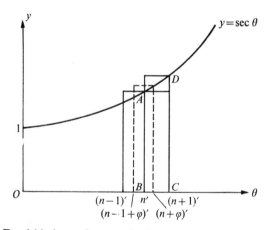

FIG. 4.14. Approximate evaluation of the sum of secants.

right for the increase from $(n-1+\varphi)'$ to $(n+\varphi)'$, where $0 < \varphi < 1$, and too small for the increase from n' to $(n+1)'$. Finally, page 26 tells us that

The speediest & surest way in half degrees to calculate the *canon nauticus* is this: first multiply the first number of the Hypotenuses by 30; then vnto the ofcome adde the summe of the differences in the table, the totall is the rumbicall line of half a degree; that beinge added to the nomber before so gotten Doth complete the *canon*. & this way is best to avoyde ouersyghtes before you make addition for euery minute.

It can be concluded that Harriot had a table formed by the addition of secants, at $1'$ intervals, and that he had considered the problem of continuity corrections. What method, if any, he had to make such corrections, does not appear. Thus the remark[55] that J. A. Lohne has established that Harriot had the mer-parts in 1594 by stereographic projection is wrong. What he did have was the same sort of solution as Wright, and the beginnings (at some date perhaps in the 1590's) of a more advanced method, but the full mathematical solution did not exist for another twenty years, and stereographic projection by itself does not (and did not) lead to the immediate construction of mer-part tables without a very considerable amount of further work, which I have described elsewhere.[56] Further, the statement in *The Principal Works of Simon Stevin* (Amsterdam. 1961), iii, 493, that the bulk of this work [the *Doctrine*] is formed by a *Canon Nauticus*, being a table of 'meridional parts' from minute to minute, is also an overstatement; the most that can be said is that it refers to such a *Canon*.

Some improved instruments for observing altitudes are considered by Harriot at his pages 31–2. These are intended to avoid the dangerous necessity of looking directly towards the sun. There is also a 'quadrante for the starres'. An attempt is made at page 32 to consider great circle sailing, but this leads nowhere and is cancelled.

A large number of the pages of this manuscript are left blank. It seems possible that Harriot had hoped to be able to provide a complete solution of the mer-parts problem, but had had to abandon this at that time, that is, about 1594. Although he kept the manuscript, he did not later revise it when, before or during 1614, he solved all the related problems it leaves unanswered. The manuscript thus gives us a valuable glimpse of an important early stage in the full mathematical solution of the mercator problem, and some indication of the difficulties which held up Harriot's work at this particular stage.

APPENDIX TO CHAPTER 4
The early development of the mercator chart

THE present section gives a brief account of the early development of the mercator chart.[57] The idea of the enlargement of the meridian scale to allow for the distortion formed by taking parallel meridians on a plane chart occurs as early as 1511. Erhard Etzlaub made a pair of Sundials (1511 and 1513), and there is a map on the case for these instruments which is said to give a tolerable mercator projection up to about 60 degrees.[58] In Mercator's own map the meridian scale is increased, but the method he used is not known. The addition of secants seems the obvious answer. Harriot refers to Mercator's work at Leconfield 241, vi.b, 4, as we have seen, and he also takes the latitudes and longitudes of various towns from this map as can be seen at BM Add MS 6786, *f*.442.

The most interesting of the early work is John Dee's *Canon Gubernauticus*. This manuscript (Ashmolean MS 242), is described in E. G. R. Taylor's edition of *A Regiment for the Sea* (Cambridge, 1963), 415–17, and the tables are printed at 420–33. An extract is given in Table 8.

TABLE 8. *D. longs on the 7th rhumb*

78. D 45. M						
	Longitude					
	Continuate			Resolute		
D	D	M	S	D	M	S
1	5	1	39	5	1	39
2	10	3	24	5	1	45
3	15	5	20	5	1	56
4	20	7	32	5	2	12
5	25	10	7	5	2	35
6	30	13	10	5	3	3
7	35	16	46	5	3	36
8	40	21	1	5	4	15
9	45	26	1	5	5	0
10	50	31	52	5	5	51

Dee's *continuate* is the d. long. and his *resolute* the first differences. The tables are for the 7 rhumbs, for latitudes up to 80 degrees, and thus the table for the fourth rhumb is in effect a table of mer-parts. Harriot had similar tables later on (Leconfield 240, ff. 263–9). Dee's values are quite good, better in fact than some later values. It is apparent that he knew how to turn d.m.p. into d.long. for a given course. Taylor suggests that these tables are of about 1558, and there is nothing unlikely about this. Dee was a friend of Mercator and had been employed by the Muscovy company as navigational adviser; later he drew a polar chart for Grenville, and aught Captain John Davis, the arctic navigator, so that his interest in high latitudes is explained. The tables *could* be used for plotting approximate great circle routes in conjunction with a gnomonic polar chart. But Dee's *Paradoxall Compass* appears not to have been a gnomonic chart, but the rather similar orthogonal polar projection. Both Davis and Polter, in works referred to below, refer to this *Paradoxall Compass*, and although no-one seems now to know for certain what it was, what is said above is not too far-fetched.[59]

The first published table of mer-parts was in Thomas Blundeville, *His exercises* (London, 1594), 2nd edition 1597. He had them from Edward Wright (whom he acknowledges with thanks), and prints them at an interval of one degree.[60] The values do not entirely agree with those published later by Wright himself. The idea is mentioned by William Barlowe in his *Navigators Supply* of 1597, but he does not give tables.

Wright's own tables appear in his very important *Certaine Errors in Navigation* (London, 1599). In this he deals with four main topics:

  (i) Correction of the plane chart (Ch. 1–5),
 (ii) Variation of the Compass (Ch. 6),
(iii) Errors of the cross-staff (Ch. 7),
 (iv) Ephemerides of the Sun, 1597–1600 (L1.1—Mm.2),
  (v) Declination of the Sun and stars (Mm.3—Oo.1, Pp.2, P.4), and
 (vi) R.A. of the Sun (Qq.2).

His mer-parts are given for latitudes up to 89° 50′ at 10′ intervals, and to one decimal place (in the 1610 edition they are at 1′ intervals and to four decimal places, but the 1599 printer, Valentine Sims, presumably would not have this). He gives some unhandy looking rhumb tables, tabulated by *d*.long. and not *d*.lat., and with the nomenclature of the rhumbs reversed (he changed it back in 1610).[61]

There is a table of magnetic variation at given places, of dip of the horizon (at 0.1v., similar to that of Harriot's *Instructions*), and of parallax of the sun for its different altitudes (0.2v). In 1610 Wright added tables of refraction for the sun and fixed stars (p. 232). At Aa.2v.—Ee.3 of the original edition there are tables of declination for given longitudes, that is, tables of sine of the declination equals sine of the obliquity times sine of the longitude. There are also these other tables:

Ephemerides of the Sun, 1597–1600,
Declination of the Sun (Mm.3—Oo.1),
Fixed stars near to the equator, and those near to the pole (Pp.2—P.4), and
The Sun's R.A. (Qq.2).

He promises tables for correcting pole star observations, and these appeared in 1610, as we have seen.

The tables of observations of meridian altitudes of the Sun, taken by a quadrant of six foot semi-diameter at London, are very interesting from our point of view. Using a latitude of 51° 32′, the resulting declination of the Sun is also given. The period covered is from May 1594 to November 1597, intermittently (thus showing which were clear days), and a direct comparison may be made with Harriot's predicted declinations in his *Instructions*.[62] That it is rare for the difference to be as much as 3′ (often the agreement is exact, or only 1′ or 2′ out) seems remarkable to me.

To return to the general question, it was Halley who said that Henry Bond first noticed the relation between mer-parts and log tangents.[63] Harriot himself may have seen this connection in 1614, when John Napier's *Mirifici Canonis Logarithmorum Descriptio* (Edinburgh, 1614) appeared. John Speidell produced logarithms of all the trigonometric functions in his *New Logarithmes* (London, 1619). William Oughtred interested himself in the subject, but did not publish his work on it.[64] Halley quotes

Oughtred's erroneous value for the mer-part of 89° 59′. John Collins wrote a work on geometry and navigation, *The Marriners Plain Scale New Plain'd* (London, 1659), in which he deals with the Meridian Line at pages 42–7. He compares the logarithmict angent with values obtained by Wright, Gunter, Snell, and others, and in saying that he has heard that Oughtred is to make a new table, he supposes that he probably has 'attained the manner of adding up those Secants by some new Propositione'. A curiosity is Richard Norris' *The manner of finding of the true sum of the Infinite Secants of an Arch, by an infinite series* (London, 1685). This little tract rehearses some of the recent history of the problem, and eventually finds a 'mer-part' for 89° 59′ 'which is not so much as $\frac{1}{4}$ of the length of the Meridian-line made by the *Addition* of the *Secants*' (page 10). At page 12 we read 'Thus I have found and shall demonstrate (elsewhere) that the Sum of the secants, however attained, hath no relation to the Meridian-line on the true Sea Chart'.

John Wallis wrote on the question.[65] He says that Wright's chart

is equivalent . . . to a Projection of the *Spherical* surface (supposing the Ey at the Center) on the concave surface of a Cylinder erected at right Angles to the Plain of the Equator. [page 1196.]

This is misleading, for the map is not a geometrical projection, in the strict sense, although the assertion is still common. Wallis produces the formula

$$s + \tfrac{1}{3}s^3 + \tfrac{1}{5}s^5 + \ldots$$

where $s = \sin \lambda$, for the mer-parts, and also gives

$$\tfrac{1}{2}s^2 + \tfrac{1}{4}s^4 + \tfrac{1}{6}s^6 + \ldots$$

for the 'Aggregate of Tangents'.[66] James Gregory was the first to prove the exact formula.[67] Isaac Barrow wrote on the problem too.[68] In respect of its use of stereographic projection, Halley's solution of 1695[69] is similar to Harriot's of 1614. Halley goes on to give solutions in series in some detail, which impressed F. J. Cajori.[70] Halley's formula was that the d.m.p. between latitudes l_1 and l_2 was given by

$$2(t/T + t^3/3T^3 + t^5/5T^5 + \ldots),$$

with a suitable scale factor, where $t = a - b$ and $T = a + b$, $a = \tan(\tfrac{1}{4}\pi - \tfrac{1}{2}l_1)$ and $b = \tan(\tfrac{1}{4}\pi - \tfrac{1}{2}l_2)$. This follows, as d.m.p. $= \ln(a/b) = \ln\{(1+t/T)/(1-t/T)\} = 2(t/T + t^3/3T^3 + t^5/5T^5 + \ldots)$. Halley determined the mer-parts of 1′, 2′, and 89° 59′ to 20 figures, page 211. Newton, too, was interested in the problem.[71] To what extent Harriot's later work on mer-parts, completed in 1614, is *equivalent* to the integration

$$\int_0^\lambda \sec\theta \, d\theta = k \ln \tan(\tfrac{1}{4}\pi + \tfrac{1}{2}\lambda),$$

is a matter of careful interpretation. It certainly gets the correct numerical results, not done before, nor repeated for a century or more, and amounts to a sound evaluation of the logarithmic tangent function; tangents are deliberately and consciously used, but as the work predates Napier's *Descriptio* (1614), it is hardly fair to ask if logarithms were known to be involved as such. Whether Harriot realized that his tables could be used for calculations involving tangents, as Napier's could for sines, is not yet clear. Certainly the exponential nature of the function is clearly visible and recognized. If we grant, as there is not then much difficulty in so doing, the direct relation between the logarithmic tangent and Harriot's obtaining of it *as a* logarithmic tangent, there is still left the question of its origin as the limit of a sum of secants. Curiously, Harriot's original approximate table, derived directly as such a sum, is much closer to this than his later work, which is based on a very profound means of *avoidance* of a limiting sum of secants as such. This is far from saying that limits or even limits of sums are avoided, as the bases of Harriot's methods include several such results. The simplest view to take is that his method was a special device for a particular problem, which led both to an anticipation of some rather specialized logarithm tables, and to the creation of much highly original mathematics.

NOTES

1. J. V. Pepper, 'Harriot's Calculation of the Meridional Parts as Logarithmic Tangents', *Archive for History of Exact Sciences* (Berlin-Heidelberg), iv (1967–8), 359–413; a more general survey, with a bibliography and list of some contemporary references to Harriot's work is in my 'Harriot's unpublished papers', *History of Science*, vi (1968 for 1967), 17–40.

2. E. G. R. Taylor, 'Hariot's Instructions for Ralegh's Voyage to Guiana, 1595', *Journal of the Institute of Navigation*, v (1952), 345–50. See D. W. Waters, *The Art of Navigation in England in Elizabethan and Early Stuart Times* (London, 1958) for the general background.

3. William Bourne, *A Regiment for the Sea and other writings on navigation*, edited by E. G. R. Taylor (Cambridge, 1953), 415–33.

4. Edward Wright, *Certaine Errors in Nauigation &c.* (London, 1599); an extract from the mercator chart tables of Wright had been published in Thomas Blundeville, *His Exercises* (London, 1594). Wright produced an enlarged edition of his important work in 1610.

5. This is described in detail in my *op. cit.* above. The question why Harriot never published this work himself was considered by me in a short paper 'Harriot's work on the true sea-chart', *Actes du XIIᵉ Congrès International d'Histoire des Science Paris 1968* (Paris, 1971) iv, 135–8. Briefly, Wright's existing tables were adequate for practical purposes; Harriot was used to dealing with so-called 'classified' material; there were considerable printing problems for such an advanced exercise; Harriot, although undoubtedly convinced of the soundness of his work, may have realized that its newness and complexity might have failed to convince his contemporaries; the meridional parts are closely related to the *differentiae* of Napier's tables of 1614, and that Harriot most probably realized this is likely from some of his calculations; and finally, he had very comfortable patronage and had no need to draw attention to himself or run the risk of controversy (from which his earlier career had not been free). It is worth adding here that an orthographic projection is shown by Harriot at BM Add MS. 6782, f. 275.

6. See in particular D. W. Waters, *op. cit.*

7. The longitude was desirable, but not attainable accurately at sea, then or until much later. Dead reckoning using traverses was the best available way for nearly two centuries following.

8. That is, the altitude when the body crosses the meridian of the observer; in high latitudes, where the body is circumpolar, there are two such altitudes, but in lower latitudes it corresponds to the highest altitude of the body. For the sun, it gives the Local Noon, within a few minutes of the modern Mean Noon.

9. John Davis, *The Seamans Secrets* (London, 1595) announced the Davis, or back staff.

10. Pedro Nuñez, *De arte atque ratione navigandi libri due* (Coimbra, 1546) i, 45–6.

11. See Richard Eden's translation of Martin Cortes, *The Arte of Navigation* (London, 1561), f. lxxiii.

12. William Bourne, *A Regiment for the Sea* (London, 1574?) and later editions.

13. Refraction also was not well understood; Harriot was working on the refraction problem as early as 1584, as the Oslo University Library copy of F. Risner's edition of the works of Alhazen & Vitellio (Basle, 1572) shows. This copy contains valuable manuscript notes by Harriot. See J. A. Lohne, 'Thomas Harriot (1560–1621) The Tycho Brahe of Optics', *Centaurus*, vi (1959), 113–21. The volume was at Universitetsbibliotet I Oslo,

qFb 7055, but I believe that a removal and rearrangement of the library has been proposed.

14. See three papers by E. G. Forbes, (i) 'Tobias Mayer's Lunar Tables', *Annals of Science*, xxii (1966), 105–16; (ii) 'The Origin and Development of the Marine Chronometer', *Annals of Science*, xxii (1966), 1–25; (iii) 'The Foundation and Early Development of the Nautical Almanac', *J. Inst. Navigation*, xviii (1965), 391–401. The Lunar Distance method is considered in detail in an article by the staff of H. M. Nautical Almanac Office, 'A modern view of Lunar Distances', *J. Inst. Navigation* xix (1966), 131–53. The two-hundredth anniversary edition of *The Nautical Almanac and Astronomical Ephemeris* appeared as *The Nautical Almanac for the Year 1967* (London, 1966), and contains an historical section at pp. 3b–3n).

15. Richard Polter, *The Pathway to Perfect Sayling* (London, 1605), f. G1.v.

16. He thus had to have some idea which way to go, and mistakes here were the cause of disasters, for example that when, as late as 1707, Admiral Sir Cloudesley Shovell and some of his fleet were lost off the Scillies.

17. As for example in Bourne, *op. cit.*, or Table 5 of the present article.

18. A brief account of the development of the mercator chart is given in the Appendix to this chapter.

19. See, for example, P. Medina's *Arte de navegar* (Seville, 1545) or his *Regimiento de nauagacio* (Seville, 1543).

20. William Borough, *A Discours of the Variation of the Cumpas* (London, 1581).

21. See, for example, Simon Stevin, *Havenvinding* (Leyden, 1599). This appeared in English as Edward Wright, *The Havenfinding Art* (London, 1599).

22. Henry Gellibrand, *A Discourse Mathematical on the Variation of the Magneticall Needle. Together with its admirable diminution lately discovered* (London, 1635).

23. Some compasses had their wires placed so as to allow for the variation of the place in which they were made, but this could lead to further confusion, as the allowances varied.

24. Attention was drawn to these papers some years ago by E. G. R. Taylor, 'Hariot's Instructions for Ralegh's Voyage to Guiana, 1595', *J. Inst. Navigation*, v (1952), 345–350, but the following account is taken from my own transcription of the papers, and will amplify her description. The papers were not given a title, and in calling them the *Instructions* I follow Taylor's lead.

25. Of the distance of *Polaris* from the pole.

26. Among the fragments is the beginning of an unnumbered Chapter entitled:
How to know your course to sayle to any place assigned; & in sayling to make true reconing to find where you are at any time; & how farre from any place desired.   (f. 491)

27. There is a facsimile of the passage in Muriel Rukeyser's *The Traces of Thomas Hariot* (New York, 1971), 3rd plate following p. 144. The transcription given in D. B. Quinn's *The Roanoke Voyages 1584–1598,* (London, 1955), contains some misprints.

28. The full titles of this and later chapters are given above at page 58.

29. Jacob Whiddon, as commander of the small ship, *Pilgrim*, was present at the last fight of the *Revenge* off the Azores.

30. R. S. Ball, *A Treatise of Spherical Astronomy* (Cambridge, 1908), p. 85.

31. Details of this problem are worked out on f. 475.

32. Edward Rosen, *Three Copernican Treatises* (New York, 1959) 2nd edn., 61–2.

33. N. Copernicus, *De revolutionibus orbium caelestium* (Nuremberg, 1543), 89v, (iii, Ch. xviii).

34. Although it may be in Leconfield 241, ii, I have not been able to find it. From Fig. 4.6,
$$\sin \varphi = e \sin \psi = e \sin (\theta - \varphi),$$
and hence, as θ increases uniformly, the longitude is given by
$$a + 2\pi t/T - \tan^{-1} \{e \sin (2\pi t/T)/(1 + e \cos (2\pi t/T)\}.$$
It is hardly possible to recover the constants directly from the tables, but $a = 95°\ 30'$, $T = 365\cdot2$, and $e = 0\cdot0358$ produce the right sort of answer.

35. *N.P.* and *S.P.* are the North Pole and the South Pole respectively, Z the zenith, Hor. the horizon, λ the latitude, m.a. the meridian altitude, Aeq. the equator, decl. the declination, S the Sun, with a dotted line to show its motion.

36. In the notation used by Harriot, $3\bar{2}.15'$ is the modern $32°\ 15'$.

37. The work referred to is Rodrigo Zamorano, *Compendio de la Arte de Nauegar* (Seville, 1581).

38. E. Rosen, *op. cit.*, 111–14.

39. The earliest printed amplitude tables are said to be those of Ioao B. Lavanha, *Regimento Navtico* (Lisbon, 1595) [*The Principal Works of Simon Stevin* (Amsterdam, 1961), iii, 382–3], but these are not in the copy in the British Museum (C. 31. e. 42). It may be that they formed a separate part. Such tables were not published in England until much later.

40. In the addition to his father Leonard Digges' *Prognostication* (London).

41. It is bound separately at Leconfield MS 241, vi. b.

42. S. P. Rigaud mentions the manuscript in his *Supplement to Dr Bradley's Miscellaneous Works: with an account of Harriot's Astronomical Papers* (Oxford, 1833), 41, very briefly, and only in the context of magnetism where he says it does not contain 'even in the form of an example any quantity which can be supposed to be an observation which Harriot had made for himself of "the declination of the needle" '. That it did not do what it did not set out to do is hardly a fair criticism.

43. This list has been dealt with in a number of places. See either D. B. Quinn and J. W. Shirley, 'A contemporary list of Harriot references', *Renaissance Quarterly*, xxii (1969) 9–26, or J. V. Pepper 'Harriot's unpublished papers', *History of Science*, vi (1967) 17–40, in particular 33–6.

44. The four columns are of course in proportion.

45. Coygnet's version appeared in the *Instruction Nouvelle* (Angers, 1581), 70–83. E. G. R. Taylor, too, is wrong in saying, in 'The Doctrine of Nauticall Triangles Compendious', *J. Inst. Navigation*, vi (1953), 134, that Harriot maintained that any difference would be so small as to be negligible.

46. E. Gunter, *De Sectore et Radio* (London, 1623). See also entry for Gunter in *Dictionary of Scientific Biography*, vol. 5 (New York, 1972).

47. The idea has got about, originally I think from Markham's edition of Hues' work for the Hakluyt Society in 1889, that Harriot actually wrote the fifth part of Hues' *Tractatus de globis et eorum vsu &c.* (London, 1594), but this is a mistake arising from Markham's misreading of Hues' text at his p. 111.

48. E.g. those in *Inman's Nautical Tables* (London, 1957), 25–100.

49. In the *Archive* article noted above. Further, the conditions for conformal mapping can be expressed in partial differential equations, whose solution shows that the mercator chart is the only solution of its type. See R. S. Ball, *op. cit.*, Chap. 3.

50. Leconfield MS 241, vi. b, p. 6.

51. Leconfield MS 241, vi. b, pp. 8, 10.

52. 2. is cancelled in the manuscript. This is indicated by the vertical bar in the left hand margin here.

53. See my *Archive* article, *op. cit.* above.

54. By a slip of the pen, Harriot writes 'the' here twice.

55. D. T. Whiteside, *The Mathematical Papers of Isaac Newton* (Cambridge, 1967), i, 475.

56. In the *Archive* article, *op. cit.*

57. Although the idea of the chart neither originated with G. Mercator himself, nor was fully developed by him, it would be pedantic not to use the name deriving from his World Map of 1569, *Nova et aucta orbis terrae descriptio ad usum navigantium emendate accomodata* (Duisburg, 1569).

58. Johannes Kenning, 'The history of geographical map projections until 1600', *Imago Mundi*, xii (1955), 17, which quotes Drecker, *Annalen der Hydrographie* (1917). Pedro Nuñez' *Tratado da Esphera* (Lisbon, 1537) includes a *Tratado em defensam da carta de marear* at ff. 59–98v. Nuñez pointed out that the rhumb line was not a great circle, but a spiral.

59. Dee and Harriot were acquainted, as has been pointed out by earlier writers, and as is shown by the copy of Antonio de Espeio's *El Viaie que hizo Antonio de Espeio en el Anno de ochenta y tres &c.* (Madrid 1586, reprinted Paris 1586 by Hakluyt) in the British Museum (Press Mark C.32.a.32) which has on the title page the inscription

Joannes Dee: *Anno* 1590. Januarij 29. Ex dono Thomas Hariot, Amici mei.

There is also a mention of Mr. Dee on the page opposite the book list considered in the last Section, but this may be to one of Dee's sons, Arthur, later physician to Charles I.

60. Harriot has a copy of this table at Leconfield 241, iv, f. 10, 'A table of Mr. Wrightes in Blundevilles Treatise of Navigation'.

61. Wright's map on this projection, with the rhumbs marked, published in the 2nd edition of Hakluyt's *Principal Navigations* (vol. ii, 1599) probably gave rise to the comment in Shakespeare's *Twelfth Night* (III, ii) 'he does smile his face into more lines than is in the new map, with the augmentation of the Indyes'. (I have this reference from D. B. Quinn's 'Sailors and the Sea', *Shakespeare in his own Age* (ed. Allardyce Nicoll) (Cambridge, 1964), 21–36.)

62. They occur at BM Add MS 6788, ff. 205–10 v.

63. E. Halley, 'An Easie Demonstration of the Analogy of the Logarithmick Tangents to the Meridian Line or sum of the Secants: with various Methods for computing the same to the utmost Exactness', *Phil. Trans. Roy. Soc.*, xvi (1695), 202–14, in his addition to Richard Norwood's *History of Navigation* (London, 1659).

64. S. P. Rigaud, *Correspondence of Scientific Men &c.* (London, 1841), i, 87.

65. 'Concerning the Collection of Secants; & the True Division of the Meridian in the Sea-Chart', *Phil. Trans. Roy. Soc.*, xv (1685), 1193–1201.

66. These may be easily verified in modern notation, for example

$$\int_0^\lambda \sec \theta \; \mathrm{d}\theta = \int_0^\lambda \sec^2 \theta \; \mathrm{d}(\sin \theta) = \int_{\theta=0}^\lambda \mathrm{d}s/(1-s^2) = s + \tfrac{1}{3}s^2 + \tfrac{1}{5}s^2 + \dots$$

67. *Exercitations Geometricae* (London, 1668), 14–17, *Analogia inter Lineam Meridianam Planisphaerii Nautici & Tangentes Artificiales Geometricae demonstrata*.

68. *Lectiones Geometricae* (London, 1670), 111.

69. *Op. cit.*

70. 'On an integration ante-dating the integral calculus', *Bibliotheca Mathematica,* 3rd series, xiv (1913–14), 312–18.

71. D. T. Whiteside, *The Mathematical Papers of Isaac Newton* (Cambridge, 1967), i, 466–7, 473–5, & pl. iv, opp. 468.

5

HENRY STEVENS AND THE ASSOCIATES OF THOMAS HARRIOT

R. C. H. TANNER

ONE of the standard items in any bibliography on Harriot is the book generally referred to as *Thomas Hariot and his Associates* written nearly eighty-five years ago by Henry Stevens of Vermont (1819–86). The full title of the book runs:

THOMAS HARRIOT/The Mathematician/the Philosopher and/the Scholar/Developed/Chiefly/From/Dormant Materials/with notices of his associates/including biographical and/bibiographical disquisitions/upon the materials of the/history of 'ould/Virginia'/By Henry Stevens of Vermont/FSA, Student of American History/ Bibliographer and Lover of Books/LONDON/Privately Printed/MDCCCC[1]

I propose here to explore what Stevens discovered from his 'dormant materials', what new items about Harriot might be drawn from some of these materials, and some new information about the fate of the Harriot papers after his death.

Henry Stevens, though he has been referred to as a scholar,[2] was in fact as he says a bibliographer and lover of books and a student of American history. His interest in Harriot came about through Harriot's role in Ralegh's colonizing venture in Virginia and the subsequent publication of the first English book on the new world, Harriot's *Briefe and True Report of the New Found land of Virginia*, 1588. A search of the remaining Stevens papers gives few clues to the 'dormant materials' on which Stevens drew, and reveals only a few non-relevant collections in American libraries.[3] In these circumstances it is perhaps not surprising that as far as Harriot is concerned I can find no dormant material in Stevens' account that is not still dormant today in the sense that it still awaits adequate scholarly publication and comment.

With the exception of Harriot's will, the unpublished papers relevant to Harriot that Stevens refers to had been seen and reported on in print before his time and in those books which he mentions as sources. Stevens must have looked at the British Museum originals himself, since he transcribed letters from Additional MSS 6789, and pronounced the contents of the other volumes as containing 'much that is waste, but much also that is of importance equal to those at Petworth'. He did not see those at Petworth, but they had been sufficiently written about by von Zach (1785),[4] Hutton (1795),[5] Robertson

(1822),[6] Rigaud (1832–3), [7]and biographical reference books culminating in the most scholarly report of Agnes Clerke (1842–1907) in the 1885 edition of the *Dictionary of National Biography* the year before Stevens died, which indicated that the will had not been discovered. Had he fully recognized its importance, Stevens would have taken pains to have the discovery immediately publicised.[8]

The discovery of Harriot's will was perhaps Stevens' greatest accomplishment in Harriot research. The will contradicts much that had previously been said about Harriot, his work, and his friends, opened up for Stevens wide new fields for investigation, and was undoubtedly the basis for most of his subsequent studies. The biography of Harriot was never completed by Stevens, and he died before seeing his volume in proof and making corrections which he certainly could have done. His son, after some hesitation, finally published the book as it stood.

Passages in Stevens' text, possibly written at different times, are occasionally in contradiction with each other. For instance, in one place Stevens claims priority in publishing in one piece the well-known Lower letter of 6 February 1610, and later mentions in his sources that this had been printed long since by S. P. Rigaud (1774–1839).[9] Another instance is that on page 38 an 'important hitherto unpublished volume' is referred to on page 39 as 'since . . . edited with valuable notes by Mr. Charles Deane'. Such discrepancies are minor compared with mistakes due to misreading or misunderstanding, which would be more serious if we were to consider the work for what it never claimed to be—a piece of true scholarship. Its value resides in its being a fount of pointers for further study; and its value would be enhanced if it could be reprinted with adequate notes and an appendix to supplement its information.

Harriot's will also gives valuable information, some of which Stevens missed. The most important misinterpretation is on page 198 where an acknowledgement of debt by Harriot on his deathbed should read: 'at this present I do owe moneys to Monseir Mayernes apothycarie'. Stevens instead has written *Mayornes, a Potycarie*. In the next entry, too, he splits the word in the same way, though the entry should read: 'More to M' Wheatley apothecary dwelling neare the Stockes at the East end of Cheapside'. In the text, page 149, Stevens drops the terminal *s* but still writes Mayorne and distinguishes him as an apothecary, as opposed to the doctor, *Turner*, both, he adds, employed also by Ralegh. It is extremely odd that if Stevens knew this, he did not also recognize that Harriot is here referring to the King's own physician, *Theodore Turquet de Mayerne*,[10] the famous Huguenot doctor who did much to introduce chemical medicine and supersede the old Galenic point of view.

More astonishing still, in the sentence immediately preceding on page 148, Stevens refers to 'drafts of the three Latin letters to a friend at Court'. These he had earlier, page 141, reported as being in the British Museum—'three beautiful letters in Latin written from Syon in 1615 and 1616 to a friend of distinction, name not mentioned, who had recently been appointed to some medical office at court, in which he describes himself and his disease. These letters show great resignation and Christian fortitude. He seemed to be getting better in 1616, and expressed himself as somewhat hopeful.' It is clear that Stevens took pains to decipher the writing, which is in fact hardly legible, but overlooked Mayerne's name. Two only are addressed to Mayerne.[11] They follow one[12] which is about Mayerne addressed to Harriot and signed *Samuel Turner*. This Samuel Turner was the elder son of Harriot's and Ralegh's doctor Peter Turner.[13]

An interesting fact is that at the end of Harriot's second letter to Mayerne, he makes a confession of faith which has been more noticed than the main text with its rather gruesome, factually far more important medical details. This confession of faith has been overemphasized by Harriot's biographers who have been worried by the charges of atheism levelled against him,[14] and any counter-evidence has attracted attention. That it was called forth in this case by a presumption of a similar religious outlook in Mayerne is very plausible, in view of his Huguenot affiliation.

Together, these documents dispel the mystery and exaggeration that has surrounded the question of Harriot's health: they show his general condition was good even at this time when the cancer he suffered from had reached seriously alarming proportions; and the exact aspect and location of the tumour in the left nostril is accurately reported. Harriot exhibits here the same powers of meticulous observation and description that are so much admired in his *Briefe and True Report of the New Found Land of Virginia*.[15] Harriot also shows a very fair understanding of the nature of his case and of the minor disturbances incidental to the medical treatment. He asks Mayerne to take particular account of them when prescribing further drugs. Mayerne made a note for himself[16] of the substances involved without precise quantification and it is not clear whether a past or future treatment is meant. It is clearly his first examination of Harriot that he here recorded. He describes Harriot as a rather melancholy type, about sixty years old (by our reckoning he would have been 55) and the first person to introduce into England the use of tobacco smoke—something that Mayerne naturally saw in a medical light. Harriot, he also notes, had suffered from the complaint for about two years. Mayerne adds that a cure would be extremely difficult (*perdifficilis*).

The tumour is described as being so large that it made the lip hard and insensitive. This explains the rumour that still lingers on that the cancer was in the lip itself. Stevens had the chance of correcting it when he referred to Dr Alexander Read's report[17] (1635, not 1638 as Stevens states). He accurately identifies the passage by Treatise, Lecture, and page number, but failed to notice that the chapter is dedicated to ulcers and tumours of the *nose*, and merely repeats the quotation already familiar in Aubrey's day, beginning 'Cancerous ulcers also seize upon these parts', where Stevens inserts in square brackets the word 'lips', in disregard of Read's specific description.[18]

Read was considerably younger than Mayerne and was called in only at the last extremity, as he himself says. But he appears to have been very much of the old school, having in fact studied in France, which Mayerne left in disagreement with the reigning Faculty in Paris over his attempts at innovation. It was for this reason that Read ranked only as *Foreign Brother* of the Barber-Surgeons' Company at the time he visited Harriot. In 1618 he had been practising in Wales: perhaps acquaintance with Harriot's friends there drew him into consultation in the last resort. Read goes out of his way to mention the Earl of Northumberland, Harriot's patron, with great reverence, and three of Harriot's circle—Hughes, Warner, and Torporley—all still alive early in 1632, when we may suppose Read prepared these lectures. It is curious that he let these eulogies all stand unchanged in the final version delivered at the end of the year at the earliest, when all of them had died except Warner, who was now a really old man bu$_t$ still active—and who outlived them by another twelve years.[19]

The distinction between Mayerne and his apothecary mentioned in Harriot's will is underlined by the postscript to one of the two letters to the physician which shows the apothecary to have acted as postbox as well as supplier of medicines. The other apothecary who had supplied Harriot on credit, 'Mr Wheately', can be identified a little more personally in the manuscript records of the Society of Apothecaries in the Guildhall Library of London.[20] The Society, founded in 1617, elected Wheatley as one of three to fill vacancies in the *Court of Assistants*. Although he appears not to have attended many meetings of the Court, his name still occurs in 1624.

The most interesting of Harriot's debts mentioned in the will is that 'to Mr. John Bill Stationer for Books'. (See Plate 3.) Stevens might have investigated this item with profit for this is the well-known John Bill,[21] King's Printer and bookseller in London from 1604 until his death in 1630. (Harriot's posthumus mathematical work, the *Artis analyticae Praxis*,[22] was issued from his office the year after John Bill died.)

Harriot's direct association with John Bill is shown by his acknowledged debt in an account for books which he incurred between 31st October 1617 and July 1618. The list is preserved among the other Harriot manuscripts at Petworth; it is a highly informative document.[23] It is headed: 'To the right wors: Mr Thomas Harriot 31 October 1617' with the date of '29 Jul. 1618' entered at the end against: 'Re in part . . . 5.0.0' and a final note: Re'd backe Alexander de Alex. 5.10.0 13 Julie 1619', showing that at that date the balance of the account, presumably reduced to £3.5.0, was outstanding and no doubt still was when Harriot died two years later.

An identification of the items listed as Harriot purchases forces appreciation of the enormous programme of reading which Harriot had embarked upon. A word of explanation regarding John Bill's activities is necessary to understand some of the listings.

John Bill had from the start of his career travelled abroad to buy books for the Bodleian Library at Oxford and he continued doing so for other wealthy clients, including King James, after he set up in London. In 1617, he began the issue of a London edition of the twice-yearly Frankfurt Mess-Katalog,[24] the catalogue of the Frankfurt bookfair which he had been regularly visiting. Harriot's list includes in two places the entry: **1** *Catalogus nundinarum 0.0.6.* What might otherwise have been taken to be simply a calendar of market-days in Britain may thus with certainty be recognized as the current Spring or Autumn number of the bookfair catalogue brought out by John Bill. To cor-roborate this, most of the foreign books and many of the British items in Harriot's bill are listed in the catalogues.

Other items in the bill reveal Harriot's known major interests, notably Kepler's *Epitome Astronomiae Copernicanae* and his two current *Ephemerides*; Snell's *Erosthenes Batavus* (1617) and his *Observations* of 1618; Quir's *Terra Australis Incognita* (1617); and even the *Mercurius gallo-belgicus*, a twice-yearly magazine on current events printed at Frankfurt which covered such things as astronomical phenomena. Another understandable purchase was that of the first *London Pharmacopoeia*, published in 1618, with Mayerne as one of the chief contributors.

The purchase of the works of the early 16th-century humanist lawyer of Naples, Alexander ab Alexandro,[25] seems, on the other hand, to stand alone; but as this item was in fact returned and credited in full, it may have been sup-plied in error. The entry 'Martin's Chronicle' is more problematical: it would seem to mean the *Historie and Lives of the Kings of England* by William Martyn,[26] published in London in 1615 for John Bill, but there is a dis-crepancy in the format, which should be 4°, but is given as 'fo'. All the other indications of format are accurate and furnish considerable help in identifying the works.

Stevens now turns to some of Harriot's associates mentioned in the will. Among these, the author quaintly lists 'the last lord Harrington' without quo-tation marks (page 97) with other 'pupils' of Harriot, because Harriot so describes him in his directions relating to his mathematical papers, and Stevens knows no more of him. Had he known, he would have been delighted to expand on such an entry. 'The last lord Harrington' in 1621 can only have been the second and last Baron Harington of Exton in county Rutland[27] who had died in 1614 aged not quite 22. He was the only son, bearing the same name John, of the John Harington created Baron at King James's coronation in 1603 and entrusted with the education of the King's daughter Princess Elizabeth.[28] She lived with the Harington family in a kind of boarding-house for highborn young ladies which the parents ran. John Harington the son had been an intimate friend of Elizabeth's eldest brother, Henry Prince of Wales,[29] whose death at the age of 18 in 1612, less than two years before that of his friend Harington, was seen then, as now, as a national tragedy.[30]

John Harington was certainly an exemplary young nobleman, studious and devout, very suited to the serious side of Prince Henry. Abroad a good deal, as belonged to his station in life, he reported assiduously to the Prince in his letters, as well as he could for the suspicions and jealousies always rife in court circles. He longed to return to England to spend the rest of his life in close companionship with his friend. But when he finally settled in England at his father's death in 1613, Henry was already dead and the Harington family estates were encumbered through the father's liberality and expenditure in the service of King James. John had a sorry time of it trying to restore the family fortunes during those last two years of his life, so that his sisters might not suffer. Until he succeeded to the barony (the lowest rank of peerage), he was Sir John Harington and could not have been referred to as Lord; and Harriot would have alluded to this circumstance had the copy of Harriot's mathematical papers at Syon House made by him antedated his peerage—unlikely in any case since he was mostly out of England then. Thus Harington's contact with Harriot as revealed by the will cannot be directly linked with the occurrence of Prince Henry's own name in at least two of Harriot's mathematical papers.[31]

However, the two manuscripts mentioning Prince Henry are of much more than passing interest and justify listing him as at least an indirect associate of Harriot. Both are included among the 'bundles' listed as given to Nathaniel Torporley to look through after Harriot's death in compliance with the will.[32] Much remains to be said about both, but for the present it will suffice to mention that one gives the solution of a cubic equation to which the words *Henricus Princeps* are appended, the other is an exercise in combinatorics with the phrase *Henricus princeps fecit* which could have been used in devising a cypher.

Stevens mentions Prince Henry only once (page 155) as the owner of a volume of great typographic beauty and rarity which Stevens claims must have served as model for the printing of Harriot's 'Algebra' in 1631. This was Vièta's three algebraic works (1591, 1593, 1600) bound together in one volume with the arms and motto of the Prince of Wales on the binding.[33]

Coupled with Harington's name in the will is that of Sir Robert Sydney, knight, Viscount Lisle,[34] who was to be given the notes that John Harington had transcribed. This Robert Sidney was the nephew of the great Philip Sidney and son of Philip's younger brother Robert, who had been created Earl of Leicester in 1618, reviving a title forfeited by the unfortunate Dudley in the reign of Elizabeth. Young Robert was then 23 and as the eldest surviving son took his father's second title, Viscount Lisle, a courtesy title without legal right. Two years earlier, in 1616, he had married Dorothy Percy,[35] eldest of the two daughters of Harriot's patron, the ninth Earl of Northumberland. In the Earl's household account-rolls that we know,[36] Harriot's pension of £100 annually compares favourably with those of the Earl's younger brother at this time; so the connection of friendship between Harriot and the son-in-law could rank as fairly close. But Harriot is meticulously deferential in constituting him also one of his four executors later on in the will, with the proviso 'if his Lordship may take so many pains on my behalf'. Four years later, in fact, in 1626, Lisle succeeded his father as Earl and was very probably fully taken up with his family and the state affairs incumbent on his new rank. But it is possible that during the intervening five years he shared with the other executors in supporting Harriot's plan that his mathematical papers should, as they thought fit, be prepared for publication by Nathaniel Torporley. It is probably not a mere coincidence that, in the same year 1626 when Lord Lisle may legitimately have retired from that scene as Earl of Leicester, Torporley received an isolated payment from the Earl of Northumberland direct.[37] Before the will was found, it had always been supposed (and is still so stated in D.N.B.), that Lord Lisle retained a half share of Harriot's papers. The will indicates that he must have carried off at least the 'fiue quires of paper, more or lesse' left to him expressly; they still may lurk somewhere among family archives.

Stevens' comments on other personages mentioned in Harriot's will are only briefly supplemented in the following paragraphs, as they are considered more fully elsewhere in published or forth-coming accounts. The famous scholar Thomas Allen (or Alleyn, 1542–1632) 'of Gloster Hall in Oxford M^r of Arts', had lent Harriot 'some written Coppies to the number of twelue or fowrteene (more or lesse)', and these were to be returned to him safely 'according to the noate that hee shall deliuer of them'. Allen liberally allowed manuscripts from his splendid library to be borrowed by other scholars and students. A note of those loaned to Harriot would be very interesting and may have included the copy of Roger Bacon's *Opus Tertium* which Harriot excerpted,[38] including apparently the fragment unknown in more modern times till discovered in part in 1909 by Duhem.[39]

Thomas Aylesbury (1576–1657), named an executor of the will, was described as 'Harriot's pupil' in the index by Stevens, and grandly 'the great-grandfather of two queens of England' (page 97). But for Harriot, Aylesbury was simply 'of Westminster, Esquier', and, at the date of the will, was secretary (since 1605) to the Earl of Nottingham, until recently Lord High Admiral. He was 'S^r Th. A' (baronet since 1627) when he wrote the letter (5 July 1632) about printing further mathematical papers of Harriot's which Stevens reprints (pages 189–90), going directly to the copy by Warner in the Pell collection of papers in the British Museum for the attribution to Aylesbury.[40] In 1634 Aylesbury became father-in-law to Edward Hyde (1609–74), created Earl of Clarendon in 1661. In the political upheavals that followed, Aylesbury was forced into exile (1642), stripped of the fortune which he had liberally devoted to the support of scholarship till then. He was the executor most conversant with Harriot's mathematics and the loss of his papers is undoubtedly a major factor in the paucity of relevant information that has reached us.

On a very different plane, another of the executors, Thomas Buckner, 'Mercer' in the City of London, may be identified as a companion of Harriot's on the Virginia voyage of 1585, though little else is known of him beyond the special mention he receives in the will as he 'at whose house being in St Christophers parishe I now lye'. This house in London City may, as has been suggested, have served Harriot now and at other times when he made the journey from Syon House in Brentford to consult Mayerne. Overnight stay on visits to the Earl his patron (still in the Tower) was otherwise provided for by the prison authorities. In this visit the will hints rather at an exceptional emergency of considerable magnitude, since Harriot estimates at 'the somme of fifteen poundes' what the executors should allow 'M^{ris} Buckner', the wife, 'towards the reparacions of some damages' that he had made, adding, however, 'or for other uses as shee shall thincke convenient'. Buckner's son was to get five pounds, but Buckner himself only his share of what the four executors would together decide to repay themselves for 'Charges on my behalfe out of the rest of my goods' when all specific bequests had been complied with.

Robert Hues (or Hughes, 1553–1632), one of the beneficiaries to whom these related, still has a somewhat misty connection with Harriot. He is said by Wood to have 'translated himself to S Mary's hall' from Brasenose, to take his B.A. 'at about 7 years standing'. So his acquaintance with Harriot may have gone back to their undergraduate days there.[41]

Henry Percy (1564–1632), Harriot's patron himself, ninth Earl of Northumberland (1585), is of course plentifully noticed by Stevens. His imprisonment for life under Queen Elizabeth was owing to the part played by his cousin and pensioner Thomas Percy (1560–1605) in the Gunpowder Plot (1605), but was terminated after sixteen years by James I in 1621, a few months after Harriot's death. He at once retired to his country estate at Petworth in Sussex where the mathematical papers directed by Harriot to be preserved in the Earl's Library survived, though now divided between Petworth House and the British Museum.

The chief legatee concerned with these papers, Nathaniel Torporley, mathematician and clergyman (1564–1632), has been the subject of many hearsay reports. A close examination of authentic evidence has still to be made, including a number of facts, like his significance (overlooked or ignored) in relation to Harriot and his circle. Like the Sidneys, Torporley was at Shrewsbury School and Christ Church, Oxford, the indications being that his father was a 'plebeian' burgess of Shrewsbury.[42]

Harriot's other executor, Protheroe,[43] got Torporley to witness his will;

and Torporley's own will in 1632 refers to John Protheroe (who died eight years previously) as his debtor for three hundred pounds paid him for an annuity of forty pounds 'which annuity I never received and is now in suite', i.e., still awaiting legal sanction owing probably to the fact that Protheroe's son (another John, born posthumously) was still an infant.

Stevens has little to say about Walter Warner,[44] the older mathematician in the service of the Earl of Northumberland whom Harriot mentions only as an authority on his 'manner of Notacions or writings'. The friendship and admiration of the much younger John Pell (1610–85) has preserved much manuscript evidence, still unassessed, on Warner's scientific activity under the protection of the ninth Earl at Syon House. Pell couples his name with that of Oughtred, as the likeliest in England, if it were not for his great age, to be πρὸς ταυτα ἰχαγόσ (proficient in all). In 1644 when Warner was dead Pell was still expecting to see 'Mr Warner's Analogickes' published.[45]

Nothing has been found so far about the servants and relations also mentioned by Harriot, though the glass-grinder Christopher Tooke is often cited in biographies and a distant connection with the contemporary and well-known family in Hertfordshire is not excluded.

Of Stevens' comments relevant to Harriot's will, those on Nathaniel Torporley reflect an insight and accuracy not characteristic of his book as a whole. Stevens devoted nearly one-fifth of his book to Harriot's mathematics—a proportion nearer the true picture of Harriot's overall activity than is deducible from many more modern accounts. The description of Torporley's two mathematical manuscripts at Sion College given on pages 170 and 172 testifies to a firsthand acquaintance sufficient for a creditable appreciation:

The more important one comprises 116 closely written folio leaves, or 232 pages, all in Torporley's handwriting. . . . it appears to be nothing more nor less than Torporley's attempt to pen out such doctrine as he found in Hariot's papers. The leaves are numbered, 1 to 16 containing a Treatise on Hariot's Theory of Numbers. Leaves 17 to 25 are Tables of [46] divisors of odd numbers up to 20,300. On the verso of leaf 25 the Theory of Numbers is resumed extending to the recto of 27. Leaves 35 to 55 comprise examples of Algebraic processes, and leaves 56 to 116 contain Tables (probably tabulae sinuum?) up to 180°. On the second leaf the Author speaks of himself as working out, or working on Hariot's principles, and also as making use of the writings of Vieta.

Translating Torporley's Latin a little more exactly, Stevens quotes further:

And since it is our principal design to explain the improvement in this science [the Properties of Numbers and Triangles] discovered by our friend Thomas Hariot; but he neither completely reformed it (which indeed was not necessary) nor gave a full account of it, but only strengthened it where it was defective, and by treating in his own way the points of the science which were heretofore more difficult, rendered them clear and easy.

With remarkable flair Stevens has picked here on the one passage in Torporley's extended and voluble writing that presents for us the very picture gained from a personal examination of Harriot's surviving papers. Stevens has, however, broken off in mid-sentence: an extensive qualifying clause follows which makes very plain that Torporley intends to be no mere amanuensis. This position is repeatedly underlined in other passages. And on folio 5 recto Torporley thus sets out the programme of his projected treatise:

Numeris compositis vel alias primis degnoscendis
Facultate Congestiva invento Hariotaeo nostroque
Divisione ingeminata
Radicalium dispensatione Hariotaea
Speciosa Logistica ab eodem perfecta a V.F. profesta

De proponimus nobis ad agendum,

so coupling himself with Harriot as co-discoverer of the 'Congestive Faculty' that was to form his second theme of discourse.

Torporley's direct references to Harriot, scattered over discursive historical and philosophizing observations, are of great personal interest in reflecting on the relationship between them and on Harriot's vast reputation in the circle of contemporaries whom Torporley addresses, though in their view Torporley was an inferior mathematician. Yet he sounds an underlying note of intimate knowledge and the same attitude is revealed in the title-page to the second document described by Stevens (and at greater length, pages 172–6).

Present-day concern with Harriot's manuscripts, however, centres on a question that Torporley's Sion College MSS answer in a manner surprising from every point of view: which of Harriot's manuscripts were in Torporley's hands? In particular, do they give evidence of more than have come down to us? They do not, and virtually every original Harriot paper used by Torporley may be identified among the two collections at the British Museum and at Petworth, though not without considerable labour for they are widely dispersed among their many miscellaneous folios, bound in the disordered state in which they were found. Torporley has meticulously crammed symbol for symbol well over 150 large sized pages of Harriot's mathematical writings into the twenty folios (35 to 55) that Stevens dismisses somewhat perfunctorily as comprising 'examples of Algebraic processes'. It is, however, astonishing and gratifying for us who are thus enabled to gather together in correct sequence correlated pages with relatively little further toil. In additon, Torporley has provided a valuable table of contents for his transcription, with a separate index to the seventeen types of algebraic equation discussed (folio 54 verso).

Four further non-transcribed mathematical works of Harriot on geometric combinatorics, triangular numbers, and progressions are listed. The transcribed topics are as follows in the table of contents:

1. *Operationes logisticae in notis.*
2. *De Radicalibus.*
3. *De numeris planis et binomialium linearum speciebus.*
4. *Apotome ex linea secta extreme et media sectione.*

5. *De speciebus irrationalibus ab Euclide omissis.*

6. *De cubo binomii.*

7. *De extractione radicis quadratae et cubicae e solido binomio.*

8. *De generatione Aequationum canonicarum.*

9. *De resolutione aequationum per reductionem* . . .

10. *De numerosa potestatum resolutione* . . .

11. *Exempla aeguationum in numeris* . . .

12. *Aliquot quaesticulae.*

13. *Effectiones.*

14. *Ad numeros triangulos, quadraticos, pentagonos &c. et illorum species.*

15. *Combinations, transpositions.*

16. *Lemmata . . . via generalis extractionis radicorum.*[47]

The most interesting section is of course the eighth in which Harriot's factorization method for the resolution of algebraic equations is built up in reverse by multiplying together linear or quadratic factors with a as the unknown taken to be positive. This is the basis equally of the exposition of Harriot's algebra in the *Praxis*; and the following section 9 includes the crucial inequalities which are Harriot's necessary conditions for resolution in positive numbers, as set forth in the *Praxis* page 78 (misprinted 72) et seq.[48]

But Torporley has transcribed far more than the *Praxis* comes near to hinting at, and, greatly to his credit, has included all the advanced treatment of algebraic equations beyond the stage of purely positive solutions, to which the *Praxis* was confined, possibly in fear of proceeding too fast with innovations; disagreement among the editors must not, however, be excluded. Opinion had not yet crystallized in 1631 even on the question of the sign of the square of a negative number, still less on that of its square root.

That Harriot was conversant with complex (or as he called them, noetic) numbers—also referred to as *impossible* even in their current use in the early 19th Century—has long been noticed without becoming general knowledge. The relevant plate in Rigaud's *Account of Harriot's astronomical papers*[49] shows in facsimile the Petworth folio giving the full solution of a quartic equation with the roots $+5, -7, +1+\sqrt{-32}, +1-\sqrt{-32}$ written exactly as we write them. The page illustrates two characteristics of Harriot's notes on algebraic equations *in numeris*: one is his habit, confusing for a newcomer, of heading the page with the conjugate equation (substituting $-a$ for the unknown a) alongside the one he proceeds to work out, each with its real roots above, from which obviously the equations are derived behind the scenes; the other is a much more general custom of his, always to produce at least one alternative treatment, as a check, or simply as a variant giving a further if not preferable illustration of method. The scarcity of verbal text is also characteristic: the symbolic lay-out is to speak for itself and rules of procedure are to emerge from inspection. Torporley adds no comments of his own. This second manuscript is obviously not a sequel to the first, but it is equally manifestly the material he intended to use for that sequel. The strong impression is that he made the transcription under great pressure. Towards the end he begins to condense even further to save space and time. Where, for example, Harriot repeats a letter the exact full number of times its power requires, Torporley abbreviates by placing that number in Roman numerals over one specimen of that letter. The idea of an exponential notation does not enter his head: the same device serves for one or two other instances in which the repetition does not represent a power.

How Torporley produces Harriot's work when he has ample leisure is exemplified in his manuscript I, where he reproduces (folios 26–7), (again literally transcribed but crammed to fill the page, though not so minutely) a complete section of Harriot's mathematical notes, those on Pythagorean triples (solutions of $x^2 + y^2 = z^2$ in whole numbers). The original stands in B.M. ADD 6782 folios 84–8.[50]

Torporley introduces the transcription to counter the impression he recognized as inevitable that he was using the project as a chance to air his own ideas. Stressing the beauty of Harriot's construction, he admits the likelihood that his own discursive commentary on it (folio 27 et seq.) will not be thought adequate and he challenges the reader to provide his own *proprio Marte*. In this Harriot again gives no verbal explanation but so tabulates his triples that a glance shows their construction rule. In this respect he has much improved on the first version he drew up at the start (folio 84), skipped in Torporley's transcription, which, however, loses much of the immediacy of appeal by sacrificing Harriot's staggered arrangement to save space. More still is lost if we translate into general algebraic formulae. Torporley exemplifies by his following commentary how awkward the result is to formulate in words. He is more concerned with Harriot's challenge to the authoritative assertion by Stifelius quoted at the outset than with the basis of Harriot's finite difference method of classification, providing him with an infinity of 'orders' where Stifelius knew of only two.

Torporley was puzzled also at a cryptic note Harriot has at the bottom of his tabulation on folio 85:

Hìc sunt omnes primì
sed hìc omnes non sunt primì.

Beginning with Harriot's introductory remark, folio 84:

Examinatur Stifelius
de numeris diagonalibus: pa.150
et Praetorius pag.ult
Dixit q/ rationes omnium laterum sunt in istis duobus ordinis.
Ego dico q/ non.
ordines sunt alij infiniti. ut per sequentis patet.

Torporley comments: 'Et notanda est eius lasciviendi consuetudo in phrasi illa (dico quod non)/qua uti solebat ioculariter ad veterum non tam imitation-

To the right wor: mr Thomas Harrot 31 octob

1	Eraslosthenis Batauus 4o	0	4	6
1	Flood de vita et morte 4o	0	1	6
1	Kepleri epitome Astronomia 8o	0	2	8
1	Soalatensis de Republica fo	0	13	0
1	Terra Australis 4o	0		7
1	Mercurius 8o	0	1	0
1	Lessius de summo bono 8o	0	3	0
1	de Iure et Iustitia fo	0	17	0
1	whites defence 4o	0	3	6
1	Bedro vmo Lecorum 8o	0	2	6
1	Silem defensio Armini 8o	0	0	6
1	Libauij fama 8o dutch	0	1	0
1	Secunda remonstrantia 4o	0	1	6
1	Alexander de Alexandro fo 269	5	15	0
1	Orthodoxographia Patrum fo	1	0	0
1	Hookers tracts	0	2	6
1	Abbot contra Tomson 4o	0	2	6
1	Mercurius 8o	0	1	0
1	Bradwardmus fo	0	15	0
1	Catalogus nundinarum 4o	0	0	6
1	Marius contra soalatensis 8o	0	3	0
1	Kepleri Ephemerides 4o	0	4	0
1	Berstj rymenaeus 4o	0	2	6
1	B of Andrews sermon 4o	0	1	0
1	Rocke of Christian warfare 4o	0	2	0
1	Cassani opera 8o	0	11	0
1	Augustinus contra Iulianum 8o	0	3	0
1	Maretis Chronicle fo	0	8	0
1	Pharmacopoeia Londinensis fo	0	7	0
1	B of Chichers sermons 4o	0	2	0
1	Catalogus nundinarum 4o	0	0	6
		12	12	11

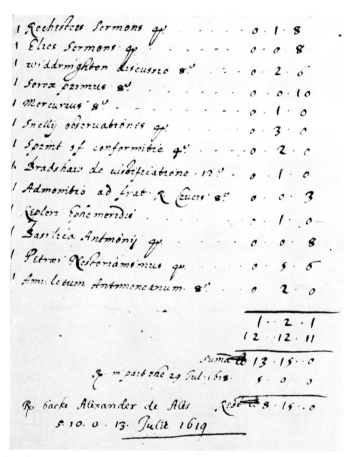

1 Rochester Sermons qᵒ	. . . —	0	1	8
1 Elies Sermons qᵒ	. . . —	0	0	8
1 Widdrington discussio 8ᵒ	. .	0	2	6
1 Sorex primus 8ᵒ	. .	0	0	10
1 Mercurius 8ᵒ	. .	0	1	0
1 Snelli observationes qᵒ		0	3	0
1 Spemt of conformitie qᵒ	. .	0	2	0
1 Bradshaw de uisbificatione 12ᵒ		0	1	0
1 Admonitio ad frat R Cruci 8ᵒ		0	0	3
1 Kepler Ephemerides			1	0
1 Basilica Antmonij qᵒ		0	0	8
1 Petræ Nestoriæ minus qᵒ		0	5	6
1 Amuletum Antmoneanum 8ᵒ		0	2	0

1	2	1
12	12	11

Summa ⅊ 13 . 15 . 0

Ite. m paid the 29 Jul. 1618 5 . 0 . 0

Ro backe Alexander de Ales   Rest ⅊ 8 . 15 . 0
5 . 10 . 0 . 13 . Julie 1619

Plate 3. The bill mentioned in Harriot's will 'to Mr. John Bill Stationer for Books'.

em quam irrisionem./Atque haud scio an iocone an serio in forma contra-
dicenti testimonium dederit/de numeris omnibus primis sed omnibus non
primis.' This is a unique first-hand contemporary glimpse of Harriot in
lighter vein. Other personal remarks in the course of Torporley's screed also
call for further study.

It must seem strange to many that Torporley selected out of Harriot's
mathematical papers so little else now recognized as pioneering work. It must
be supposed that other discoveries were already common knowledge, as was
certainly the case with Harriot's evaluation of the area of a spherical triangle
in 1603.[51]

Torporley's name occurs rarely in Harriot's manuscripts, among two
hundred authorities, ancient or contemporary, whom he refers to for one purpose or another. In one place it appears in cypher (B.M. ADD 6787, folio
241^v) beside a quadratic equation in the symbols of Stifelius and Recorde.
Torporley's own work on spherical triangles, published in 1602,[52] is never
mentioned as far as I know. But at least two pages of text in his handwriting
on that subject were found among Harriot's (B.M. ADD 6787, folios 126-7,
both verso, the rectos being blank). Among other evidence,[53] the cypher which
they both used[54] testifies to a closeness between them at different times in their
life. This is not so evident from Harriot's will in 1621, since he expected his
friend to have some trouble in mastering his novel mathematical symbolism.
By the time of Torporley's transcript, however, he had certainly completely
mastered it, but showed little sign of having adopted it as his own. He was
probably not inclined to give up a lifetime's habit of verbal exposition, with a
pedantic love of complication, while genuinely admiring Harriot's feat of
sobriety and simplification. Torporley takes it for granted that he is expected
to reproduce with absolute faithfulness what Harriot had designed (folio 26,
lines 27-8):

Nam cum esset ille tantae authoritatis apud noscentes . . . consultum plane fuerit,
quae sua erant integra et intaminato, ne litera quidem immutata describerem.

We may well therefore imagine Torporley's shock when he found the
Praxis printed with scarce regard for literal reproduction and drastically cur-
tailing the scope of Harriot's doctrine. However justified in this respect, his
consequent tirade against the editors, unfinished and perhaps never intended
for public release, has been dismissed in much the same spirit as Stevens evinces
in opining that it was (page 173) 'begun in senile peevishness . . . and discussing some algebraic questions with the fancied errors of the editors'
(regarded by Stevens as 'all eminent mathematicians' above Torporley's standing). And the suspicion (page 175) is endorsed 'that Torporley's age and dila-
toriness compelled the accomplished executors to take the editorial matter in
hand themselves *et hinc illae lacrimae*.' A more exact evaluation of the circumstances is afforded on a less superficial inspection of this document.

T.H.—8

NOTES

1. This work, though well known, is understandably rare since it was published in an edition, limited to thirty-three Large Paper and one hundred and sixty-two Small Paper copies.

2. A. C. Crombie, J. V. Pepper, D. B. Quinn, J. W. Shirley, and R. C. H. Tanner, 'Thomas Harriot (1560–1621): an original practitioner in the scientific art', (London) *Times Literary Supplement*, 23 October 1969.

3. Correspondence with Stevens' biographer, Wyman Parker, Olin Librarian of Weslyan University, Middletown, Connecticut, and with descendants of Stevens, still antiquarian booksellers and publishers, though no longer in London, revealed a collection of papers at the Clements Library in Ann Arbor, Michigan, which proved, upon examination, not to be relevant. Another collection at the Guy W. Bailey Library of the University of Vermont belongs to the period before 1864 and, hence, cannot concern his work on Harriot. The later papers of Stevens up to his death appear to be in the Lawrence Clark Powell Library of the University of California at Los Angeles, and these demand further study which I have not been able to give them.

4. See especially Baron von Zach, 'Anzeige von den in England aufgefundenen Harriotschen Manuscripten . . .'. London, 26 Nov. 1784, in J. E. Bode's *Berliner astronomisches Jahrbuch*, etc., Berlin, 1785.

5. Charles Hutton (1737–1823), *A Mathematical and Philosophical Dictionary*, 2 vols. London, 1796. The article on Harriot, reprinting von Zach, is in volume 1, pp. 584–6.

6. Dr. A. Robertson, 'An Account of some Mistakes relating to . . . Harriot's MSS', *The Edinburgh Philosophical Journal*, VI (1822), pp. 313–8.

7. Stephen P. Rigaud, *Supplement to Dr. Bradley's Miscellaneous Works: with an account of Harriot's Astronomical Papers,* Oxford, University Press, 1833.

8. Even the publication in 1900, limited as it was, did not forcibly bring the will to public attention. The will was rediscovered by an unknown 'Mr. Walford' and printed as if new by Henry R. Plomer in an article 'The Will of Thomas Harriot, Mathematician and Astronomer (1560–1621)' in *The Home Counties Magazine*, VIII (1906), pp. 240–7. In spite of this, the second edition of the *Dictionary of National Biography*, issued in 1908, continued to reprint Agnes Clerke's article on Harriot with the statement that the will has not been found. So far as I know, this has not been corrected to this date.

9. The first part of the letter had been published by von Zach as a letter from Henry Percy to Harriot. Rigaud found the second half, and on the basis of the signature, ascribed it correctly to Sir William Lower.

10. Sources for the life of Sir Theodore Turquet de Mayerne (1573–1655) are listed in Irene Scouloudi's thesis, 'Sir Theodore Turquet de Mayerne (1573–1655)', *Proceedings of the Huguenot Society of London*, XVI (1937–41), pp. 301–37.

11. British Museum, Additional MSS 6789, ff. 446$^{r \& v}$, 447^r.

12. *Ibid.*, f. 442^r.

13. Peter Turner (1542–1614) is indicated in the PRO records (*Cal. St. P. Dom.* 1603–10, 307) as having attended Sir Walter in the Tower in 1606. His son, Samuel, graduated like his father from a foreign university, but is best known for his political activities as a royalist in later years. Another son, Peter (1585–1651), a mathematician, succeeded Henry Briggs as professor of geometry at Gresham College. Both Samuel and Peter entered Harriot's college, St. Mary's Hall at Oxford, at the turn of the century.

14. See, particularly, Dr. Jean Jacquot, 'Thomas Harriot's Reputation for Impiety', *Notes and Records of the Royal Society of London*, XI (1952), pp. 164–86.

15. Harriot's *Briefe and True Report* and the circumstances of its publication in London occupy sixty-four pages of his book.

16. Mayerne's own case note on Harriot is to be found in the British Museum, Sloane MS 3086, f. 57^r. This note begins: *Mr. Hariot. Vir admodum melancolicus. Annorum circiter sexagint. primus ex Virginia innexit in Angliam usum fumi tabaci. Ulcus* χαρχυνῶδες *in nare sinistra quod septum nasi depascitur & pro magnitudine sua habet labia dura & innersa. Non serpit multum intra narem. Hoc malum patitur aeger a biennio & medicamentis sedulo adhibitis*

id perstitit ne abiret in deterius. Observami aegris maxime noxias esse pinguedines. (Abbreviations expanded.)

17. Dr Alexander Read, *The Chirurgicall Lectures of Tumors and Ulcers* . . . , London, 1635, p. 307. The new edition of Read's *Works* (1650) plainly distinguishes the two topics by dividing the lecture into two halves. See my 'La place de Thomas Harriot dans l'histoire de la medecine et de l'astronomie', *Gesnerus*, XXIV (1967), pp. 75–7.

18. The section concerned begins on page 299: 'Lect. XXVI. *Of Ozaena*'. The second sentence starts 'Of all the ulcers of the nose . . .'. The Harriot passage is on page 307, and is followed by further advice of a general nature on nasal tumors. It is not until page 310 that we read 'As for ulcers of the lips'.

19. The passage is entirely out of character; nothing like this digression appears elsewhere in the treatise. Unfortunately it has been adopted into Harriot lore as evidence that Torporley was supported at Syon House by 'the Noble Earl in the Tower' which was not so, see below, note 36.

20. This information I owe to Leslie Matthews, author of many authoritative works on the history of pharmacy, including his *The Royal Apothecaries*, London, 1967.

21. See E. Arber, *A Transcript of the Stationers' Registers, 1554–1640*, 5 vols. London, 1875–94, Index I. Also R. G. McKerrow, *Dictionary of Printers and Booksellers in England, Scotland, and Ireland, and of Foreign Printers of English Books, 1557–1640*, London, 1910.

22. Thomas Harriot, *Artis Analyticae Praxis ad Æquationes Algebraicas noua, expedita, & generali methodo, resoluendas,* Londoni, Apud Robertum Barker, Typographum Regium, et Haered, Io. Bilii. Anno 1631. Brought out ten years after Harriot's death, the contents purported to be selected from the papers he left behind. This work was undoubtedly the outcome of joint efforts of the executors of Harriot's will, and of Nathaniel Torporley, literary executor under the terms of the will, with Walter Warner as *de facto* editor.

23. Petworth collection of Harriot Manuscripts, HMC 241/IV/9.

24. *Catalogus vniuersalis pro nundinis Francofurtensibus, &c,* London, Apud Ioannem Billium. See *The Cambridge History of English Literature*, 1909, Vol. IV, Chapter XVII, 'The Book-Trade, 1557–1625', p. 406.

25. His *Opera Juridica* in 7 volumes folio appeared at Frankfurt in 1616–17. See D. Maffei, *Alessandro d'Allessandro, giureconsulto umanista, 1461–1523*, Milano, 1956.

26. William Martin or Martyn (1562–1617), Recorder of Exeter.

27. John Har(r)yngton (1592–1614), Lord (1613). For source material, see Ian Grimble, *The Harrington Family*, London, 1957. Sources include the edition of family papers made by Henry Harington (1755–91) in 1769, in the not altogether complete re-edition by Thomas Park (1804), where it supplements Thomas Birch's *The Life of Henry Prince of Wales, Eldest son of King James I. Compiled chiefly from his own Papers, and other Manuscripts, never before published,* London, 1760.

28. Elizabeth (1596–1662), Queen of Bohemia (1613), eldest daughter of James I (1566–1625).

29. Henry Frederick (1594–1612), Prince of Wales (1610).

30. See Thomas Birch, *op. cit.*, note 27, who gives much information about John Harington.

31. British Museum, Additional MSS 6782, f. 27^r, and 6783, f. 75^r.

32. British Museum, Additional MSS 6789, ff. 448–50. The list is transcribed in 'Nathaniel Torporley and the Harriot Manuscripts', *Annals of Science*, XXV (1969), pp. 339–49.

33. This volume is currently in the British Museum, where it has a new shelfmark (C. 74.e.5). The binding, which is quite beautiful, is one of the standard ones used between 1610 and 1612, when Henry was between sixteen and eighteen.

34. Robert Sidney (Sydney) (1595–1677), 2nd Earl of Leicester (1626).

35. Lady Dorothy Percy (1598–1659) married Sir Robert Sidney about January, 1615/16.

36. See John W. Shirley, 'The Scientific Experiments of Sir Walter Ralegh, the Wizard Earl, and the Three Magi in the Tower,' *Ambix*, IV (1949–51), pp. 52–66, and G. R. Batho, *The Household Papers of Henry Percy*, London, 1962.

37. Batho, *op. cit.*, p. 163. Rumour that Torporley was more fully supported by the Earl is not borne out.

38. British Museum, Additional MSS 6788, f. 566$^{r \& v}$.

39. Reprinted and completed in A. G. Little, *Part of the Opus Tertium . . . including a fragment now printed for the first time,* Aberdeen, University Press, 1912.

40. In 1841 the youthful Halliwell misassigned this letter to Torporley; see J. O. Halliwell, *A Collection of Letters illustrative of the Progress of Science in England from the Reign of Queen Elizabeth to that of Charles II,* London, the Historical Society of Science, 1841.

41. Wood, ed. Bliss 1815, II, p. 534. For the mathematical connection see J. V. Pepper, 'Harriot's Calculation of the Meridional Parts as Logarithmic Tangents', *Archive for History of the Exact Sciences,* IV, 5 (1968), pp. 359–413. See particularly p. 365.

42. Shrewsbury School Registers. I am much indebted to the Librarian, J. B. Lawson, for information available there.

43. John Protheroe of Hawksbrooke (1582–1624) is not noticed in the *D.N.B.*, and passing reference to him in accounts of Harvey's discovery of the circulation of the blood (which did not connect him with astronomical or genealogical matters) recently provoked the question, 'Who is the mysterious Mr. Protheroe?' (C. Webster, review of Sir G. Keynes, *The Life of William Harvey,* in *British Journal of the History of Science,* CXI (1967), p. 406).

44. For information about Walter Warner (1560?–1643), see my 'Thomas Harriot as Mathematician: A Legacy of Hearsay', *Physis, Rivista internazionale di storia della scienze,* Anno IX (1967): Part I, pp. 235–47; Part II, pp. 257–92. See especially pp. 265–6.

45. See C. de Waard and B. Rochot, *Correspondence du P. Marin Mersenne,* Paris, 1970, Vol. XI (1642), p. 244 n. (where earlier references are listed) and p. 310. British Museum, MS Birch 4278, cited in S. P. Rigaud, *Letters on Scientific Subjects,* 1841, Vol. i, p. 78.

46. Stevens writes 'the', meaning 'prime'. But only as many are indicated as suffice to reduce a considered number to a convenient earlier item in the table, of course.

47. The last item refers to a section transcribed with item 10; the others are in order of transcription. The fact of 16 headings requires to be collated with item 1 in List A (*Analytiques in 16 bundles*) of the Harriot manuscripts entrusted to Torporley (note 32) with some caution, since one or two other items in this list are also relevant (notably item 38 which coincides with 4 above, and 39 with 3 above).

48. The originals of Torporley's transcription are as follows for these two items: Additional MS 6783, ff. 183–163 (backwards); 6786, ff. 495:, 203–5; 6783, ff. 98, 99, 101–12, 198–84 (backwards), 113–18, 130, 161?, 144–39 (backwards), 150–60, 162, 138–31 (backwards), 146–9, 199–202, 86–77 (backwards); 6782, ff. 399–88 (backwards); Petworth HMC 241/I ff. 12–1 (backwards); Additional MS 6782 ff. 417–402 (backwards), 400, 401; 6783, ff. 215–16, 219, 217–18, 72–3, 219, 74–5. (Here Torporley inadvertently transcribed f. 76, out of context by virtue of alien symbolism, Torporley's insertion of Harriot's equality sign for 'aequuntur' in the original confusing the evidence further.) Petworth HMC 241/I ff. 14–16; Additional MS 6783, ff. 93–4, 96–7.

49. S. P. Rigaud, *op. cit.,* note 7, p. 250, and Plate V.

50. The possibility that Torporley used another draft of the same work cannot be excluded. There are small differences, including one error, corrected in Torporley's version without comment. Analogous small discrepancies occur in other first and second drafts among Harriot's mathematical papers.

51. British Museum, Additional MS 6786, f. 106. A passing mention by J. E. Hoffmann, *Geschichte der Mathematik I,* 2nd ed., Berlin, 1963, p. 172, is not meant to imply a reference of Brigg's *Trigonometria Britannica* (1633) there discussed as the source. The fact without date was mentioned by Briggs in a letter to Kepler, 20 February 1625 o.s.

52. *Diclides coelometricae . . . ,* London, 1602.

53. See, for instance, J. V. Pepper, 'A Letter from Nathaniel Torporley to Thomas Harriot', *British Journal of the History of Science,* III (June, 1967), p. 285–90.

54. See Ethel Seaton's 'Thomas Hariot's Secret Script', *Ambix,* V (1853–6), pp. 111–14.

6

HARRIOT, HILL, WARNER AND THE NEW PHILOSOPHY

JEAN JACQUOT
Centre National de la Recherche Scientifique, Paris

HARRIOT'S mind was equally at ease in mathematics, astronomy, and physics, and was apt to apply the first to the study of the other two. He could observe with the same rigour the motions of distant celestial bodies and the path of a ray of light through different media. His scientific investigations raised fundamental problems of which he was fully conscious. His exploration of the skies with the telescope, which parallels Galileo's, also questioned the validity of the traditional world-order, based on the opposition between the Heavens and the Earth, their natures, and their motions. The Copernican theory had challenged the world-order by making the Earth move with the other planets. The asperities of the Moon's surface disproved the celestial globes' perfect smoothness; the Sun's spots brought evidence against the Heaven's inalterability. Harriot was also prepared, as it appears from the letters of his disciple William Lower, to reject from the Copernican system the last vestiges of the old astronomy, the circular orbits of the planets and the sphere of fixed stars.[1] On the other hand he had recourse to atomism to explain the properties of matter, and of transparent bodies in particular.

Considering the scope and the originality of his research, one may wonder to what extent he felt the need of a new natural philosophy to replace the old, and to what extent he was able to shape its elements into a coherent pattern. Unfortunately the evidence to be found in his papers is fragmentary. As for the persistent reports concerning his impiety, they must be examined with caution.[2] They were circulated, as early as 1592, by adversaries of Sir Walter Ralegh, were repeated by divines anxious to see a judgment in Harriot's manner of death, and eventually found their way into Aubrey's and Wood's biographical collections. The Reverend Nathaniel Torporley, whom Harriot trusted as a friend, wrote in his *Corrector analyticus* that Harriot seldom erred as a mathematician, but sometimes as a bold philosopher, and notably as a man. And he left among his manuscripts an outline of a refutation of atomism. where Harriot is clearly designated as his chief opponent.[3] There is sufficient correspondence between the arguments attributed by Torporley to Harriot and the evidence in the latter's writings of his use of atomism to conclude that atomism occupied a central position in a body of opinions which was adversely described as 'atheism', 'deism', or 'philosophical theology'. He once wrote to Kepler that he could not philosophize freely,[4] and his association with Ralegh and Northumberland, who had been sentenced for treason, was an additional motive for prudence. There is nothing in his extant papers that may be construed as being opposed to the Scriptures, or the main articles of Christian faith. On the other hand he has left a dignified expression of his belief in a natural order established by God, and of his submission to the divine will.[5] It is possible for him to have been sincerely religious, and to have conformed to the ways of worship of his country and times, and at the same time to have held philosophical opinions that were at variance with the letter of the Scripture or the dogmas of the Church. Atomism could not easily be dissociated from other aspects of Democritean philosophy, and postulating the indestructibility of matter inevitably led to denying that the world had been created. According to one Mr. Haggar, who was a mathematician and well acquainted with Harriot, he could not believe in the story of Genesis, and would say *ex nihilo nihil fit*.[6] Torporley considered that the dogma of Creation was at stake in the controversy of atoms, and sought to prove the contrary maxim: *ex nihilo omnia*. Ancient atomism offered the model of a universe indefinitely extended in space and time, where everything was subject to generation and decay but was made up of indestructible particles of matter. This view could fit neither with Christian eschatology nor Aristotelian cosmology. But such a universe could be conceived as homogeneous, all its parts being subject to the same physical laws. And this suited the purpose of the new astronomy which tended to dispense with qualitative distinctions between different regions of the cosmos.

Copernican astronomy and the concepts of atomism and an infinite universe were related for the first time by Giordano Bruno. But it is well known that the Copernican system had found supporters at an early date in Elizabethan England, and had been competently described by Robert Recorde and Thomas Digges. When Bruno stayed in England from 1583 to 1585, he found a scientific milieu which was congenial to him and stimulated his speculations. The Italian dialogues containing the main features of his cosmology were composed during that period. Their influence upon the circle of the Earl of Northumberland must have been considerable but, except in the case of Nicholas Hill, it is difficult to assess. It is idle to ask whether Harriot without the stimulus of Bruno's thought would have had recourse to Democritean principles in order to relate distant fields of scientific inquiry. But it might be rewarding to set Harriot in perspective, to try and define his position in a line of evolution which leads from sixteenth-century philosophy, steeped in Neo-Platonic and Hermetic speculation (as was still the case with Bruno), to seventeenth-century mechanism.

A study of Walter Warner's papers is useful for such an assessment. He was ten years younger than Harriot, and was at the same time his associate and his disciple. He wrote more abundantly than his elder on principles of natural philosophy, and what he has to say bears a relation to Bruno's, Hill's, and Harriot's own writings. It is difficult to tell how far he is indebted to the latter's oral teaching. Comparison will show that he shared Harriot's views on the nature of matter and the universe, but also that he ventured into fields that, to my knowledge, Harriot never explored. After Harriot's death Warner received encouragement from two amateurs of science, William Cavendish (Earl and, later, Duke of Newcastle) and his brother Charles, who both worked in close association with Robert Payne and Thomas Hobbes. In his relations with these men who came to know Mersenne and his circle, and took part in the scientific and philosophical controversies of the 1640's, Warner appears as a transitional figure, and I hope to show that he contributed to the expansion, and transmission to a new age, of ideas which originated in Harriot's lifetime.

Bruno's conception of the universe combined the materialism of the ancient Atomists with Neo-Platonic and Hermetic speculations.[7] Creation *ab aeterno*, the infinity of the universe, and the plurality of worlds were by no means new notions. Their possibility had been discussed by generations of Schoolmen who found it difficult to reconcile their rejection by Aristotle with the idea of God's omnipotence.[8] But with Bruno this possibility becomes a certainty. As he seeks to prove in the first dialogue of *De l'infinito, universo e mondi*, God's creative power and goodness, being infinite, could not refuse existence to all that had a possibility of coming into being. Yet this did not impair God's free-will, as freedom and necessity coincided in Him. As has been already noticed, this cosmology was in contradiction with a literal interpretation of the Bible[9] and the belief in the Creation of the world in time, its final destruction, and the reward of men in Heaven, or punishment in Hell, according to their conduct in this life. Such belief was necessary to keep the common people in the path of virtue.[10] But the learned, inspired by divine love, were devoid of fear and derived incomparable satisfaction from the contemplation of an infinite universe in which God is everywhere present.

Bruno tells us, in *La causa, principio e uno*, that he considered at first that matter was the only substance in nature but he came to recognize two substances, form and matter, and to distinguish an active and a passive power. Form was the cause which organized matter according to design and maintained perfection throughout the universe by continually actualizing all possible forms of being. Bruno still retained the Platonic distinction between the divine Intelligence and the Soul of the World, but in his mind they tended to coincide, Soul being the form-giving principle of the Intelligence, active through the whole universe. And ultimately the active and the passive powers, form and matter, could be considered as complementary aspects of the same reality. The notion of a world infused with divine energy was inspiring to the mystic. But Bruno's cosmic vision raised the problem of the nature of the individual soul and of its survival after death, a problem which did not receive a definitive answer in his work.

The earliest evidence of the influence of the ancient Atomists and of Bruno's speculations in the circle of Northumberland is to be found in Nicholas Hill's *Philosophia,* which was published in Paris in 1601.[11] Hill was, according to Aubrey, 'one of the most learned men of his time: a great mathematician and philosopher'. He was the steward of Edward de Vere, Earl of Oxford, whom he accompanied in his travels. At a later date he was taken into the retinue of the Earl of Northumberland. But he was compromised in one of the plots for the succession of Elizabeth I and left the country. He is supposed to have settled in Amsterdam, where he practised physic, and to have committed suicide by poison in 1610, after the death of his son. He had the reputation of a Lullianist and an alchemist. Besides his printed book he left manuscripts on the essence of God and the eternity and infinity of the world.[12]

In his *Philosophia* Hill claims not to be dogmatic, and the book is made up of the juxtaposition of aphorisms and various reflexions. From these disconnected fragments, nevertheless, a relatively consistent picture emerges. God is conceived as a source of energy and a formative power. He is not the unmoving mover of the Aristotelians. He must not be considered abstractly but as an active principle at work through the whole universe and in all its parts. In the divine essence to be, to be able to, and to act are the same. Since it is better to be than not to be, to do than not to do, and since God's power is infinite, his power can only manifest itself in an infinite universe and through eternity.[13] The whole scheme of things is subject to a law which is co-essential and co-eternal with God. The understanding of causes and the certainty of science are grounded in that law and in the divine unity underlying the plurality of worlds and the diversity of phenomena.[14]

Besides this active principle, the primary constituents of nature are time, space, and matter. Time and space are infinitely extended and homogeneous. So is matter but it is discontinuous, being made up of atoms. The latter's resistance and the existence of a vacuum enable the active virtues to operate all the motions and changes which can be observed in the universe. Atoms have the shape of the regular solids, and their various combinations account for the differences in density, porosity, asperity, smoothness, and other properties of bodies.[15]

Homogeneity of space and matter imply the rejection of the opposition between celestial and sublunary regions. The heavenly globes are the same as ours. Light and fire are the same in all parts of the universe. Hill advances various proofs of the Earth's motion, and quotes Hermes, Nicholas of Cusa, Copernicus, Bruno, and William Gilbert. He associates Copernicanism with the notion of an infinite universe. The ideas of Gilbert, whose *De magnete* had appeared only a year before, were familiar to Hill who denies the existence of levity as opposed to gravity and attributes the latter to magnetic attraction.

Hill also seeks to account in terms of magnetic influence for the relative position of celestial bodies and to explain the tides by the combined effect of the Earth's motion with lunar and solar attraction.[16]

Light seems to be conceived by Hill, like magnetism, as a manifestation of the active principle. But his meaning is not easy to define, as here he usually does not dissociate observation from mystic symbolism of Neo-Platonic inspiration. This is expressed through images of expansion from a centre, or descent from extreme purity through degrees of material grossness. Light, which he calls the impression of the deity in nature, is of itself invisible, and is revealed by the opacity or transparency of the matter which is opposed to it (transparency resulting from the homogeneity and rarity of the particles of matter in a given medium). Hill also speaks of 'primary incorporeal light' which, through its association with matter, gives form to all things and, though degraded and obscured by impurity in the process of generation, nevertheless effects all the operations of life in the universe. The perception of light through the eye is compared to intellection and to discovery as a sudden illumination of the mind after a methodically pursued investigation. The act of vision also leads to admiration, contemplation, and philosophical knowledge.[17]

Hill, as we can see, never speaks of light simply as a phenomenon, and it is not easy to tell whether he considers it as a manifestation of the active principle or a metaphor of the same. Such notions are not easy, either, to reconcile with Democritean materialism and, not infrequently, Hill contradicts himself. For instance, sometimes he speaks of light as being incorporeal, and sometimes as being an extremely refined substance. He also speaks of 'quintessence' as of a celestial substance free from earthly stain which is similar to the breath of God, the influence of superior bodies, or the soul released from the bonds of flesh. Elsewhere man is described as a microcosm participating in all things in nature. There are several references to astral influences and to the operations of alchemy. The extraction of the great elixir, or the transmutation of metals, is compared to the generation of the second person of the Trinity. On the other hand chemists are relieved of the blame of pursuing empirical knowledge, their aim being the welfare of men.[18]

The whole universe is conceived as animate, God being present as energy (prima hypostasis energetica) in the souls of the whole, of the Earth and the celestial globes, and of the animals which people them. The rotation of the planets and the distances they keep from the Sun are devised in order to preserve in all parts of their surface the temperate heat which they need for the maintenance of life. The Earth's animal nature is evidenced by its motion, its vital effluvia, its fecundity. It generates all possible forms of animal life, man being the last offspring of a long series of species. And it is difficult to imagine the length of the revolutions of time that were necessary to produce them.[19]

'Primary seeds' are defined as the indissoluble conjunction of divine virtue with atoms arranged in a certain pattern, 'generative seeds' as a combination of such primordial seeds. The seed of man, or any other animal, already contains, in a fluid state, the anatomy of the species which later becomes manifest to sense, by adjunction of matter to the existing pattern.[20]

Hill shows great interest in the chain of physiological and psychological procedures which enables man to receive impressions from the external world and to act in consequence. One of the senses in which he uses the word 'species' is that of an emanation from an object which affects an organ of sense. He is not of a single mind about the nature of such emanations. Light and heat, he says, are not qualities in themselves but in respect of the sense they affect, and a certain quantity is necessary to produce the effect. Things diffused by radiation act *per punctualem contactum*. Thus the pain caused by heat is due to fiery particles which penetrate the part affected and produce an unpleasant sensation of discontinuity. Yet elsewhere, as we have seen, light, though assimilated to fire and endowed with a penetrating power, is said to be incorporeal.[21]

Nevertheless he has valuable things to say about sensation, imagination, and intellection which are conceived as continuous processes, the sense impressions being coordinated in the phantasy, and the intellect sifting carefully the information thus transmitted. He also explains how the images resulting from sense impressions are memorized, and revived by an internal stimulation of the sense organ which received them. And he describes the way images of similar things are unified and abstracted to become intelligible forms. The function of the intellect, according to Hill, is also to choose the appropriate response to a given situation. The will is an urge to act according to the intellect's representation of the good. The image of the object desired provides the stimulus which sets the members into motion, but the whole process presupposes an adjustment of the means to the circumstances and to the mode of working of the organs of motion. Passions are also described as disturbances of the humours and the spirits of the blood.[22]

Nicholas Hill calls the soul the divine act in man, the action of the primal energy in the human frame considered as a well-disposed organism, the union of God with the most subtle material part of ourselves. This association begins with the embryo, and the soul is responsible for the growth of the body. But illness and age submit the body to a contrary process of decay, with a corresponding decline of human faculties. Hill is deeply preoccupied with the problem of death and immortality. There is no regression in nature and the disintegration of the corpse frees its material components for other purposes, the primordial seeds do not perish, and the 'inner man,' perhaps, is called to a higher office. In a sense death is a purification, a liberation from the bounds of flesh, and a return to unity. Hill undoubtedly believes in the indestructibility of the divine life-giving principle, but he does not seem to believe that the soul retains its individuality or identity after death. It is true that he expresses the hope of spending eternity exploring the innumerable worlds and understanding their cause. But elsewhere he speaks of the extinction of the human intellect. And, at the very end of the book, he affirms that the longing to retain separate individual existence is against the common desire of all things of the same nature to unite or, to speak in religious terms, is against the promised union with God as the reward of our labour. What is significant, as in the case of Bruno, is that the religious impulse, the yearning for an after-life, has found a new object: no longer an other-wordly Paradise, but a boundless universe teeming with life, with its endless transformations.[23]

In such a universe, with the uniformity of its space and matter, and the ubiquity of its active principle, the workings of nature are simple and intelligible. The perplexity resulting from the multiplicity of sense data can be surmounted by the correct use of reason; its incorrect use and deductions from uncertain premises are the main source of error. The object of science is not an approximation of truth, it is absolute certainty. The use of reason is also of basic importance in the spheres of ethics and religion. Moral virtue is the expression of right reason in the whole conduct of life. Observing the uniformity and simplicity of nature's operations breeds constancy in the mind. The knowledge of God begins with the study of the simplest effects of nature just as arithmetic begins with the study of the first numbers. The intelligibility of things does not detract from their nobility, and inscrutability does not add anything to God's glory. A man made pious by philosophy will not swerve from religion. The necessities of geometry, the reasons of physics, and clear experiments command our faith and win our assent, while our mind accepts reluctantly the authoritarian decrees of the Church. But this philosophical theology must not be revealed to the vulgar. Religion must maintain the multitude in the path of virtue by teaching that God will punish the sinners in another life, which is meaningless if the universe is eternal. For all his heterodoxy Hill nevertheless expresses Christian feelings, though in a paradoxical way, saying for instance that the mystery of God-made man is more stupendous in an infinite universe. And he claims in a preface to his young son that he does not advance anything dogmatically and that he is ready to abjure whatever in his book is repugnant to the Catholic faith.[24]

Hill's book is not exempt from confusion and contradictions, yet it is not a jumble of opinions derived from many sources. True, it is made up of fragments printed without apparent order. But this form of exposition is deliberate. It may have been chosen to eschew the reproach of teaching a doctrine, or to stimulate reflexion. It is not difficult to reconstruct from these fragments a philosophy which is an attempt to reconcile Neo-Platonism, Hermeticism, Democritean atomism, and the new astronomy. In other words Hill seems to aim at the sort of synthesis which Bruno had attempted, and it is significant that the book appeared in Catholic France, just a year after Bruno was burnt in Rome. Though he is named only once, it appears as a tribute to his memory and, in spite of the cautionary preface, as a challenge to the authority that had condemned him.

Hill retains the preoccupation of the Renaissance Plotinians and Hermeticists with the continuity between divine unity and the multiple manifestations of existence, and still conceives many degrees of transition between the spiritual and the material. His view of the universe is still very different from the mechanistic systems which were to be proposed in the course of the seventeenth century. Yet his concern with problems such as the nature of the soul and its relation to the body, the origin and growth of our mental faculties, and the situation of man in a universe which so widely differed from the traditional model is characteristic of the new century. He has been described as a precursor of Hobbes and Locke because he sought to show that our ideas were derived from sense experience.[25] The outlook of these philosophers, of course, widely differs from his own. Yet the description he attempted of such processes as sensation, imagination, intellection, will, and action opens new vistas. And Walter Warner (whether he was directly influenced or not) sought to describe such processes more amply and more precisely. What he has to say about energy (*vis*), space, time, and matter also bears a strong resemblance to Hill's own ideas on the first principles of natural philosophy.

The Earl of Northumberland shared Hill's interest in the 'method general of all atomical combinations' and its application to the practice of alchemy.[26] As for Hill's emphasis on the correct use of reason, rigorous demonstrations, and clear experiments, its counterpart is to be found in George Chapman's poem in praise of Harriot as a moral figure and a man of science.[27]

Nothing certain concerning Harriot's religious or philosophical opinions can be inferred from reading Hill's book. Hill's *Philosophia,* being an attempt to combine different trends of thought which were influential in the Northumberland circle, only adds to our knowledge of Harriot's background. But whatever the ideas and preoccupations they had in common, there is a striking difference between Hill's book and Harriot's papers. Hill speaks of demonstrations and experiments in the abstract, while Harriot discusses general problems, such as the form and extension of the universe, or the structure of matter, in concrete relation to scientific observation and mathematical reasoning. To limit ourselves to one example: his position in the controversy about the existence of the sphere of fixed stars is known from a letter of William Lower's[28]. William Gilbert, in his *De magnete*, claimed that the sphere did not exist, and that the stars were situated at various distances from our globe.[29] Bruno held that each star was a sun and that whatever the place of the observer in the universe, he would see as many stars as if he were upon Earth. Kepler[30] still believed in the existence of this sphere of fixed stars, though he denied its motion. And he argued that an observer in the sign of Cancer would be surrounded by huge stars but would be unable to see the stars in Capricorn on account of their distance. Kepler also thought that the sphere of fixed stars was situated at a considerable distance from the solar system because no stellar parallax could be observed. In his letter, Lower quotes Harriot's own objections to Kepler's argument. Between the distant stars which Kepler supposes to be fixed on the sphere enclosing the world, and the orbit of Saturn, Harriot argued, there may be a considerable number of lesser stars which escape our eye, and there may be planets in the solar system that we fail to see. We also gather from the letter that news which Lower had just received from Harriot added strength to this hypothesis. What the news was is not specified but, judging by the date, Lower's excitement, and his request for 'all sorts of thes cylinders', it undoubtedly concerned the observations made by Galileo, and Harriot himself, with the telescope.

What interests us here is Harriot's approach to the problem. He sought to meet Kepler's serious objection to the void between the stars and the solar system. And whatever his own intuition may have been, he did not rely on metaphysical speculation, but on evidence. He was primarily concerned, like Galileo, with observation, and the invention and improvement of optical instruments. The use of the telescope could not prove that the universe was infinite, but added strength to the supposition that it was. It did show that celestial bodies were far greater in number than the eye could discover, that the stars varied considerably in size and probably in distance, and that it was unlikely that our world was limited by a sphere. In a similar way, his observation of the Moon's surface and of the Sun's spots added strength to the hypothesis that celestial bodies were made of the same matter as the Earth and were subject to generation and decay.

But Harriot did not rely on observation alone. In his notes *De infinitis*[31] he seeks to demonstrate, by reasoning on mathematical series, that there must be a *minimum finitum* beyond which further division is impossible. And that this *minimum* is 'multiplicable infinitelie infinite till a quantitie absolutely un-multiplicable be produced which I may call universally infinite'. He also seeks to prove that these notions of *minimum finitum* and *maximum infinitum* could be applied equally to mathematics and geometrical figures, and to the physical world. In other words he admitted the existence of the atom and of an infinite universe. It also appears from some of his notes, connecting the notions of *plenum, vacuum*, motion, and cause, that he attributed all the effects in nature to the local motion of atoms or bodies made of atoms.

That Harriot explained reflexion and refraction by the atomic structure of matter we know from his letters to Kepler.[32] Light meeting a transparent body followed a different path according to the resistance of atoms or the absence of resistance in the vacuum between them. We also know from Torporley's refutation of Harriot's theory that he held atoms to be eternal, hard, un-alterable; the properties of bodies, such as weight, homogeneity, solidity, or brittleness depended on the size, shape, and configuration of the atoms they were made of.

The study of Walter Warner's papers is rewarding, because he shared Harriot's views on the nature of matter and the universe, and part of his work was in the same fields, but also because he ventured into fields that, to my knowledge, Harriot never explored. Our knowledge of Warner is derived mainly from Aubrey's *Lives*[33] and Warner's letters and papers preserved at the British Museum.[34] To these sources may be added the accounts of Henry Percy, Ninth Earl of Northumberland, now at Alnwick Castle, which Shirley has examined.[35] Warner was already in the service of the Earl in 1591 and later, in 1616, became his pensioner. Harriot's name appears for the first time on the Earl's pay-roll in 1593, and the two scientists worked together over a long period. Both took part in the experiments of Ralegh and Northumberland in the Tower; Robert Hues, the third of the 'Magi', was to join them at a later date, in 1615. Warner seems to have acted as the Earl's librarian, and supplied the prisoners with books from Syon House, where he resided at the time, with Harriot.

Harriot's will appointed Nathaniel Torporley, John Prothero, and Sir Thomas Aylesbury as his literary executors. But it is well known that the *Artis analyticae praxis* (1631) was the only volume of Harriot's works to be published. Aubrey states that the *Praxis* was printed by Warner. This is confirmed by a letter addressed by Aylesbury to the Earl of Northumberland on 5 July 1632, to support Warner's request for a special allowance to cover his extraordinary expense in attending to the publication of Harriot's book after the copy was finished. This expense was greater than Warner's means could bear, including the Earl's pension and the help of his friends. Aylesbury was disposed, with the assistance of Warner, to undertake the publication of other works of Harriot, provided that Warner received the compensation required.[36] But we know that the project did not materialize. The Earl died four months later; Aubrey writes that Henry's son and heir, Algernon, maintained Warner's pension, but there seems to be some confusion in his mind:

Sir Thomas Alesbury obtained of Algernon, earle of Northumberland (son to that earle, prisoner of the Tower) a continuation of the annuity, dureing Warner's life, upon condition that he should, out of M. Hariot's papers, drawe out some piece fitt to be published, which he did, under the title aforesaid [i.e. the *Praxis*] 1631, London: but did not set his name to it, and accordingly Warner had his money as long as he lived.[37]

Since the *Praxis* was published before the death of Algernon's father, it could not be considered as the fulfilment of the condition for a continuation of Warner's annuity. He may have done further work preparing Harriot's manuscripts for the press, but there is no evidence of this, and we cannot tell for certain whether his pension was maintained or not. But Aubrey tells us elsewhere that he also received:

some allowance from Sir Thomas Alesbury with whome he usually spent his sumer in Windsor Park, and was welcom, for he was harmless and quiet. His winter was spent at the Woolstable, where he dyed in the time of the Parliament of 1640, of which, or whome, he was no lover.[38]

Warner had made a Canon of 100,000 logarithms which, with other manuscripts, passed into the hands of Herbert Thorndyke, prebendary of Westminster,[39] after the death of Warner. The Canon and related material were inventoried in a letter of Thorndyke to Pell (23 December 1652) requesting him to peruse them and see whether they could be published, but one bundle of 10,000 was found missing and the project was dropped. Pell's notes show that he considered the Canon to be their common work, though Warner had been responsible for the ordering of the theoretical part.[40]

Judging from an inventory of his papers,[41] and from the extant material, much of his work besides mathematics and geometry, was concerned with optics and with the study of money and alloys. His papers on optics include tables of refraction resulting from observations made with Aylesbury in July 1627,[42] and a tract on the image reflected in a spherical concave mirror.[43] This tract, and a project for the making of a 'perspective glass', were submitted to William and Charles Cavendish and were discussed in a correspondence in which Robert Payne and Thomas Hobbes were also involved (1634–6).[44] Hobbes was in possession of Warner's treatise on refraction, which Mersenne published in 1644,[45] along with a treatise on optics by Hobbes himself. Warner did much work on money and exchange, no doubt at the instigation of Sir Thomas Aylesbury who was Master of the Mint. A treatise on the subject has been preserved; it consists of a series of definitions, problems, and theorems.[46]

All these reveal a many-sided personality, but I would like to draw attention to two sets of papers, which are bound with other material in Add. MSS 4394–5. The first consists of loose folios dealing with the first principles of natural philosophy.[47] The other is a first draft of what was meant to be, apparently, a treatise on the vital functions of man. Its scope and extent are not easy to assess. Folios 132 to 271 of MS 4394 and folios 1 to 48 of MS 4395 certainly belong to it. But these are made up of five sections marked respectively DDD, HHH, LLL, MMM, NNN, which are not bound in order.[48] It is specified at the end of DDD that the next subject is discussed in EEE. And it seems obvious that there were at least 13 (or 14 if I and J were two distinct letters), since there is a section marked NNN. But I have not found the sections corresponding to the 8 or 9 missing letters. The fact that each of the letters is repeated three times may perhaps suggest that these sections were meant to be included in the third part of a treatise of vast proportions. Section DDD starts with a discussion of blood circulation and gives substance to the story told by Aubrey and others that Harvey got the idea for his famous discovery from Warner. This section has been noticed by historians of medicine on that account, but to my knowledge no attempt has been made to connect this section with the four others. There is no apparent connection between these and the loose leaves on first principles which have been mentioned before. But I shall try and set all these fragments in perspective as witnesses of Warner's attempt to integrate different fields of natural philosophy into a unified system. We shall start from first principles. To account for the universe, Warner defines four basic concepts: time, space, matter, and energy (*vis* or 'virtue radiative').

Time and *space* are the prerequisites of all existence. Time is continuous and eternal. Space is infinitely extended and also continuous and eternal. They are both simple and homogeneal, inalterable and exempt of active force. Space offers no resistance, and all things are contained in it. It is imperceptible to sense and its existence can only be inferred by abstraction from corporeal objects. Its infinitude can also be inferred. A straight line can be imagined to be extended *ad infinitum*, and in all dimensions of space. Space rightly conceived is nothing but magnitude or quantity, the *principia* of quantity (point, line, surface, volume) being also the *principia* of space. Warner also clarifies the notions of *unity*, *plurality*, the *whole*, the *part*, *division*, and *composition*, distinguishing material and mental procedures. Of 'mental division' for instance, he writes that it 'is the imaginary distraction of the phantasme or species of a thing continuall retained in the phantasie, the thing it self remayned unaltered, which division may be performed by the operation of the fantasie whether the thing be divisible by nature or art, as thinges materiall, or not subject to any division . . . as space, and time, and lumen'.[49]

And now we come to *matter*. Warner criticizes Aristotle's 'confused and irresolute doctrine of *materia prima*'. 'For to say that it has no actuall existence but is only and merely in potentia and never reducible into act is as much as to say it is nothing . . .' 'If the things themselves and particulars of the universe have actuall being and existence as they have, theyr matter must have the same, for particular things are nothing els but severall portions of matter invested with divers and severall formes.'[50] Things are in a continual process of change and generation. This does not happen by chance, but in a certain order, by several gradations or dispositions of matter according to the diverse quantities, or shapes or combinations of its constituent parts, or atoms. 'And though they are subordinate one to another . . . there is none of them so prime but it may become secondary and that which is secondary or last to be prime, though not immediately, yet by circulation of some changes and transitions'.[51] Phenomena of condensation or expansion can be observed in bodies, but they do not affect the ultimate constituents of matter. In that sense matter resists matter and matter cannot penetrate matter. Warner thinks that 'although things do infinitely differ according to the infinit variety of formes and magnitudes and other properties of these resulting,' matter in respect of its inward substance 'is homogeneall and simple . . . and therefore in that sense it is said to be one through the whole univers.'[52]

The qualities which our senses perceive, such as hardness, softness, brittleness, heaviness, are diversified according to the arrangement of the atoms,

Plate 4. Two of Harriot's sunspot drawings. (a) The first observation, dated 8 December, 1610. (b) Observation numbers 49–52.

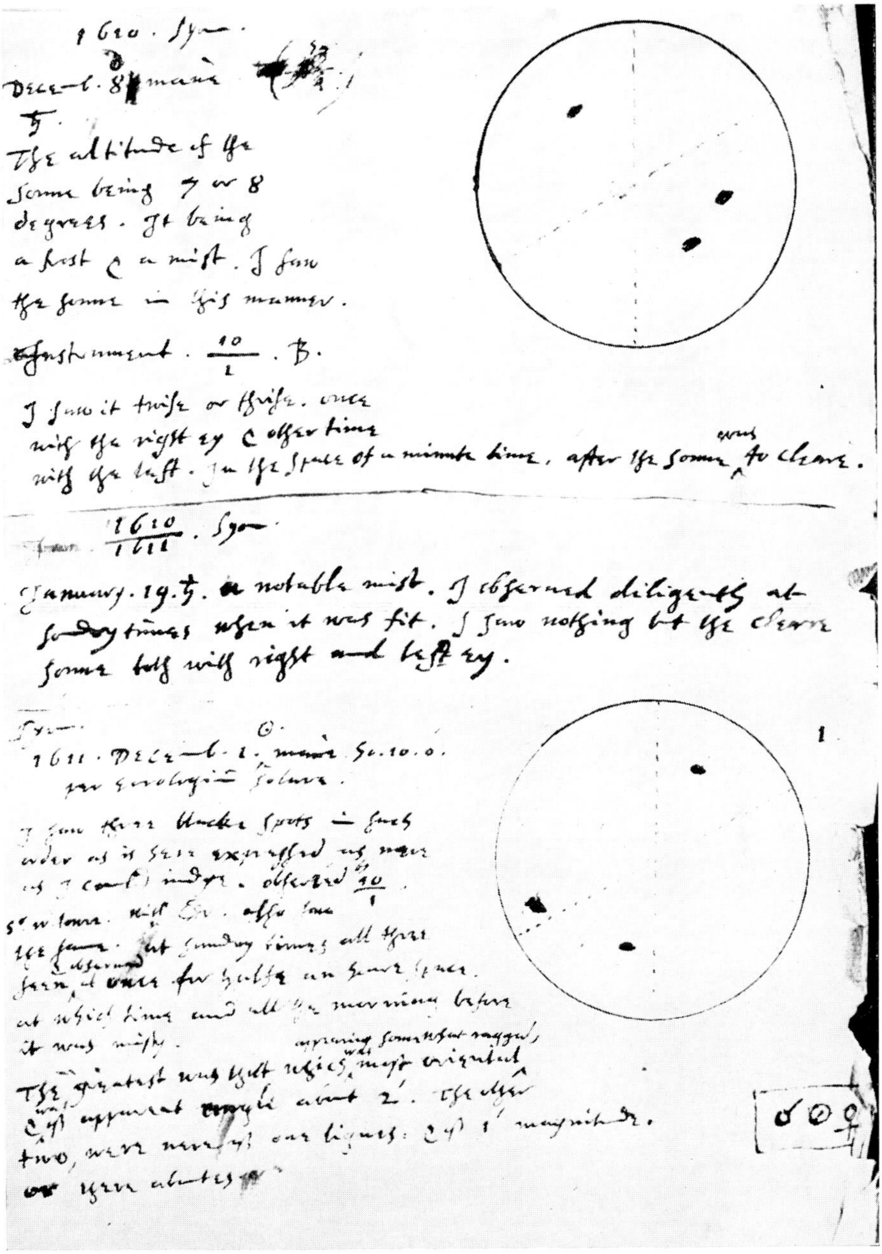

1610. Syon.

Decemb. 8 mane

♄.

The altitude of the sonne being 7 or 8 degrees. It being a frost & a mist. I saw the sonne in this manner.

Instrument. 10/1. B.

I saw it twise or thrise. once with the right ey & other time with the left. In the space of a minute time, after the sonne was to cleare.

1610/1611. Syon.

January. 19. ♄. a notable mist. I observed diligently at sondry times when it was fit. I saw nothing but the cleare sonne both with right and left ey.

Syon. ☉.

1611. Decemb. 1. mane ho. 10. 0.

per horologium solare.

1

I saw three blacke spots in such order as is here expressed as neare as I could iudge. observed by 10/1

... also saw the same. but sondry times all three I observed seen, at once for halfe an houre space. at which time and all the morning before it was misty.

The greatest was that which appearing somewhat ragged, was most oriental & was of apparent magnitude about 2′. The other two were nere of our lignes: 2 of 1′ magnitude. or there abouts.

♂ ☉ ♀

Syon. $\frac{1611}{1612}$

February . 17 . ☽ . Ho . 7^{a}. ($6\frac{3}{4}$. 12^{a}.

Through thick ayer & a litle misty the sonne appearing sufficiently fayer, I saw but 8 spots . whose position as in the first figure. That nere the ecliptick hath now an other by him not seen before. That which was southerly yesterday & dim not now to be seen. The greate one nere the verticall is dim on the north side seeming to have 2 dim ones adjoyning. That westerly is not now double distinct as the day before. At 12^{h} all the sky being cleare and the sonne, I saw the great spot with $\frac{10}{1}$ & $\frac{20}{1}$ but no more. my sight was after dim for an houre.

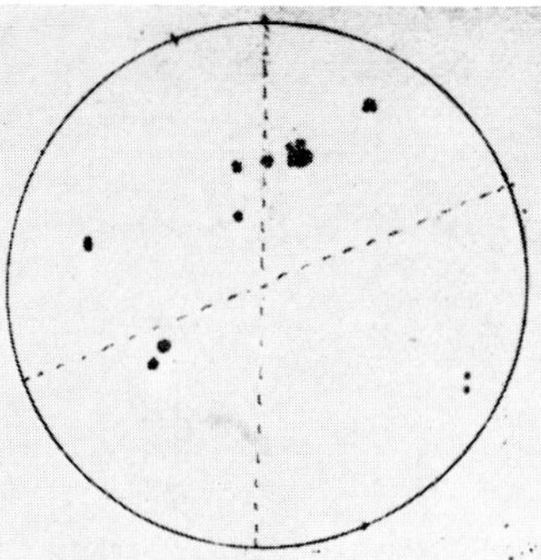

49

February . 18 . ♂ . Ho . 7^{a}. ($6\frac{3}{4}$.

Through thick ayer & sometimes thin cloudes I saw 8 spots in such manner as is set downe in the second figure. The great one had two litle ones to the southward nere adjoyning but distinct. The two that were southerly before are now three distinct. The great one seemed somewhat long.

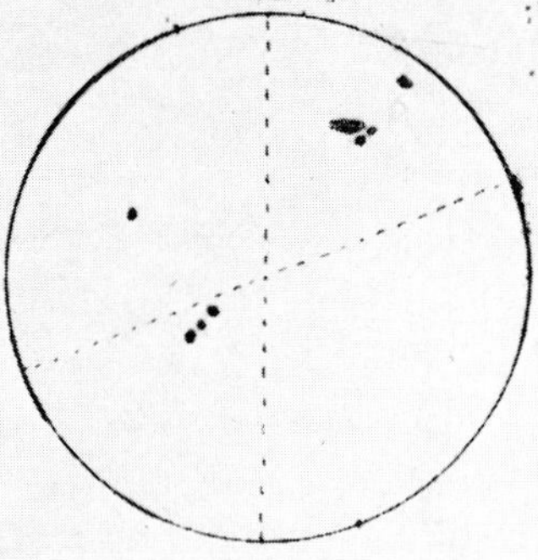

50.

February . 19 . ☿ . Ho . 5^{a}. (12^{a}.

Here 5^{a} afternoone through thick ayer whiles the sonne appeared, being somewhat to bright. The former great spot I saw now devided in such manner as it expressed in the 3 figure, both partes being long & dim at the endes especially. I saw then also an other spot small, on the east parte nere in the place as is expressed. I saw the great spot also at 12^{h} devided, through thin cloudes, but no more.

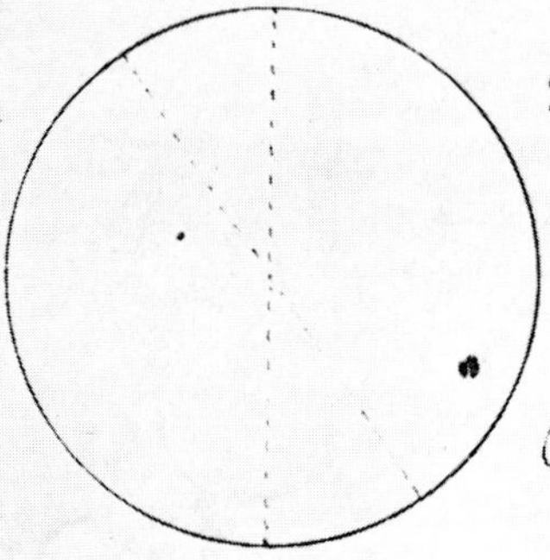

51.

(w)

February . 20 . ♃ . Ho . 7^{a}. ($6\frac{3}{4}$.

Through a frosty mist the sonne somewhat with the brightest. I saw the old great spot devided nere the edge with a litle dim one nere the most westerly part. Also 3 more towardes the east, of which the most northerly very dim. The two other more perfect. But none of the 3 seen with $\frac{10}{1}$. There position as in the 4 figure. The devided one in the west well seen with $\frac{10}{1}$.

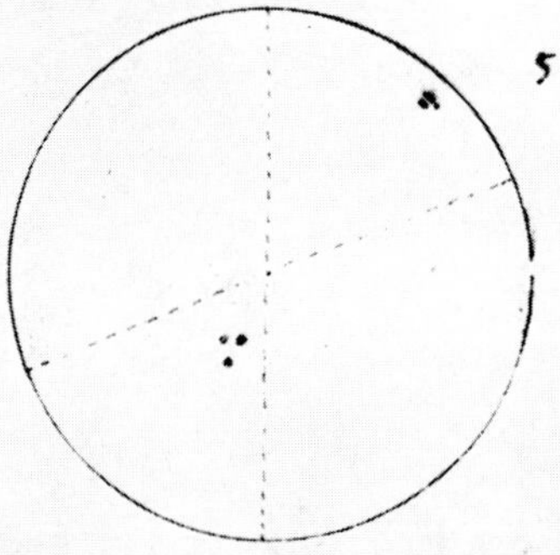

52.

which are the constituent particles of bodies. We have no means as yet to know whether the Sun and Moon are made of the same matter as the Earth but the hypothesis of universal homogeneity of matter is the simplest, and it agrees with theory and experience.[53] Warner thinks that matter is eternal and therefore not created. And he seeks to prove it. To say that it was made out of matter already existing is to reject the explanation *ad infinitum*. If it was made out of nothing it must have been made in an instant for there is no degree or transition from nothing to *hoc aliquid*. But it could not have been made in an instant because making supposes motion, as every effect is motion or is accompanied by motion. But every motion is made in time. Therefore matter was not made at all and has always existed, and it can also be shown that it is indestructible.[54]

Warner discusses at length the notion of *cause*, the relation of the agent to the patient and the conditions required for the production of the effect, or alteration of the state of the patient. The effect is produced as soon as all the conditions required are satisfied. But as has already been noticed, the effect is motion, or a new state resulting from motion, and this cannot be produced in an instant:

for as whatsoever is moved must necessarily be moved in time so e converso whatsoever causeth an other thing to be moved or altered should in like reason require time for that causation . . .[55]

But once the motion or state has been imparted it persists until it is modified by a new cause:

If a thing be set in motion or in any state and afterwards left by the cause that motion or state whatsoever is it self a sufficient cause of his owne continuence till it be resisted hindred or altered by some contrary . . .[56]

This leads Warner to examine the case of the motion imparted to a body at rest and to formulate an approximation of the principle of inertia:

In the alteration from quiet to motion it is manifest [. . .] that the state of the patient being by supposition motion during the application, it doth keep and continue the state of motion without interruption after the recesse of the agent eternally unless it be hindred or stopped by a contrary force and look in what degree of velocity it was at the very instant of the separation of the agent, in that state of the same velocity it doth continue till the next encounter.[57]

Warner further discusses the case of a body in motion subject to a contrary agent and the reduction of speed, change of direction, or alteration to a state of rest resulting from the action. But in his discussion of causation, Warner admits that the action may be either corporeal or virtual, and the effect may be produced by immediate contact, or mediately.

Since matter is passive, and does not move of itself, but can only be moved, Warner has to introduce a fourth principle besides time, space, and matter to account for all the phenomena of the universe. He calls it *vis*, the cause of motion. It is immaterial but possesses extension. While matter resists penetration, portions of *vis* encountering each other interpenetrate and mingle. Warner writes that matter and virtue radiative do fill the universal space. But elsewhere he admits the existence of a vacuum. He considers light as something distinct from matter, and as such, we suppose, it must be considered as one of the manifestations of *vis* as he understands it. On one occasion he attributes the sensation of colour, like all sense impressions, to the atomic structure of the object. But elsewhere he accounts for it by the effect of *vis* upon the retina and the visual spirits. The two explanations may be complementary and he seems to think that sense perception, like other natural processes, is the result of the configuration and local motion of particles of matter, the cause of motion being energy. Warner's system, therefore, is not rigorously mechanistic. It retains a certain degree of dualism. Warner's vocabulary is practically free of theological or metaphysical connotations. Yet this virtue radiative filling the universe is still reminiscent of the Neo-Platonic Soul of the World and seems to have much in common with Bruno's *Causa*.

These papers of Warner's on first principles are only notes, or first drafts, yet they enable us to distinguish the elements of a system of the world which Warner intended to support by carefully wrought out logical arguments. From this point of view they are more valuable than Hill's book, and they are less fragmentary than Harriot's papers and letters on the same subject. How much Warner owed to Harriot for his ideas we cannot tell. And we cannot know either to what extent Harriot's own ideas were affected by Bruno's philosophy. But we may be sure that both Harriot and Warner shared the same convictions concerning the eternity of the universe. Both accepted the principle, *ex nihilo nihil fit*, but Warner's reputation does not seem to have suffered from it, as Harriot's did.

I shall now attempt to deal briefly with the incomplete draft of a treatise of Warner's on the vital functions of the human organism. Blood circulation, though by no means the only subject treated, occupies a central position in this description of all the operations necessary for the maintenance of life. And the draft bears a certain relation to the treatise on blood circulation alluded to by biographers, mainly to raise the question of the priority of Warner's claim to the discovery. We read in a set of manuscript notes on the Earl of Northumberland and his associates:

Another was Mr Warrener the inventor probably of the circulation of the blood, of which subject he made a treatise consisting of two books which he sent to Dr Harvey, who epitomized, and printed them in his own name; he usually said that Dr Harvey did not understand the motion of the heart, which was a perfect hydraulick.[58]

Aubrey's version of the story, which is based on Pell's testimony, is substantially different:

Warner did tell Pell, that when Dr. Harvey came out with his Circulation of the Blood, he did wonder whence Dr. Harvey had it: but comeing one day to the earl of Leicester, he found Dr. Harvey in the hall, talking very familiarly with Mr. Prothero (Wallice ap Roderic) to whom Mr. Warner had discoursed concerning this exercitation of his De Circulatione Sanguinis, and made no question but Dr. Harvey had his hint from Prothero.[59]

According to the first source Warner had communicated his treatise to Harvey. According to Aubrey, Warner merely supposed that Protheroe had repeated to Harvey what he had told him concerning blood circulation: Harvey was not accused of having appropriated the whole argument of Warner's treatise, but suspected of having received a hint from a person who had heard him discourse on the subject. The first source quotes no authority for the story of Harvey's plagiarism, but names two reliable witnesses who had seen, or possessed, Warner's treatise on blood circulation:

Sr Thomas Ailesbury Master of the requests a great officer in the Mint told me that he had Warriners book, and that I should have it, but coming to London he found his library, wherein were many rare, and curious books, plundred, and that amongst the rest taken away; Dr Pain that very ingenious and learned canon of Christ Church told me, that he had seen pervied this book of Warreners.[60]

Robert Payne, as has already been noted, was an associate of William and Charles Cavendish, and of Thomas Hobbes, and had discussed with them, and Warner himself, Warner's work on optics.[61]

As for Aubrey's memorandum: 'Dr. Pell sayes that Mr. Warner rationated demonstratively by beates of the pulses that there must be a circulation of the blood', it receives some support from a note by Warner, distinct from the manuscript under discussion:

A schematisme or literall designation of the harts reciprocal motion in both his progresses the corporal and the pectorall as they are distinctly but yet concomitantly continuable.[62]

It appears from Pell's story, as reported by Aubrey, that Warner was convinced he was the real inventor. Historians of medicine have examined Warner's draft on this point, and concluded that though Warner might have discovered independently the principle of blood circulation, Harvey alone had provided the decisive experimental demonstration.[63]

But the draft in question cannot be used incontrovertibly either to dismiss or support Warner's claim of priority. First the draft is not the treatise *De circulatione sanguinis* alluded to by Pell and Aubrey, and known to Aylesbury and Payne. It is true that it contains matter concerning blood circulation but it is incomplete and, as we shall see in a moment, the first extant section begins after blood circulation has already been described. Finally the draft is difficult to date[64]. It might have been written after the publication of Harvey's *De motu cordis* (1628), though it is reasonable to suppose that Warner's interest in anatomy and vital functions can be traced back to the years of captivity of

Northumberland and Ralegh in the Tower, during which, as we know from the Earl's accounts, dissection was practised[65].

Biographers of Harvey, and commentators on his famous book, dismiss Warner in a foot-note. But perhaps his ideas on physiology deserve to be better known, not only in relation to Harvey's discovery, but as part of his own philosophy. The following passage will give an idea of his approach:

It may be noted that the life of animals or state of animality is *status fluens*, a state in continual flux and mutation and in *continuo fieri*, as is that of fire or flame and of the sea and the earth and indeed of the whole univers. So as no individuum can be understood to be the same at one time that it is at another precisely, *id entitate numerali* but only *per equivalentiam* as we understand of an old ship that hath had all or most of her pieces changed.[66]

Whether he deals with the universe or the little world of animal life he is concerned with the incessant flow and renewal of things. Blood circulation occupies a central position in his description because the continuation of life depends upon it. But he is concerned with all biological cycles and their inter-dependence. He is consequently interested in the relationship of the individual with its surroundings and the activity which enables it to satisfy its vital needs and make up for its organic waste.

The extant papers start with section DDD, when blood circulation has already been discussed, but what we have yields abundant evidence of his knowledge of the anatomy and function of all the organs involved in the process. Warner describes the fabric of the heart muscles as being made of fibres, 'direct, transverse and oblique' to allow for dilatation and contraction[67]. He understands that systoles correspond to the propulsion of blood into the arteries and diastoles to the supply of the heart of blood from the veins[68]. He is aware of the circulation of blood from the left ventricle and the aorta through the different organs and back to the vena cava, and the right auricle and ventricle. He is also aware of the interconnection of capillary arteries and veins, and speaks of the 'inosculatory or venarteriall circulation of the blood'.[69] He also understands the circulation of blood from the right ventricle to the lung and back to the left ventricle, and describes the 'dispersion and distribution of the branches of the asperous artery (=trachea) through the whole body of the lungs exactly accompanying the branches of the venous artery and of the arterious vaine to the very capillar points of them' which proves, he adds, that nature intends to mix air and blood to be conducted to the left ventricle'[70]. He is also aware of the part played by circulation in conducting the products of digestion to the various organs where they are required. His purpose in this section however, is not to describe circulation, but to seek what is its active principle, which after examining various hypotheses, he finds in the influx of animal spirits which is transmitted from the brain through the nerves to the fibres of the heart.

This is what he calls the pneumato-hydraulic motion of the heart, which involves the blood and the nervous system. Actually the whole living organism is involved in the process. The products of digestion receive a further elaboration in the bloodstream, and are distributed to the different parts of the body, while the wastes are eliminated. The 'matter-plasmatick' serves for the refection of the organs and tissues. Spirits extracted from the blood are collected in the brain. Part is retained for operations such as sense perception, imagination, intellection, voluntary motion. To this purpose, the animal spirits are connected by 'nerve-canallets' with the organs of sense, from which they receive impressions from the exterior, and with the other organs from which they receive internal impressions. They are also connected with the organs of voluntary motion, the first purpose of which is to obtain materials from the exterior to make up for the loss of substance incurred in the course of the various organic activities. Another part of the animal spirits is concerned with the maintaining of spontaneous motion, in particular the contraction and dilatation of the heart[71].

I have just briefly mentioned these points which Warner discusses at length in sections DDD and HHH. But before I conclude I would like to give an idea of his views of the locomotive faculty, because it takes into account mental as well as organic processes. As in the case of the spontaneous motion of the heart, Warner looks for an active principle. It cannot be the pleasure associated with food. This is a stimulant, but it is secondary, being based on the 'phantasiation' (or recollection) of an earlier sensation. The first stimulant then must be the dull sensation of pain in the digestive tract which is known as hunger and the feeling of dryness and heat resulting from the thickness of blood, which we call thirst. This stimulates the appetite but voluntary motion cannot take place without the agency of the cognitive spirits. In other terms the appetitive faculty is subordinate to the locomotive faculty, which in its turn is subordinate to the rational.[72]

Warner distinguishes several degrees in the relation of our intellect to objects of desire or aversion. First these objects are apprehended simply and recognized as pleasing or displeasing. Secondly they are recognized as good or bad in relation to us. Thirdly they are also recognized as good or bad in relation to us but with the additional consideration of the possibility of obtaining them or not, or avoiding them or not, which implies some form of reasoning or 'syllogizing', comparing their present phantasm or image with those of similar objects retained in our memory. But before we reach the final stage when a decision can be taken and the action accomplished, some further reasoning is necessary: our intellect must compare the images or representations of our own motions, and of the means to be used to obtain what is desired. It must compare or balance the good and the evil on either side, to determine what is most expedient. And only then can the act of volition take place, and the action be performed.[73] The faculties involved are not innate, but acquired by way of repetition and habit. Through the repeated experience of pain, relief from pain, and pleasure, the animal learns what is good or bad for its conservation and protection.[74]

Warner makes a further distinction between the effects produced upon corporeal organs, and the effect upon spirits: consciousness of pain is distinct from pain itself. It is as necessary for the intellect to apprehend the malignity of pain by speculating upon it as for sense to receive the impression of pain. But between these two levels there remains a continuity residing in the nature of the spirits sensitive and intellective, which are similar in substance, though they represent different degrees of elaboration. Pain which is transmitted by sense is perceived by the intellect as sorrow, that is as apprehension of danger and of the destruction of the self. But the process can be reversed. Sorrow may in its turn have a destructive effect by creating a disturbance of spirits, and the neglect of the function of restoration. A relation of the same order is observed between a sensation of pleasure and a feeling of joy.[75]

Though the levels of living matter, sensation and intellection are distinguished, the ingestion of aliments, their further elaboration in the digestive tracts and the blood stream, and the use of part of them to renew the spirits are considered, in this draft, as a continuous process. The spirits are apparently conceived by Warner as rarefied matter, obtained by vital operations analogous to those which can be artificially produced by chemistry. But what is the action of *vis* or virtue radiative in the living organism? And is there such a thing as the individual soul? These questions are not raised in the sections of the manuscript we possess.

A final observation. Warner's approach to the discussion of pleasure, pain, joy, sorrow, sensation, intellection, and volition is strikingly similar to that of Thomas Hobbes in early manuscripts such as the *Elements of Law*, or the criticism of Thomas White's *De mundo*[76], as well as his published work, *De Homine* and *Leviathan*. That Hobbes had some knowledge of the ideas expressed in Warner's draft can be deduced from his letter to William Cavendish, Earl of Newcastle:

For the soule I know he has nothinge to give your Lordship any satisfaction. I would he could give good reasons for the facultyes and passions of the soule, such as may be expressed in playne English, if he can; he is the first—that I ever heard of—could speake sense in that subject. If he cannot I hope to be the first.[77]

The tone is rather disparaging, but Hobbes, though doubting Warner's capacity to give his ideas clear formulation, is ready to admit that Warner is the first to speak sense on the subject of the faculties and passions of the soul. The last sentence, 'If he cannot I hope to be the first', seems to mean: 'If he cannot express himself clearly on the subject I hope to be the first'. But the whole passage is based on the distinction between 'being the first to have sound views on the question', and 'being the first to give them clear philosophic formulation'. Hobbes suggests that he is also working on the subject, and hopes to forestall Warner. Does he mean that Warner is the first person he had met with ideas similar to his own on the subject, or that Warner is really a pioneer, from whom he has received precious hints, and whom he wants to emulate? The wording of the passage is too ambiguous for us to decide. But at least we can conclude that Warner's research in that field was not unknown to Hobbes, and that it had a stimulating influence upon him.

From Bruno's infinite and universal cause, to Harriot's speculations on the structure of matter, to Warner's attempted formulation of the first principles of natural philosophy and inquiry into the workings of living organisms, and finally to Hobbes' own philosophy *de corpore* and *de homine,* we seem to have travelled a long way. Though the work of Northumberland's associates remained largely unpublished and, in the case of Warner, was partly lost, they were not an isolated group. The new ideas which originated, or were developed, in their circle, were eventually transmitted. The story of the half-century which precedes the formulation of classical science and philosophy would be incomplete if this group was not taken into account, though much work remains to be done.

NOTES

1. In his letter to Harriot of 6 February 1610 (soon after the publication of Kepler's *Astronomia nova*), Lower writes that Kepler 'establishes soundlie and as you say overthrowes the circular astronomie'. Quoted by Robert H. Kargon, *Atomism in England from Harriot to Newton,* Oxford 1966, pp. 20–1. Lowers' reference to Harriot's view of the fixed stars is discussed further below.
2. They are discussed in my paper on 'Thomas Harriot's Reputation for Impiety', *Notes and Records of the Royal Society of London,* vol. 9, May 1952, pp. 164–87, where all the data are given. Harriot's own reaction to these attacks is reflected in a list he had compiled of books referring to him. Cf. David B. Quinn and John W. Shirley, 'A Contemporary List of Hariot References', *Renaissance Quarterly* (vol. 22), 1969, pp. 9–25.
3. *A Synopsis of the Controversie of Atoms,* Birch MSS 4458, pp. 6–8, published in appendix to my article (*Notes and Records, ut supra*).
4. Letter of 13 July 1608, *Kepleri Opera omnia,* ed. Frisch, vol. II (1857) p. 74. This was more than two years after his arrest and imprisonment at the time of Northumberland's trial.
5. Letter to his doctor (1616), Add. MSS 6789, f. 446 v.
6. This was told to John Aubrey by Seth Ward, bishop of Sarum: *Brief Lives,* ed. A. Clark, p. 286.
7. This aspect is treated by Frances A. Yates, *G. Bruno and the Hermetic tradition,* London 1964. On his view of the universe, cf. Paul-Henri Michel, *La cosmologie de G. Bruno.* Paris 1962.
8. For a full treatment of these discussions in Scholastic philosophy cf. Pierre Duhem, *Etudes sur Léonard de Vinci* (first published, Paris 1909, reprint 1955), vol. II, Ch. IX and X, and notes E.F.
9. In *Spaccio de la bestia trionfante* Bruno seeks to establish that the Egyptian (Hermetic) tradition is more ancient than, and superior to the Hebrew. The equivalence of religious myths is emphasized in that dialogue, where the existence of Pre-Adamites is also discussed in connection with the discovery of ancient monuments in the New World. Harriot wrote in his *Report* that the religion of the Virginians, though inferior, was based on beliefs similar to those of Christianity. That he was one of the mathematicians who, according to Thomas Nashe, would prove the existence of men before Adam is highly probable since *Pierce pennilesse* (1592), where this statement occurs, appears in the list of books containing references to him (D. B. Quinn and J. W. Shirley, article cited, p. 20).

10. *De l'infinito, Opere italiane*, ed. Lagarde (Gottinga 1888), pp. 304–18, and Cf. Pico della Mirandola, *Oratio de hominis dignitate* in *Commentationes*, Bononiae 1496, f. 137 v.

11. *Philosophia Epicurea, Democritiana, Theophrastica proposita simpliciter non edocta, per Nicolaum Hill Anglum, Londinensem*. Parisiis 1601. Second edition, Geneva 1619.

12. Cf. J. Aubrey, *Lives*, ed. Clark, I, pp. 319–20; A. Wood, *Athenae Oxonienses*, ed. Bliss, II, pp. 86–7, and manuscript notes on the Earl of Northumberland and his associates, Bodleian, Rawlinson B 158, pp. 153–5. His manuscripts were once in the hands of Thomas Henshaw FRS (1618–1700), and William Backhouse of Swallowfield, Berks (1593–1662). Copies were made for Edmund Sheffield, First Earl of Mulgrave, and John Everard D.D. (1575?–1650?). Henshaw was an expert in the occult, Backhouse was a Rosicrucian, Everard translated Hermetic works (*Pymander, Asclepius*) and, in his 'unregenerate days' was a Neo-Platonist. I have been unable to trace Hill's MSS (with the exception of a poem *Sanctus Spiritus vere Deus est* (MS Tanner 305, f. 110 and 112)) and would be grateful for information concerning them.

13. N. 363, 368, 370, 376. These, and the following references are to the numbered aphorisms and fragments of the book.

14. N. 36, 37, 444, 445.

15. N. 352, 391, 410, 436, 454.

16. N. 20, 49, 107, 131, 205, 237, 434, 435, 438.

17. N. 165, 245, 246, 284, 299, 300, 304, 334.

18. N. 63, 263, 280, 309, 310, 365, 394.

19. N. 64, 73, 139, 253, 376, 378.

20. N. 2, 3, 4, 5, 112, 169.

21. N. 56, 60, 61, 203.

22. N. 21, 22, 87, 88, 100, 101, 186, 190, 191, 192, 193, 207, 208, 273, 274.

23. N. 111, 118, 122, 153, 168, 276, 340, 341, 345, 411, 478, 509.

24. N. 25, 143, 144, 145, 161, 172, 178, 399, 404, 444, 445, 454, 499.

25. Cf. Grant McColley, 'Nicholas Hill and the *Philosophia epicurea*', *Annals of Science*, 1939, (pp. 390–405), p. 401.

26. *Advice to his Son*, quoted by R. H. Kargon, *Atomism in England*, p. 14.

27. *Poems*, ed. P. Bartlett, pp. 381 ff. Cf. my book: *George Chapman*, Paris 1951, pp. 26–7, 218–20; David B. Quinn and John W. Shirley, 'A contemporary list of Hariot References', pp. 23–4.

28. 21 June 1610, to Harriot, quoted and discussed in 'T. Harriot's Reputation . . .' (*ut supra* n. 2) pp. 174–6.

29. Bk. VI, ch. III, pp. 215–16 of the original and of the facsimile translation (London 1900, reprint Basic Books, New York, 1958).

30. *De stella nova Serpentarii, Opera,* ed. Frisch, vol. II, pp. 608–9.

31. Add. MSS 6782, ff. 362–74 and cf. Harleian MSS 6002, ff. 2–10. Discussed in 'T. Harriot's impiety . . . " pp. 177–9 and in Kargon, *Atomism in England*, pp. 24–6.

32. Kepler, *Opera*, vol. II, pp. 67–76.

33. Ed. Clark, vol. II, p. 291, also I, p. 286 and II, pp. 15–16. Cf. Anthony Wood, ed. Bliss, I, pp. 460–1.

34. Most of the extant papers are in Add. MSS 4394–4396, and 6754–6756. Letters from Warner, to him, or about him, are to be found in other volumes. Some have been reproduced by J. O. Halliwell *A Collection of Letters Illustrative of the Progress of Science in England*, London 1841.

35. John W. Shirley 'The Scientific Experiments of Sir Walter Ralegh, the Wizard Earl, and the Three Magi in the Tower, 1603–1617'. *Ambix*, vol. IV, 1949–51, pp. 52–66.

36. Add. 4396, f. 90. A copy in Warner's hand. The Lord to whom it is addressed is not named. Warner, Harriot and Aylesbury are mentioned only by their initials, but the circumstances make the identification certain.

37. Aubrey, II, p. 291.

38. Ibid, II, pp. 15–16. The Woolstable was near Charing Cross.

39. He had received them from Tovey, beneficed in Leicestershire, who had married Warner's niece. He transmitted them to his successor Dr Richard Busby.

40. Add. MSS 4279, ff. 275–8. On f. 278 Pell wrote: 'Hujus operis Warneri-Pelliani capita

12 Warnerus designavit'. Follows a table of twelve chapters, modelled on Warner's own notes in Add, 4396, f. 1. Ff. 1–39 of this volume concern the theoretical part of the Canon.—In a letter from Amsterdam to Charles Cavendish, 7 August 1644, Pell had expressed the fear that 'all Mr Warner's papers, *and no small share of my labours therein*' had been lost. (Add. 4278 f. 179, italics mine).

41. Add. 4394, f. 106. 'An Inventorie of the Papers of Mr. Warner', with a receipt dated 14 December 1667: 'Received the abovesaid papers from Dr. Thorndyke which I promise to return upon demaund', signed 'John Collins'. All the items are crossed out, except four concerning money. Aubrey notes that Warner 'wrote a Treatise of Coynes in relation to mint affaires, of which Mr. John Collins has a copie'. According to A. Wood, John Collins was Accomptant to the Royal Fishery Company.

42. 'Ex observationibus diligentissimis Tho: Aylesbury and Walt: Warner; Westmonasterii mense Julio 1627 apparent'. Follow tables of refraction from 1 to 90 'Ab Aëre ad Vitrum' and 'Ab Aëre ad Aquam'. Add. 4395, ff. 138, 140, and cf. f. 99. There is more material on refraction in this volume.

43. *De loco imaginis in visione a speculo concavo reflexa*, Add. 6756, ff. 5–22. (Copy by the scribe of Charles Cavendish.)

44. The second tract, on the making of a telescope, is apparently lost, but the problem of its construction is formulated in Add. 3495, f. 103. The correspondence is summed up in my paper 'Sir Charles Cavendish and his Learned Friends', *Annals of Science* (8) 1952, pp. 19–20.

45. *Problema ad tabulas refractionum construendas*. In Mersenne's *Universae Geometriae Synopsis*. Charles Cavendish left a manuscript copy of the tract in the hands of J. Pell 'about the beginning of June' 1640; Add. 4417, ff. 38–9.

46. Add. 6754, ff. 2–74 v. A fair copy, not in Warner's hand.

47. The classification of these papers is difficult because the same basic concepts occur in most fragments. I shall not discuss it here but I sum up the substance in what seems to be the logical order.

The main groups are:

—MS 4394, ff. 129r–130v (Of states, alterations, causes), cf. MS 4425, 3v (*causa—status—alteratio*);

—4394, ff. 384r–385v (on matter and states) continued on 4395, ff. 191r–200v (states of formation, motion, alteration, existence, cause);

—4394, ff. 387r–389v (*vis*);

—4394, ff. 386r (matter), 396r–403v (matter, atoms, time, space); cf. 4395, f. 212 (*materia*), continued 4394, f. 382r–383v;

—4394, ff. 387r–389v (*vis*);

—4395, ff. 201r–211v (existence, time, space, plurality, continuum);

—MS 4425 contains a fragment (on matter and motion) f. 4 r/v; cf. 4395, f. 95r (*de motu*).

These papers are discussed by R. H. Kargon, op. cit., pp. 35–40.

48. DDD: 4394, ff. 132r–175v
HHH: *Ibid.*, ff. 177r–218v
LLL: 4395, ff. 1r–70v
MMM: 4394, ff. 219r–264v (to be read *retrograde*)
NNN: *Ibid.* ff. 265r–271v.

49. 4395, f. 208v.

50. 4394, f. 396r.

51. *Ibid.*, f. 396v.

52. *Ibid.*, f. 398v.

53. *Ibid.*, f. 399v.

54. *Ibid.*, ff. 382r–383r.

55. 4395, f. 198r.

56. *Ibid.*, f. 198v.

57. *Ibid.*, f. 199v.

It is difficult to ascribe a date to these papers, and to this passage in particular. But Warner died before Descartes published the *Principia* (1644) where the formulation of his first law of Nature is to be found (Part II, pr. 37).

58. MS quoted *supra*, n. 12, pp. 152–3.

59. Aubrey, ed. Clark, II, p. 291.

60. P. 153: 'pervied = purvayed' (sold) seems implausible.

61. *Vide supra*, pp. 109 and 117.

62. MS 4396, f. 29v. This note fills a blank verso in the theoretical part of the Canon of logarithms, a work with which Pell was acquainted. (Cf. supra n. 40). The 'schematism' where S, M, D probably stand for systole, motion, diastole, is as follows:

							Puls.	Corp.	
Actus	Pausa						Actus	Pausa	
SMD	DMS	SMD	DMS	SMD	DMS	SMD	e a	a e	
							SMD	DMS	SMD

63. G. Rolleston, *The Harveian Oration*, 1873, pp. 56 ff.: M. P. Bayon, 'Allusions to a circulation of the blood', *Proceedings of the Royal Society of Medicine*, Feb. 1938, vol. 32, pp. 711 ff.

64. Rolleston dates MS 4394 as c. 1610; Bayon inclines to date it later, c. 1635. But this volume, which contains the parts of the draft concerning blood circulation, is of a composite character, papers of different origin being bound together. Kargon, op. cit., p. 36, n. 7, thinks that another set of papers, on the first principles of natural philosophy, which we have already discussed, was probably written during the 1620's, and certainly before Torporley's death in 1632, because some of Warner's material on the subject is to be found in Torporley's papers at Sion College. But apart from some of Warner's work on optics, which can be precisely dated, we are reduced to conjectures.

65. Payments for drawings or paintings of the dissection of the head and skull appear c. 1617, unfortunately the last year of the period for which the accounts have survived. Cf. John W. Shirley, 'The Scientific Experiments . . .' (Op. cit. *supra* n. 35). p. 63. The anatomy of the brain is discussed by Warner (Section HHH, 4394, ff. 177 ff.) in relation to blood circulation, the nervous system, and the formation of spirits.

66. 4394, f. 161v.

67. *Ibid.*, f. 133r/v.

68. *Ibid.*, f. 137v.

69. *Ibid.*, f. 142v.

70. *Ibid.*, ff. 133v–134r.

71. *Ibid.*, ff. 137–139v.

72. 4395, ff. 1r–16r.

73. 4394, ff. 264v ff. (reading *retrograde*).

74. *Ibid.*, ff. 254v ff. (*retrograde*).

75. *Ibid.*, ff. 251v ff. (*retrograde*).

76. Bibliothèque nationale, Paris, MS Latin 6566 A. A critical edition by Harold W. Jones and myself has just appeared: Thomas Hobbes, *Critique du 'De Mundo' de Thomas White*, Editions Vrin-LNRS, Paris, 1973. English translation is in preparation.

77. Paris, August 25, 1635, *Historical Manuscripts Commission*, Portland MSS, p. 126. (The preceding paragraph criticizes Warner's project for a burning-glass.)

7

THOMAS HARRIOT AND THE FIRST TELESCOPIC OBSERVATIONS OF SUNSPOTS

JOHN NORTH
Oxford University

One [mathematician] saith the Sun stands, another he moves, a third comes in, taking them all at rebound: and lest there should any Paradox be wanting, he findes certain spots or clouds in the Sun, by the help of glasses, by means of which the Sun must turne round upon his own center, or they about the Sun. *Fabricius* puts only three, and those in the Sun, Apelles 15. and those without the Sun, floating like the Cyanean Isles in the *Euxine* Sea. The *Hollander* in his *dissertatiuncula cum Apelle* censures all. . . .[1]

Democritus Iunior [Robert Burton],
The Anatomy of Melancholy . . . , Oxford,
1621, p. 329.

IT is a melancholy thought that Robert Burton, whose book was first published in the year of Harriot's death, should have known no better than to omit his compatriot's name from his list of paradoxers. Burton evidently knew of the controversy over priority in the discovery of sunspots, and he must have ignored the name of Galileo quite deliberately, for with Galileo's writings he was very familiar; but of Harriot's work he was in all probability totally unaware. What was true of Burton in 1621 was to remain true of many a later historian. Thus in a recent discussion of Galileo's observations of sunspots, running to more than three score pages, Bernard Dame was able to include Harriot's name only in a footnote, as one who 'a peut-être observé les taches avant Galilée'.[2] He observed that Harriot's observations were not known until 1784, and not published until 1833. In saying as much, although he made no mention of Arago, he reminds us of that passage where Arago, in a life of Galileo and in connexion with this very question of priority over the observation of sunspots—laid down his 'règle aux historiens des sciences'.[3]

Arago's guiding principle was one of public utility: 'Le public ne doit rien à qui ne lui a rendu aucun service', and 'en matière de découvertes, comme en tante autre chose, l'intérêt public et l'intérêt privé bien entendu marchent toujours de compagnie'. Publication meant everything to Arago, and in reading him we are reminded of William Lower's plea to Harriot in a letter of 6 February 1610, where Lower has spoken of Harriot's discoveries passing to other men:

Al these were your deues and manie others that I could mention; and yet to[o] great reservednesse hath robd you of those glories . . . Onlie let this remember you, that it is possible by to[o] much procrastination to be prevented in the honor of some of your rarest inventions and speculations. Let your countrie and frends injoye the comforts they would have in the true and greate honor you would purchase your selfe by publishing some of your choise workes.[4]

But Lower's lament was not quite the same as Arago's principle of the historical excommunication of writers without influence. Of course if a man were to have spent his life in a hermit's cell drafting political constitutions for his own amusement, his prospects of inclusion in a constitutional history would be quite properly slender. But even taking an extreme view of Harriot's isolationism, and supposing that he conceived of mathematics and astronomy as wholly personal intellectual enterprises, he was neither inconsistent nor foolish, unless it is foolish not to beg for admiration. Galileo wished to know, and also to be known. Harriot seems to have wished only to know. His surviving writings are far less extensive and discursive than Galileo's, and had they been otherwise they would not still be awaiting publication.

When we look to Harriot's solar observations, we find records made on two hundred or so days, with very few personal asides, a few rough calculations, and nothing more. Galileo, on the other hand, was by this time exposed to the public gaze. He gave glory to senates and to princes, in the expectation of rewards, and it was important that he not only reveal new truths, but also master the art of establishing priority in his discoveries. When in 1613 he published his 'history and demonstration relating to sunspots and their phenomena',[5] it was in the form of three letters to Mark Welser, a leading citizen of Augsburg, in which an attempt was made to refute a rival claim to the discovery. But the letters were much more besides: Welser, who had prompted them by his having published three letters on sunspots from Christoph Scheiner (under the long pseudonym 'Apelles latens post tabulam'),[6] had obliged Galileo to reply to a question about the nature of the spots. Scheiner was a Jesuit, and Welser a banker to the Jesuits. With great intuition and tact, Galileo in his replies helped to erode opposition to Copernicanism, and to the notion of an immaculate and lucid Sun, although it is doubtful whether Galileo's letters much affected Scheiner himself. In the course of the polemic, and with Welser's help, we may as it were interrogate Galileo closely. There is no such possibility with Harriot, for whom we must piece together what fragmentary evidence survives, and hope that something significant emerges.

THE DEBATE ON PRIORITY OF DISCOVERY

This is a tedious problem, but not entirely barren, historically speaking. It is now well known that spots were seen on the face of the Sun long before the advent of the telescope. Chinese observations go back at least to 28 BC,[7] and Humboldt has collected together a very useful list of references to sunspots in European and Islamic annals,[8] of which perhaps the most interesting are those in the *Annales Regi Francorum* (for 807 AD), and in Einhard's life of Charlemagne (before 814 AD).[9] The former was interpreted at the time as a transit of the planet Mercury, lasting for what we know to be an impossible eight days. In the same century, the philosopher al-Kindī explained away similar observations as a transit of Venus (lasting for a nonsensical 91 days), and before 1199 Ibn Rushd used the Mercury explanation once again. Even Kepler, who had observed a sunspot by projecting the image of the Sun through a small hole into a darkened chamber during what he believed would be a transit of Mercury on 18 May 1607, was totally but quite naturally misled by his expectations into thinking that he was indeed seeing Mercury.[10]

There are clearly two vastly different sorts of connotation for sunspot records. Looking back with the advantage of our present knowledge that a sunspot is a relatively cool area forming a slight depression in the photosphere of the Sun, one might say that sunspots were not truly found until, at the very least, a proof was offered of their solar nature. Curiously enough, Stephen Rigaud took an almost equally severe historical position, and consequently refused to entertain the idea that with his earlier observation Harriot had discovered anything. He had not, said Rigaud, obtained 'more than a transient view of a phenomenon, which had been seen before his time, even with the naked eye', adding that it was 'a misapplication of terms to call such an observation a discovery'.[11] Speaking of Scheiner, Delambre said, not that he made no true discovery, but that if he had a telescope then it followed that he could see the spots: 'il n'y a pas grand mérite à cela'.[12] As Delambre pointed out, Scheiner was less happy in his conjectures than Galileo. He was an inferior geometer, and a less practised astronomer.

This was all part of a very proper reaction against the tactics used by the astronomers and their factions in the original dispute over priority, in which rhetoric had meant more than logic. The dispute had its repercussions on very many nineteenth century writers whom it would be pointless to list: it should be sufficient to say that in imposing some sort of criterion of historical validity which was not ostensibly designed to favour a chosen party, Delambre and Rigaud were untypical of their time. Nevertheless, with Rigaud's argument begins the slippery path to a very corrosive paradox of historiography. Why did he not go on to deny Galileo's discovery of sunspots, on the grounds that our knowledge of them suggests that they are different from the objects known to Galileo? If the historian defines his conceptual terms once and for all in order to escape this paradox, he runs the risk of being accused of not playing the priorities game impartially. Alternatively, should he emphasize that he writes of a conceptual world which is in a state of flux, he will be accused of writing with a grey historical uniformity. But a continuum is not necessarily homogeneous. Harriot left no indication of his attitudes to the physical nature of sunspots, let alone to their significance for theology and Aristotelianism, a matter which was uppermost in Galileo's thoughts. We have no explicit indication even of their supposed location. But slender as is the evidence, Harriot's observations show him to have been a remarkably good astronomer, the peer of Galileo in matters of observation, and superior in many small respects to Scheiner, Fabricius, and the rest.

Harriot recorded what we must suppose was his first observation of sunspots as follows:[13]

1610 Syon
Decemb 8^d mane ♄ [= Saturday]. The altitude of the Sonne being 7 or 8 degrees. It being a frost & a mist. I saw the Sonne in this manner. Instrument. $\frac{10}{1}$.B. I saw it twise or thrise. once with the right ey & other time with the left. In the space of a minutes time. After the Sonne was to cleare.

(See Plate 4.) Little more than a month later, he found the Sun to be clear:

$\frac{1610}{1611}$ Syon

Jannuary. 19. ♄ [Saturday] a notable mist. I obserued diligently at sondry times when it was fit. I saw nothing but the cleare Sonne both with right and left ey.

If we are to judge by his surviving papers—and I am not at all sure that we should— nearly a year went by without further observation. On 1 December 1611, in the company of Sir William Lower and Christopher Tooke, he began a systematic study, numbering his observations from this time.

A number of objections may be raised at once to Rigaud's argument that Harriot was at first merely making simple observations of a phenomenon not as yet understood. No astronomer fully appreciated sunspots from the moment he first saw them. The telescopic observer had the inestimable advantage of being able to study carefully sunspot shapes—and hence avoid the planetary interpretation which no less an astronomer than Kepler had previously offered. In Harriot's very first drawings he gave the spots a hard and irregular outline, and on the whole he is unlikely to have thought them planetary or nebulous in character.[14] His second numbered record, although admittedly by this time he must have heard of the speculations of others, refers to the phenomena unambiguously as 'spots in the Sonne', and the appellation never changed.

Our second objection is that Harriot's pages, as they survive, are almost certainly fair copies. We know the appearance of his rough observing notes, from two leaves in the volume of his lunar observations.[15] Are we to suppose that his curiosity during the period from December 1610 to December 1611 never got the better of him? We know that he looked in vain for the spots on 19 January. Are we to suppose that he let matters rest there? He will be shown to have performed a calculation of the sunspot rotation period spanning the interval 8 December 1610 and 28 November 1611, both of which dates are outside the period of the *numbered* observations. No record of any observations of 28 November or of any other date in the interval survive. Scheiner's records subsequently printed and thus available to Harriot,[16] include an observation of 28 November 1611, and we may imagine that Harriot was making use of this in his calculation. But how, without a chain of intervening observations, did he conclude that there was a connexion between the states of the Sun on the two dates? I shall suggest a solution subsequently. On the whole it is hard to believe that on 1 December 1611 (a highly significant date, as will be explained) Harriot embarked on a systematic programme of recorded observation without due rehearsal.

Rigaud supposed that such of Harriot's sunspot observations as were made with understanding began only on 1 December 1611, and this is very surprising since Rigaud offered what is undoubtedly the true reason for Harriot's great concern over the sunspot configuration on that day.[17] Against the written record and the drawing for 1 December, there are—prominently displayed—the symbols for a conjunction of the Sun and Venus. Maginus in his *Ephemerides* had predicted a superior conjunction,[18] but interest was aroused in what would happen, since there were many who, subscribing to a Ptolemaic view, hoped to see a transit of the planet across the face of the Sun. None was seen, of course. Scheiner's second letter to Welser[19] correctly drew attention to the opposite directions of the apparent motions of the sunspots and Venus, but Galileo took the wind out of Scheiner's sails by pointing out that his calculations proved nothing against those who maintained that Maginus had compiled faulty tables, or that Venus was too small to be seen against the Sun, or that Venus shone by her own light, or that the orbit of Venus was above the Sun. As A.-G. Pingré amusingly commented, 'Galilée étoit un Aristarque un peu trop difficulteux sur les découvertes et observations de ses contemporains'.[20] At all events, there is ample testimony to the general interest stimulated by this important prediction of the *Ephemerides* of Maginus, and that this is why Harriot commenced a careful programme of recorded observations is easy enough to accept, without our supposing at the same time that he made none other in the previous year.

Harriot never published his findings. The first printed account of telescopic sunspot observation was of those by the Frisian Johannes Fabricius, *De maculis in Sole observatis, etc.* (Wittenburg, 1611, dedicated the Ides of June, that is, 13 June). For Fabricius, the spots were certainly on the Sun's surface, whose rotation he observed. He remarked that he had been first led to examine the Sun when looking for an irregularity of the limb, of which his father had informed him by letter (folio C2 verso). Perhaps the first careful modern study of the work of Fabricius was made by Arago, who concluded that the observations date from March 1611.[21] An important document in the form of a rare book, *Prognostication* (1615), by David Fabricius, his father, was reprinted by Gerhard Berthold in 1897. There it is maintained that Johannes, then a student of medicine, in his father's presence first found the spots on

27 February 1611, old style.[22] It is now known that Simon Mayr (Marius), in his own *Prognostication* for 1613, and again in his *Mundus Iovialis* (Nurnburg, 1614), corroborates the father's statement, adding in the second work that Fabricius's name had been suppressed on religious grounds.[23]

The East Frisian's book was soon joined by those of Welser's Jesuit correspondent, Scheiner. Although the letters were not printed until 1612, Scheiner long afterwards maintained in his *Rosa Ursina*[24] that he first saw the spots in March 1611,[25] and this confirmed a statement in his letter of 12 November 1611 that seven or eight months previously, with a friend, he had first seen the black smudges. Although Scheiner was to become the principal authority on sunspots during the later seventeenth century, his early writings are not especially good. His first letter shows—and Galileo was quick to point out the error—that he believed the spots to move in a contrary sense to that of the planetary circulation. He also doubted whether the spots adhered to the Sun. In the *Rosa Ursina* he tried to cover up his first error by maintaining that the Sun had a movement about two different axes. The first book was a polemic directed against Galileo. As for the remainder, Scheiner's examples date from 1625, and they are not here of much concern.[26]

Galileo apart, there were other early observers of sunspots. The painter Ludovico Cardi de Cigoli, friend of Galileo, wrote to him on 16 and 23 September 1611 that Cresti da Passigmani had been able to see as many as eight spots, in telescopic observations made at Venice.[27] In November Galileo was informed by Paulo Gualdo that sunspots were under observation in Germany.[28] From this time, over and above the Welser correspondence, references to the subject are frequent. As for interpretations, they span a wide range of specious ingenuity. Jean Tarde, for example, a canon of Sarlat in France, who in visiting Galileo had been irritated by his reticence over the principles underlying the telescope, wrote a treatise (*Borbonia sidera, etc.*, 1620) ridiculing Galileo's views, and contending that the Sun, 'eye of the world', was incapable of experiencing ophthalmia—and hence that sunspots were not a part of the Sun, but planetary. Claimed for the house of Bourbon by Tarde, as his title implied, there was later an attempted *coup* on the part of the Belgian Jesuit Charles Malapert, who wished to have the supposed planets circulate to the glory of the Hapsburgs (*Austriaca sidera, etc.*, 1633).[29]

The evident desire to flatter a potential patron is only one of many reasons for the bitterness of the controversies over priority at this time. Nationalism and a desire for personal fame were equally important motives, the former tending to outlive the latter, and religious dissension cannot be ignored. It has been said that the charge of heresy brought against Galileo, which resulted in his trial and confinement, was in part the result of a deposition made by Scheiner to the Inquisition in Rome.[30] Yet another whose claims to priority have been pressed, this time by Ernst Zinner, was Johannes Baptista Cysat, a friend of whom Scheiner spoke in his letter to Welser of 12 November 1611.[31]

The evidence is in the form of a record of a lost manuscript, in which first Cysat and then Scheiner are reported as having seen the spots on a cloudy morning of 6 March 1611.

If the sunspot debate over priorities was acrimonious, this was undoubtedly because large doctrinal issues were at stake, but also because the great Galileo was involved, and Galileo chose quite deliberately to try to capture yet another crown of laurels to add to his collection. His published letters to Welser on sunspots served a double purpose, first as propaganda for the Copernican theory, which he hoped in due course to be compatible with Church dogma, and second, as a defence of his scientific eminence, in the face of what he conceived to be a personal attack by Scheiner. The force of Galileo's scientific arguments in these letters left little to be desired. He argued that by their random formation and inconstancy the sunspots were more like flat and thin clouds than planets, but that they were, if not on the Sun, at least within its atmosphere. He pointed out that the duration might vary from one or two days to thirty or forty, that a monthly rotation might bring a spot back into view, fore-shortening of the shape of the spot occuring near the limb. He explained that the apparent daily motion of each spot diminished as the limb was approached, and that motion was a correct function of angular distance from the solar equator. He saw that the spots favoured a central zone of 28° or 29° width, and he maintained what must have seemed utterly paradoxical to his contemporaries, namely that the intrinsic brightness of the spots was at least that of the brightest parts of the Moon. In all this he proved himself a master of his craft. In dating his first discovery, however, the craft was of another sort.

Dame has set forth Galileo's three principal statements on the matter, noting that if we follow the evidence of the *Dialogo sopra i due massimi sistemi* (1632; Imprimatur 1630), Salviati, on the third day, is made to claim Galileo as their discoverer, in July or August 1610, while he was still at Padua:[32]

The original discoverer and observer of the solar spots (as indeed of all the other novelties in the skies) was our Lincean Academician; he discovered them in 1610, while he was still lecturer in mathematics at the University of Padua. He spoke about them to many people here in Venice, some of whom are yet living, and a year later he showed them to many gentlemen at Rome . . .

If, on the other hand, we are to take seriously a letter from Galileo to Maffeo Barberini of 2 June 1612—nearer the occasion by almost twenty years—we conclude in favour of December 1610, since it was then 'about 18 months ago' that, in looking at the setting Sun, he 'perceived several dark spots . . .'. In December he was in Florence. Or again, we might take a letter to Guiliano de'Medici of the 23rd of that same month of June, which places the first observations fifteen months earlier (March 1611), when he is known to have been in Rome. Mention of the subsequent occasion on which he showed the sunspots to a number of important personages in the gardens of the Quirinal is repeated, and attested from other sources.[33]

In a court of law, Galileo's opponents might well have said of the date 'E pur si muove'. They might even have recalled the disparate statements Galileo made in connexion with the re-invention of the telescope, for as Edward Rosen has indicated in an excellent summary of the evidence,[34] Galileo first heard of the Dutch telescopes in or around the end of June 1609 (according to a letter to his brother-in-law),[35] made his first telescope six days before going to Venice, apparently in mid-July,[36] and yet in *Il Saggiatore* (1623) maintained that the interval between hearing of the telescope and making one was no more than a day. In *Sidereus nuncius* (1610), however, he explains how he first heard about the telescope, how the rumour was confirmed a few days later, and how he then gave his attention to the problem, which he solved after a little while (*'paulo post'*). As Rosen very aptly remarked, by the ordinary rules of evidence the early version is preferable to the later.[37]

To complete this Protean chronology, Galileo was in Venice for 'more than a month' showing an improved telescope to the Venetians before presenting it to the Venetian Senate on 25 August 1609, a date confirmed by official documents. Accepting with Rosen that 'more than a month' might mean six weeks, we should have Galileo's first demonstration of the (improved) telescope around 10 July, and his first attempt early in July. These dates are all, of course, in the Gregorian calendar. Harriot's first recorded telescopic observation, that in which he made what is the first known telescopic drawing of the lunar surface, is in that calendar to be dated 5 August 1609.[38]

HARRIOT AND GALILEO

Galileo's fame apart, his writings are of such importance to the history of early seventeenth-century cosmology that Harriot's knowledge of them is a matter of great interest. Harriot's earliest known telescopic observation of the Moon, of 26 July 1609 (O.S.) 9 p.m., was made almost three weeks before Galileo presented his telescope to the Venetian Senate, and Harriot must then have been entirely ignorant of Galileo's telescopic activities.[39]

Galileo first saw three of Jupiter's satellites on 7 December 1609 (N.S.). His last observation of the 64 to be recorded in *Sidereus nuncius* is dated March 1610, and the book was dedicated on 12 March and published on 13 March of that year.[40] This book had a number of undated Moon drawings, which in the Frankfurt printing of 1610 were rendered by crude wood-blocks, but in the Venice edition are printed from fine copper plates comparable in quality with Harriot's later drawings. Harriot had no need of the Italian Moon drawings, but we do know that he made ample use of the Jupiter observations, which he himself supplemented by a series commencing 17 October 1610 (O.S.).[41] A letter from William Lower of 11 June 1610 (O.S.)[42] acknowledges a letter from Harriot in which he reports on Galileo's findings, and asks for a copy of the book, meaning *Sidereus nuncius*, of which Harriot certainly then knew and probably possessed. Sir Christopher Heydon had read it by 6 July 1610, as Rigaud has pointed out,[43] and Harriot had probably received a copy at much the same time. Jupiter was then too close to the Sun, conjunction having occurred on 1 June (O.S.), but by 17 October the two were separated by almost exactly 100°.

Harriot's use of Galileo's observations of Jupiter's satellites is manifest in several of his calculations, and in particular in his calendar conversions between the two styles when working out the period of first satellite partly on the strength of what are obviously Galileo's records from *Siderius nuncius*.[44] In its way equally good evidence of the esteem in which he held the Italian astronomer is provided by Harriot's repeated attempts to rearrange the sentence

> Salve umbistineum geminatum Martia prolis.

That this is what Harriot was doing on the verso of a leaf in MS Leconfield 241 (containing on the recto the first rough notes on the observations of the satellites) is obvious from the fact that he has written down an alphabet showing the frequencies of occurrence of different letters, following them by a number of rearrangements in awkward Latin. Thus the first three are:

> Mi tantum Jupiter laus gloria summe brans me,
> Montibus et silva variis martem mage plenum,
> Ignem lunarem in sat. paruum et mobilem visitas.

All of these would be acceptable rearrangements of the original if we were to drop the 'in' from the last sentence. The three arrangements are in a marginal note ascribed to 'M. Thorp', presumably Nathaniel Torporley, while another follows, ascribed to M. W., probably Mr. Warner.[45] The fourth attempt mentions Mars, but then, beginning with the words 'Galilaei Prosopopaea ludibunda', the whole tone of the exercise is lowered with a couple of interpretations, obscene, but in more convincing Latin, the first of them ascribed to an author whose initials are now erased. And so Harriot proceeds down the page with what seem to be his own suggestions, to resume yet again in the same section (page 30, Rigaud's numbering), while scattered through the volumes of his papers in the British Museum there are at least fifty further attempts, all presumably his own, to solve the anagram.[46] These, in fact, are all attempts to solve the anagram which Galileo had communicated to Kepler:

> s/mais/mrm/il/m/epoe/taleum/ibun/enugttauiras.

Kepler's solution was that from which Harriot apparently began ('Salve umbistineum . . .'), a solution which shows that Kepler thought Galileo to have found two satellites to Mars. The correct solution was

> Altissimum planetam tergeminum observavi
> (I have observed the most distant planet to be in three parts),

an allusion to the form of Saturn, which would in due course be seen surrounded by rings, but which to Galileo then seemed like a sphere with two
handles. Kepler published the challenge and his solution in his *Dissertatio
cum nuncio sidereo nuper apud mortales misso a Galilaeo Galilaeo*, published in
Prague, 1610.[47] 'Harriot was obviously working from that source. The date is
uncertain, but it could well have been before 14 December 1610, the date of
observation no. 13. Against his observation of 11 December 1610 we can
perhaps see traces of a sense of humour, if not of a contemplated cryptographic rejoinder:

> Thomas Hariotus
> oho trahit musas
> oho trahis mutas
> oho sum charitas

The self-same phrases are written down on a sheet now among the papers in
the British Museum,[48] and a further nine rearrangements, with variants, are
to be found in the same volume.[49] It is possible that Harriot's 'oho' was in
some way analogous to Galileo's representation of Saturn's telescopic appearance as 'oOo', but if so the Harriot anagram must have been later than
his attempted solutions of Galileo's.

Kepler had owned a copy of *Sidereus nuncius* from 8 April 1610, when one
was sent to him by Galileo through the Tuscan ambassador, with an invitation
to comment on its claims. (He had actually seen the Emperor's copy previously.) His *Dissertatio* was written by 19 April, and was printed in an expanded version by the 3rd May 1610.[50] Knowing that Kepler was in correspondence with Harriot, it is not at all unlikely that Harriot read Kepler's reply
before, or at least simultaneously with, Galileo's original. It is worth observing
that Harriot's efforts at a solution, starting from Kepler's sentence, are on the
reverse of the sheet containing his first rough satellite records—or, conversely,
as the case may be. Harriot has actually at one point added a precise page
reference to Kepler's *Dissertatio*, with the date 6 October 1610.[51]

It has already been made plain that Harriot's first observation of sunspots
owed nothing to Galileo, and even by the end of 1611, knowledge as to the
several observations made earlier in the year does not appear to have been
very rapidly diffused, judging by the apparent self-righteousness of the parties
in the subsequent priority debate. Harriot is not known to have benefited at
any stage, for example, from the solar image-projection technique of European astronomers—advocated in one form or another by Fabricius, Scheiner,
and Galileo, and already used by Kepler in his unfortunate solar observations
of 1607.[52] This does not, of course, mean that Harriot was ignorant of the
possibility of producing a solar image by projection, either with or without a
lens. Among his papers in the British Museum are some in which he not only
considers at great length the mathematics of image formation by a section of
a sphere (or, as would now be said, by a thin lens), but actually calculates the

image size for a particular lens, taking the solar semi-diameter as 16'.[53] Else-where we find related diagrams, some of doubtful significance, but one show-ing solar image formation on a screen by a hole (*foramen*).[54]

HARRIOT'S METHODS OF OBSERVATION

Harriot has left us two hundred drawings of the solar surface, all but the first in a numbered sequence. Taking into account the fact that he often observed several times in the course of a day, and occasionally omitted to make any drawing for a given day (especially when he was away from Syon) we find that he has left notes of 450 separate observations. Harriot above all else was at the mercy of the weather, which provided him with the means of diminish-ing the intensity of the Sun's light. He first saw the sunspots 'it being a frost and a mist, (8 December 1610), and on the crucial day, 1 December 1611, he 'observed for half an houre space at which time and all the morning before it was misty'. Clouds were occasionally helpful, but more often not: 'I saw [a cluster of four] twise in a short time through a thinne rag of a cloud, the cloudes quickly obscuring the Sunne' (4 December 1611). By 12 December there was snow, which did not appear to matter much, and on 13 December there was mention of 'thick ayer', a phrase which was subsequently to be often favoured, and of 'coloured glasses', to which we shall later return.

It would be difficult to summarize Harriot's statements of meteorological conditions did he not at length settle for a small number of basic phrases. 'Thick ayer' (by which I understand distant or slight water vapour or dust) might alone be enough, although it might at times leave 'the Sonne . . . some-what to cleare' (14 December 1611). 'Thin cloudes', often qualified as white, as misty, or occasionally as fast moving, played their part, and mist alone (that is, mist near at hand) often sufficed. Harriot may be said to have recorded observations as made through thin cloud on 114 days, through thick air on 70 days, through mist on 60 days, and under conditions when the Sun was too bright to make observing easy on 22 days. These figures underscore not so much the folly of direct solar observation as the advantages of the Thames valley climate for reducing the light of the Sun to what Harriot called a 'tem-perate light'. The Thames vapours were as always a mixed blessing, however, for against the Moon map of 11 September 1610 we find:

I could not set downe the figure of all, nether this but by memory because I was troubled with the reume.

Four days later he was constrained to add to another lunar drawing simply 'The rume'. Harriot generally observed soon after sunrise or soon before sun-set, although he was prepared to make his drawing for any hour of the day when conditions were favourable. Occasionally he had only a short time to make his drawing. 'I saw the Sonne thorough misty cloudes for the space of a minute', he wrote on 26 December 1611; and on 25 April 1612, 'the Sonne tarrying but a little while, I set downe there places & number but by coniecture'. On three occasions in the following June he was likewise obliged to conjecture positions, and the fact that he made such notes as 'the distance of the 2 most westerly may be somewhat a misse' (19 August 1612) suggests that he had a certain confidence in the general correctness of his work. That the surviving records are a fair copy of lost originals seems clear enough, both on account of the few alterations needed, and the fact that in the three successive entries for 5, 6, and 8 May 1612 he at first wrote 'April', correcting the mistake later.[55]

Harriot was occasionally careless with his sight. Under 'fayre' conditions, with some mist, he was able to see spots on one occasion with the naked eye: 'Two of the greatest were well seen in the mist (of the cluster [of 10 spots] without instrument)' (23 April 1612). On 1 March 1612 he had looked at the Sun without clouds with his telescope of magnification 20, and twelve days earlier he wrote:

At 12^h all the sky being cleare and the Sonne I saw the great spot with $\frac{10}{1}$ & $\frac{20}{1}$ but no more. My sight was after dim for an houre.

There are several other instances of his having looked into a clear Sun. The hazards of this sort of work are obvious, and the blindness of Galileo and Cassini is often mentioned by way of warning. Rigaud[56] quoted John Greaves, who for some days after measuring the diameter of the Sun thought he saw 'a company of crows flying in the air at a good distance'. Such 'spots before the eyes' surely explain why Harriot was in his first observation anxious to point out that he truly saw what he drew, and with *both* eyes. Rigaud, who adopted an excessive scepticism over the significance of this first observation, has it that Harriot had 'unexpectedly seen what he could hardly persuade himself to be real.[57]

At only one point does Harriot mention the use of coloured glasses, to diminish the solar brightness (13 December 1611):

I observed thorough the thick ayer and also through my coloured glasses but saw no more: it seemed to me that a greate glasse wold make them appeare devided or more different.

It is natural enough to assume that he here refers to flat pieces of coloured glass, such as were already used by Dutch navigators in taking solar altitudes.[58] Apian had long before recommended coloured glass for eclipse observation in his *Astronomicum Caesareum*.[59] Scheiner, in his letters to Welser, had four different ways of viewing the sunspots, one being to use in addition to his telescope a blue or green plane glass of appropriate thickness, or a thin blue glass alone when the Sun was covered with vapour or thin cloud. Is this the sort of thing Harriot meant? The only reason for doubt is not very conclusive. 'Glass' in Harriot's day commonly meant lens, mirror, or telescope, and in its second occurrence in the quotation the word was certainly used to refer to a telescope. A 'great glasse' capable of improving the resolution of the image is unlikely to have been a thicker slab of coloured glass. It is conceivable that Harriot had telescopes with lenses of coloured glass, but not perhaps very probable, since he never refers to coloured glasses again, and since, as we saw, he hurt his eyes in the following April.

HARRIOT'S INSTRUMENTS

'Glass' was not the word commonly used to designate the telescope in Harriot's writings, when 'instrument' has a clear lead over 'trunk'. The earliest Moon drawing (26 July 1609) has merely a marginal note '$\frac{6}{1}$', meaning that a telescope with a linear (effectively angular) magnification of 6 was used. This instrument was never again mentioned. As for the remaining instruments, we may summarize chronologically the evidence of the entire contents of MS Leconfield 241 as follows:

$\frac{10}{1}$ and $\frac{10}{1}$B: An instrument of this magnification was Harriot's joint favourite, judging by the number of times it was mentioned (thirty-three at least, and perhaps on several occasions by implication). First mentioned 17 July 1610 (Moon). 'Instrument $\frac{10}{1}$B' occurs first on 8 December 1610 (first sunspots record), once again on 11 January 1612 (sunspots) and once by implication in a detailed lunar observation of 9 April 1611, where this note occurs:[60]

Sr Nicholas Sanders & Christopher were with me & also observed in my garret. Instruments. $\frac{10}{1} \cdot \frac{15}{1} \cdot \frac{32}{1} \cdot \frac{11}{1}$.
       two one one one

Although instrument B was not mentioned again, it was probably often used whilst not distinguished from its partner.

$\frac{20}{1}$: Harriot's other favourite instrument, first mentioned 4 August 1610 (Moon), and on at least thirty-three other occasions, perhaps more implicitly. It was used, like, $\frac{10}{1}$ for all types of observation. On the whole, instruments were not specified in the Jupiter records. That the words 'trunk' and 'instrument' were synonymous is evident from their application to the same telescope, as in Jupiter observations for 14 December 1610 ('my truncks $\frac{10}{1} \cdot \frac{20}{1}$') and 25 January 1611 ('my instrument of $\frac{20}{1}$'). Thus also under 3 December 1611 (sunspot record made at Syon):

Sr William Lower & Christopher saw them with me in several trunckes. $\frac{10}{1} \cdot \frac{8}{1} \cdot \frac{20}{1}$.

$\frac{11}{1}$: Mentioned on only one occasion, in a lunar context, noted above, and certainly then used at Syon (9 April 1611).

$\frac{32}{1}$: Mentioned twice, on 9 April 1611 as in the previous entry, and against a lunar map of the same date on another leaf.

$\frac{15}{1}$: Mentioned on 9 April 1611, as already noted, and again on 9 February 1612 in a sunspot record made in London, where it is possible that the instrument was now kept.

$\frac{8}{1}$: Mentioned only once, in the sunspot record of 3 December 1611 noted above.

$\frac{30}{1}$: The third most frequently mentioned instrument, although only five times noted. It does not appear until 20 January 1612 (sunspot record), unless we are to identify it with $\frac{32}{1}$, which is unlikely.

$\frac{50}{1}$: Mentioned once only, on 27 January 1612, in a sunspot record made at Syon: The southerly [spots] are fayer and great and with $\frac{50}{1}$ seemeth more. He [the Sun] was well seen with $\frac{10}{1}$ but some of the rest not at all, and some difficultely.

Speaking generally, Harriot may be said to have seldom troubled to record the instrument he used, in the sunspot records he made after June 1612. Occasionally he supplied from memory the details of the telescopes he had used—'*memoriter*'.[61]

The greater number of Harriot's observations were made at Syon House,[62] apparently from his garret.[63] Change of residence does not appear to have stemmed the flow of the observations. 'London' was the place of sunspot observations for 7–12 February 1612, and of some unnumbered ones for 12–25 February and 3–7 April 1612, during which interval he was observing from Syon, perhaps suggesting help from a friend. He was in London again between 9 June and 24 July 1612,[64] (a rather scrappy record made at Essex House being included for 25 June), and 6–26 November 1612. His second recorded observation of a satellite of Jupiter (16 November 1610) was 'London at Neales in Black Friers' and he was still in London for the next (19 November), although soon back at Syon, where on 7 December 1610 he twice recorded that Sir William Lower saw two satellites—for the first time, in fact, He made similar observations early in the next year (17 February) 'at D. Turner's house in Little St. Ellens', and on the circumstances of his London observations he is more precise when he four times states (Jupiter, ten observations numbered jointly 81, 25 April 1611 and after) that Christopher[Tooke] observed 'in a gutter', the words 'of a house' being once added.[65] Returning to Syon on 10 May 1611 it was 'we saw . . .', and the phrase is occasionally used in the sunspot records where no other person is specified by name, but where Christopher Tooke is almost certainly always intended, being often also named.[66]

We have no evidence of Harriot's having used a mounting with any of his telescopes. Some drawings with the scarcely legible caption:

in a payre of stone stayres 2 iron barres beare the Instrumentis[67]

in my opinion illustrate some sort of furnace for retorts or glass vessels in certain of the alchemical experiments which come later in the manuscript.

There is another deceptive line, in the same section, dated 1601/1602:

New glasses luted with blackest lute.

The glasses were in no sense optical instruments, but chemical retorts, lute being a mud traditionally used to seal (that is, to lute) the same.

It is curious that Harriot does not use the word 'cylinder' for his telescopes, since this is the word used by Lower, replying to Harriot's letters:

I have received the perspective cylinder that you promised me and am sorrie, that my man gave you not more warning, that I might have had also the 2 or 3 more that you mentioned to chuse for me. Hence forward he shall have order to attend you better and to defray the charge of this an others, for he confesseth to me, that he forgot to pay the work man. (6 February 1610)[68]

Lower goes on to describe the appearance of the Moon through what he once calls the 'instrument'. Four months later he writes:

We are here so on fire with thes things that I must render my request and your promise to send mee of all sortes of thes Cylinders. My man shal deliver you monie for anie charge requisite, and contente your man for his paines & skill. Send me so manie as you thinke needful vnto thes obseruations. (11 June 1610)[69]

Lower has in the same letter spoken of observing 'this last winter' with his own cylinder. Writing again on 4 March 1611, he mentions his cylinder, and remarks his inability to see Jupiter's satellites, adding

I impute it to the dullnesse of my sighte, for onlie with your greate glasse I could se them in London.[70]

The 'greate glasse' reminds us of Harriot's use of the phrase, which here apparently refers to the instrument of magnification 20.[71] It seems not unlikely that Lower was simply using a more polite equivalent to Harriot's word 'trunk', which might have referred to a tube of rectangular box-like construction, as a water conduit (*Shorter O.E.D.*, 'Trunk' II. 5), but might equally have had a circular section (ibid., I. 1, 4). Sir Christopher Heydon, in a letter mentioned above,[72] spoke in July 1610 of 'our ordinary trunks', which shows that the word had an early currency.

The word 'glass', as we have already seen, offers great scope for ambiguity. It has been continually used of a refracting telescope,[73] and of its lenses. That it could refer to a mirror is well known from the writings of a number of Harriot's near contemporaries, such as Leonard and Thomas Digges, John Dee, and William Bourne.[74] Harriot was probably using the word in this sense in his *Briefe and True Report* (1588):

Most thinges they [the Indians] sawe with vs, as Mathematicall instruments, sea compasses, the vertue of the loadstone in drawing yron, a perspective glasse whereby was shewed manie strange sightes, burning glasses, wildfire woorkes, gunnes, bookes, writing and reading, spring clocks that seeme to goe of themselues, and manie other thinges that wee had . . .[75]

The variety of English words for the telescope was a reflection of the uncertain terminology throughout Europe. In *Sidereus nuncius* Galileo used the words *organum* and *instrumentum*, but most commonly *perspicillum*. His favourite Italian word was *occhiale*. Kepler, in his *Dissertatio cum nuncio sidereo*, used *perspicillum* most often, but also *instrumentum*. Harriot, who after the first sunspot record—which was probably copied out a year later—used the word 'instrument' on 7 December 1610 (Jupiter records), and in the context of lunar drawings on 9 April 1611 when he used it in a Latin form (*Instrumento* $\frac{3}{1}\frac{2}{}$). In all probability he was following the usage of Galileo or Kepler. He apparently never used 'telescope', or its strict Latin equivalent.[76]

Very little is known of the optical performance of Harriot's telescopes, at least by comparison with those of Galileo's which survive. Of Harriot's we know their magnification, and in some instances their field of view. Rigaud was sceptical about the significance of Harriot's field measurements, but does not appear to have correctly understood them. Evaluating them care-

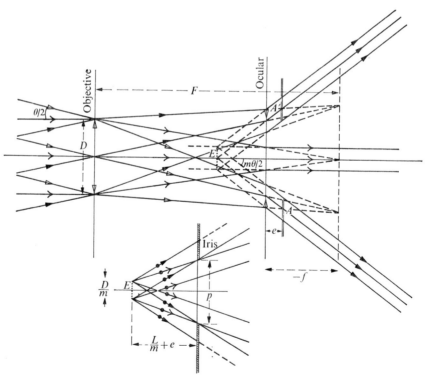

FIG. 7.1. A diagram of the early Dutch or 'Galilean' telescope.

fully, and making one or two reasonable suppositions about the instruments, we may make a rough comparison with others of the time.

Harriot almost invariably stated the angular separations of Jupiter's satellites from the planet itself, and this usually to a minute of arc, but occasionally to a quarter minute (as for example, on 25 January 1611), or even less (as on 12 December 1610: 'one other westerly, as I thought 10″ or 15″ a [Jupiter]; hardly seen'). We do not know how he gauged these distances, but since, by the time they were recorded, Harriot was in possession of Galileo's work, it is reasonable to suppose that he used Galileo's method. This, which was given near the beginning of the first chapter, involved the observer in the use of a series of object-glass diaphragms of different sizes. Galileo is not very clear on the subject, but it seems that he calibrated his diaphragms empirically, calculating (in terms of its size and distance, using a table of sines) the angle subtended by an object which exactly filled the diameter of the field of view. He first recorded the separation of Jupiter's satellites on 12 January 1610, and subsequently gave 'approximate' separations to an implied accuracy of 20 seconds of arc. Harriot found the semidiameters of the orbits of four satellites to be 14′, 9′, 6′ and 3′ 30″,[77] and Galileo's figures would have been close to these. All these data were probably arrived at by a subjective estimate based on the supposed diameter of the body of Jupiter (taken by Harriot to be a little under 2′)[78] and the fraction of the supposed field of view occupied by the planets' separation. Both were wrongly estimated, the first no doubt partly by virtue of the indistinctness of the image produced by telescopes of the time; and the second because the conditions determining the field were not properly understood by Galileo and his assumed followers, nor even by Rigaud.

The diameter of the field of view of a Dutch or 'Galilean' telescope (θ), illustrated in Fig. 7.1, is shown in Appendix I to be given in minutes of arc by the equation

$$\theta = \frac{10800.(p \pm D/m)}{\pi} \frac{}{(L+em)}$$

where the negative sign gives the clear field, and the positive sign the field with its peripheral dark ring (darkness increasing with radius) formed from light of partly obscured pencils. Here p is the diameter of the pupil of the eye, D is that of the objective aperture, or rather of any diaphragm covering it, m is the magnification, L is the distance between the centres of the two lenses, taken to be in normal adjustment for a distant object, and e is the optical distance of the eye pupil from the centre of the ocular. In writing of the 'field of view' I imagine that all our authors were including the dark peripheral field.

Galileo's method, as explained, took no cognizance of the importance of p, or for that matter, e. More recent treatises have taken no account of D or of e. All early observers, following Galileo, however, presumably made estimates of θ by daylight when p (for an observer looking into a telescope) is of the order of 5 mm, rather than at night ($p = 8$ mm), when measurements were made. Given a reasonably typical aperture (D) of 20 mm, and a magnification of 20, the ratio of an angle supposed correctly measured to the true angle would be 3:2.

We may calculate the true angles subtended at any time in the past in order to discover how close this explanation comes to accounting for the errors of Harriot and others. That the diameters of the orbits subtend different angles at different times follows from the changing geometric distance of Jupiter. On 1 January 1612, for example, Jupiter was 156° removed from the Sun, and at approximately 4·3 astronomical units from the Earth. For the sake of simplicity, consider the case of opposition, a few weeks later, when the distance was 4·202 units. The eccentricities of the orbits of satellites I-IV are all small, and the mean distances from Jupiter are (in astronomical units) 0·00282, 0·00449, 0·00716, and 0·01259. These orbits at Jupiter's opposition then subtended the angles 2'·31, 3'·68, 5'·87, and 10'·31 (approx.)—Increasing then in the ratio 3:2, to follow through our imaginary example, it appears that that erroneous estimates of the angles, using Galileo's method, would have been 3'·47, 5'·52, 8'·80. 15'·46. Comparing these with Harriot's 3'·5, 6', 9', and 14', the explanation offered here for his source of error must be admitted plausible. He was mistaken in adopting Galileo's method, and so, in exactly the same way, was Rigaud mistaken to imply that it was above reproach. Thus, for example, he wrote:

Harriot's quantities were more roughly taken. He gives no reason to think that he had made any previous experiments like Galileo, who determined the value of his apertures by the length which they included of a line at a given distance.[79]

Rigaud is misleading when he says that we have no reason for thinking that Harriot performed the requisite measurements. We know that at least in one instance (see (1) below) he had a preconceived idea of the field of one of his telescopes, and we also know from his papers in the British Museum that he made measurements to calculate the field of view of the human eye.[80] Rigaud goes on to criticize Harriot gratuitously for what he takes to be inconsistent statements as regards the field of view both of the $\frac{2 \cdot 0}{1}$ instrument and $\frac{1 \cdot 0}{1}$B. The former inconsistency is only apparent, and is very simply explained, for on one occasion the observations were of the Sun, which would have contracted the pupil, whilst the other occasion was by night.[81]

Harriot made four different statements relating to field of view, which we here collect together in order to extract from them what information we may: (1) Instrument: $\frac{2 \cdot 0}{1}$. Date: 7 December 1610. Jupiter record no. 8.

'Two seen on the west side, a little under. Sr W. Lower also saw them here. The nerest fayrest. The farther not well seen within the reach of my instrument of $\frac{2 \cdot 0}{1}$ of 14' dyameter.'

The distances marked on the drawing are 7′ and 12′, −13′ being added as an alternative. Compare the record (no. 40) for 25 January 1611, where the outermost satellite, likewise marked as 12′ or 13′, was 'scarce se[en] within my instrument of $\frac{20}{1}$'.

(2) Instrument: $\frac{10}{1}$B. Date: 11 January 1612. Sunspot record no. 26.

'One of the spots was in the verticall, the semidiameter of my instrument B$\frac{10}{1}$ from the upper edge and the whole diameter from the lower.'

A marginal note adds 'B 30′ ', and Rigaud appears to take it that this indicates a field of view (for $\frac{10}{1}$B) of 30′.[82] He writes:

'. . . we find a notice in the margin, "B 30′ ", which, if it is meant to describe the angular value of the field of view, will be another instance, in addition to those already adduced. . . . of the little precision with which these estimates were made.'

But the record itself is unambiguous. The field was half as large again as the angular diameter of the Sun, which on the date in question was approximately 32′·5. The marginal note can only have referred to the supposed solar diameter, and the field supposed was thus 20′. Harriot's 'little precision' was not invariably as little as Rigaud's.

(3) Instrument: $\frac{20}{1}$. Date: 16 July 1612. Sunspot record no. 133 (London).

'With $\frac{20}{1}$ I see a little more than ⅓ of the diameter of the Sonne, that is, 11′ or 12′.'

Comparing (1) and (3), it appears that the field of $\frac{20}{1}$ was, to use Rigaud's words 'not very precisely determined'.[83] But only in (1) do Harriot's words suggest a *prior* determination of the field (14′). In (3) he is reporting what he sees, without any preconceived notion of what he *should* see. And what Rigaud overlooked is that, as already explained, Harriot would indeed have seen a smaller field when looking at the Sun than when looking at Jupiter, or at some terrestrial object for calibration purposes. Harriot would not have realized why, but where others would have evaded the apparent inconsistency by omission or distortion of the evidence, he did not, and to accuse him of imprecision is to misjudge him. As an observer, the evidence is that he was at least Galileo's equal in the care he took, although perhaps working with inferior instruments[84] and certainly with an inferior night sky.

(4) Instrument:—? Date: 21 October 1612. Lunar observation of the moment of quadrature ('6 houres before at the least by Tycho Brahe').

'At that time the rounde vally (a) was ⅓ from the lower poynt and ⅔ from the higher. because ab was the diameter of mine instrument, and ac semidiameter'.

The lunar marking (a) was on the line of division of the dark and light halves of the Moon. Harriot had earlier said that the line of division was observed to be straight with his 'trunke of $\frac{20}{1}$', 'and if it was not, it rather lacked by some other judgements'. What we know of the field of $\frac{20}{1}$ does not accord with the present statement, which rather suggests $\frac{10}{1}$. We note that when he observed the same phenomenon in April of the previous year he mentioned five instruments, but attempted to judge the line of division by $\frac{10}{1}$.[85] (He did so without instruments on 11 January 1611.) Harriot is unlikely to have calculated or observed the precise angular diameter of the Moon for the day in question, but more probably took a round figure of 30'. The field of view was thus approximately 20', which is to be compared with the field found under heading (2) above for $\frac{10}{1}$B, rather than with any of the data for $\frac{20}{1}$.

After the details of a Jupiter observation of 24 May 1611 (no. 89+9), Harriot made an estimate of the angular separation of Jupiter and Mars, which was nearby: '[Mars] by our instrument was about 31' or 32' of from [Jupiter]'. He comments that they were 30' or 31' apart the night before, and that the emphemerides would have then been 16' or 17' apart. He does not say how he estimated the separations, which were greater than the field of either $\frac{10}{1}$ or $\frac{20}{1}$. It is possible that he used the $\frac{8}{1}$, or made up the distance in two or more steps, using intermediate stars as points of division.

Harriot indicated on several occasions that he was able to see solar detail more easily the larger the magnification used. This is a complex optical problem in the absence of a detailed knowledge of the lens systems used, since considerations of the angular resolving power of the telescope, flare, interference effects, and other aberrations of the image must all enter into any assessment of its distinctness. However, even with a clear aperture of a quarter of an inch, which is as small as any diaphragm Harriot is likely to have used, he should have been able to resolve two stars 18" apart. The resolution of sunspots is a more difficult problem than that of stars, but the diffraction limits on resolution set by his instrument would not have limited the markings he was considering, when he wrote, for example, (20 January 1612, sunspot record no. 32):

Under the 3 [sunspots] one semed fayer & great & seen alone with the smaller instrument ($\frac{10}{1}$ but with $\frac{20}{1}$ $\frac{30}{1}$ one more westerly dim yet certayne, & an other smal one easterly & close by'.

Likewise on the following day he could see eight spots, but only seven with less than $\frac{20}{1}$. On 31 January he introduced his largest magnification:

'... the southerly are Fayer & great & with $\frac{50}{1}$ seemeth more. he [the Sun] was well seen with $\frac{10}{1}$ but some of the rest not at all, & some difficultely.'

On further occasions he remarks that a spot was seen 'only with $\frac{20}{1}$','only with $\frac{30}{1}$', or 'only with $\frac{20}{1} . \frac{30}{1}$', and on 25 May 1612, when he could see twelve spots with an unspecified instrument, 'with $\frac{10}{1}$ they seemed to be but 9'.[86] That he could see more with his instruments of greater magnification cannot be shown to have been a consequence of increasing aperture (and hence resolving power) with increasing magnification, although it does seem probable that there was some such connexion.

In order to attempt to derive further detail of Harriot's telescopes (focal lengths, overall length, and aperture) from the fragmentary information already found, we have in effect only three equations in the four variables F, f, L, and D, on the assumption that we know the field (θ), eye distance (e, arbitrarily taken to be 5 mm), and pupil size (p, assumed to be 5 mm, taking a reasonable estimation for a daytime assessment of field). The first equation is that written above, for θ. The second and third are

$$F+f = L,$$
and
$$F = -mf.$$

We obviously cannot solve these equations without making some further assumption, and our safest course is to suppose that the aperture was of the size to be expected of a spectacle lens. All the evidence suggests that the earliest objectives in telescopes of the Dutch type were made on the lathes of the makers of eye-glasses, with standard tools. We know from his will that Harriot possessed such tools. The maximum clear aperture is unlikely, therefore, to have been appreciably less than 20 mm, or much more than about 35 mm, with 25 mm as a likely figure. Taking the above simultaneous equations for each of the three cases, we find these solutions (all in millimetres, and taken to the nearest 5 mm):

Instrument	θ max	$D = 20$ mm			$D = 25$ mm			$D = 35$ mm		
		L	F	$-f$	L	F	$-f$	L	F	$-f$
$\frac{20}{1}$	14′	1370	1445	70	1430	1510	75	1555	1635	80
$\frac{10}{1}$B	20′	1150	1280	130	1240	1375	140	1410	1565	155

Those two of Galileo's telescopes which are still in a complete (if not original) state, have characteristics not vastly different from those of the two Harriot instruments of which the fields of view are known. The following summary table lists some of the parameters of the two complete Galileo instruments, a further object-glass which he is known to have used, and here conjectured to have been part of an instrument of magnification 30,[87] an extant telescope in a miliary baton once belonging to Gustavus Adolphus of Sweden (of the period 1628–32), and a telescope made by Gascoigne and known from his description (c. 1641).[88]

	F	$-f$	L	θ (actual)	D	m	θ (calc.)		
							$p = 8$ mm	5 mm	3·5 mm
Galileo I	1327	95·2	1232	~15′	26	14	26′·0	18′·1	14′·2
Galileo II	956	48·8	907	~15′	16	20	30′·0	19′·8	14′·7
Galileo III	1689	56·3	1633	—	38	30	17′·9	12′·1	9′·2
Gustavus Ad.	453	60	393	15′·5	15·2	~7·5	—	—	—
Gascoigne	1136	30·5	1035	—	30·5	11·2	33′·8	24′·3	19′·6

From this table and what we have seen of Harriot's notes on the subject, it is easy to see how great were the difficulties under which the earliest telescopic observations were made. To map the Moon, for example, with an instrument capable of revealing only a quarter of its area at any one time (i.e. with field diameter ~15') required great patience and skill, and Harriot's method of mapping by recording sets of three lunar markings which appeared to be in a straight line was an ingenious—and as it turned out, well executed—solution. (There is evidence that he used the same method with sunspots, since he occasionally mentioned the fact when three or more were in line.) Quite apart from the field of view, few of us now realize how very small was the disk of light seen in the telescope by one looking at the Sun or Moon. To look down Galileo I, for instance, is to see as much light as one sees darkness inside the barrel of a Colt 45 revolver at a distance of two feet. Abetti found that with Galileo I the photosphere of the Sun showed its characteristic granular structure, that little spurious colour was introduced, and that two spot nuclei 17" apart were well separated. In the Moon he found he could see much more detail than was shown in Galileo's manuscript drawings. Jupiter was not seen well defined, and for some positions of the eye could be seen double. Satellites became difficult to distinguish when within 15" of Jupiter. With Galileo II, images were less luminous, and clarity was sacrificed to magnification. Jupiter's satellites could now, however, be distinguished when 10" away from the parent planet. The third object-glass was better than either of the others, and small spot nuclei could be resolved at an approximate separation of 10". We have at present no idea of the quality of the images formed by Harriot's telescopes. Limited as this was by the properties and quality of the glass, and of the finish of the lenses, it is not impossible that further relevant information will come to light in the optical papers at present being studied by J. A. Lohne.

Apart from his telescopes, we know very little of the astronomical instruments available to Harriot. He must have used and might even have designed one of the finest armillary spheres to have survived from Elizabethan times.[89] Passing to Sir Josias Bodley, and in principle presented by him to the Bodleian Library in Oxford in 1601, it reached the library in 1613, and is now to be seen in the Museum of the History of Science nearby.[90] Standing nearly four feet high, and with its three lions supporting an unusually complex system of armillae,[91] the instrument is a fine example of the art of casting in brass, and no doubt in marked contrast with a sphere Lower was obliged to have had made in Traventi out of the hoops of a barrel.[92]

Harriot probably possessed a number of astrolabes. As a device for measuring angles in experiments on optical refraction, the astrolabe is frequently mentioned, and in the lunar records of MS Leconfield 241, for 9 April 1611, we find the entry

per stellas clock or watch
9^h.43'   9^h.46'   Altitudo Canis Minoris $\overline{19}$.56' by my cathol.
                                  Astrolabe, not yet a right line, but almost.

The astrolabe by which he has calculated the time from the altitude of the named star was what Gemma Frisius had called his 'astrolabum [sic] catholicum',[93] which bore a universal astrolabe of a type known in the middle ages as the 'saphea Arzachelis'.[94] This was not an instrument for any but an expert astronomer. It is worth adding, however, that the astrolabe gave the local time much more reliably than did the timepiece. Although Harriot knew, for instance, that longitude could be found by means of 'a perfect watch, or Clock, arteficially made by a Clock-maker',[95] he cannot have held out much hope for an early solution, if we are to judge by his remark made at the foot of the same leaf as the lunar quadrature observations:

'The next morning about $8^h\frac{1}{2}$ my watch was to forward from the Sonne by a $\frac{1}{4}^h$ & somewhat more.'

THE ROTATION OF THE SUN

Whether or not Harriot used an astrolabe in drafting his sunspot records is a matter for conjecture, although there is one way in which he might well have done so. Each of his drawings, including the very first of 8 December 1610, has superimposed on the solar disk two broken lines as diameters, one invariably vertical, and the other at variable angle to it. The vertical must be along the great circle through the centre of the Sun and the zenith. Were the Sun near the horizon, as was usually the case, this vertical would have been easily judged. The other line undoubtedly represented the plane of the ecliptic. The first intimation of this is in the record of 8 December 1611:

'I saw the cluster of 4 also at 2^h in the afternoone, they with the ecliptick being declined.'

Elsewhere '☉ in 90 gradu' means that the two broken lines are perpendicular, the ecliptic being parallel to the horizon (e.g. at 9^h 50^m, 18 March 1611). Between the drawings numbered 122 and 155 (inclusive)[96] the lines are not inserted, but on 6 September 1612 we are told that 'the eclipticks were drawn at one time 10 dayes after the observations', and in a similar vein, on the following 6 and 8 November occurs the remark 'eclipt. coniect'. This is an odd remark, since the ecliptic is not in any sense immediately observable. The most natural way of conjecturing the angle between the verticals and the ecliptic would have been to use an ordinary astrolabe, noting the angle between the tangent to the Sun's position on the ecliptic circle and the tangent to the azimuth line through that point, when the instrument was set correctly for the time of day—by solar altitude, in fact. I have verified a score or so of the angles at which the lines are drawn, including those 'conjectured' by Harriot, and find that without exception they are reasonably accurately placed, the error seldom exceeding two degrees. There is thus no doubt that Harriot's use of the word 'ecliptic' is the conventional one.

What did Harriot suppose the significance of the ecliptic line to be? As a

T.H.—11

Copernican he accepted the fundamental nature of the plane of the ecliptic as that followed reasonably closely by the planets in their orbitings around the central Sun. He saw the rotation of the spots, and readily assumed that they turned about the same axis. Through Salviati in the *Dialogo* (1632), Galileo tells—speaking of himself, of course—how the discoverer and observer of sunspots first took the axis of the sunspots' rotation to be perpendicular to the ecliptic, 'since the arcs described by these spots on the sun's disc appeared to our eyes as straight lines parallel to the plane of the ecliptic'.[97] He went on to explain how the spots were seen to move together and disperse, but how such alterations in their course were accidental, as were the changes in terrestrial clouds, which nevertheless follow the Earth with the general daily rotation'. 'Several years later' than the letters to Welser, the observation of a slight curvature in the apparent path of a very prominent spot[98] caused Galileo to appreciate the inclination of the Sun's axis to the poles of the ecliptic, and he went on, in the *Dialogo*, to make great philosophical capital out of his discovery.

Harriot's sunspot records do not reveal any such appreciation of the true axis of solar rotation. They show very clearly, however, that the distances of spots from the ecliptic line, although roughly constant were not precisely so. He remarked occasionally on the fact that three spots which had been in line were no longer so, or conversely, and that a spot had moved 'in or nere the ecliptick' (14 February 1612), and even that a southern trio had moved (7 January 1612) so that they were parallel to the ecliptic when they were not so on the previous day. But in none of these cases is there reason to think that Harriot thought the movements to be more than 'accidental', to use Galileo's word. There were, after all, many other ways in which the spots changed in their accidents. They might appear as from nowhere, they might grow 'dimmer' or 'blacker' or 'fayrer', they might grow or diminish in size, and change in shape. They might divide into two or more parts, or merely grow 'ragged'. All these changes Harriot observed and recorded, and he never suggested that the changes in direction in relation to the ecliptic were of any deeper significance than they.

Although it seems that Harriot failed to appreciate the true inclination of the solar axis, yet he paid closer attention to the periodic time of solar revolution than did Galileo. The sidereal period of the rotation as accepted by Carrington[99] is approximately 25·38 mean solar days, making the mean synodic period—namely that which we observe from the Earth—27^d· 275. Actually an immense complication is introduced by the longitudinal drift of sunspots, that is, the variation in periodicity with latitude. This we shall overlook, but it must be borne in mind when we are appraising Harriot's measurements that the equatorial sunspot period (synodic) is only 26^d· 87, and that at latitude 30° this increases to 28^d· 45. The length of the synodic lunar month (from new moon to new moon) is approximately 29^d· 53, but the sidereal month (the time to return to a fixed star) is approximately $27^{d.}$ 32. Most early observers and many later ones spoke of the 'monthly' sunspot period, some of the later ones overlooking the fact that they were comparing a sidereal period with a synodic, but others, as for instance Scheiner, were simply mistaken as to the sunspot rotation period. Scheiner in his third letter made this out to be in excess of thirty days, that is appreciably more than the synodic month, and Galileo at one stage put the period at more than twenty-eight days.[100] Galileo seems to be of the same mind, making the period 'about one lunar month', again almost certainly meaning a synodic month.[101] A difficult problem in accurately establishing the period was that of recognizing a spot, which was bound to have changed after a fortnight's absence from sight. It was possible to follow a spot over the visible hemisphere, but the difficulty here was that its arrival and disappearance were rarely seen, and never clearly seen. Harriot solved this problem in a simple way, and was probably the first astronomer to give a reasonably accurate period for the rotation. When, by 7 April 1612, he had accumulated a collection of 57 drawings of the solar disk, he wrote down without explanation a series of figures beginning thus:

$$\left.\begin{array}{l}\text{Decemb. 1}\\\text{Decemb. 9}\end{array}\right\} \ 2.8.3 \text{ II } 13.$$

$$\left.\begin{array}{l}\text{Decemb. 13}\\\text{Decemb. 18}\end{array}\right\} \ 3\tfrac{3}{4}.5.4\tfrac{1}{2} \text{ II } 13\tfrac{1}{4}.$$

Such equations—for the use of the 'Gemini' sign of equality shows them to be such—continued until there were eleven in all, the last ending on 26 February. As Rigaud remarked, the numbers 'seem connected with the time of the Sun's revolution, but it is not easy to understand how they are supposed to contribute to the determination of it'.[102] The points are to be read as addition signs. We notice that the middle number always agrees with the number of days in the interval stated. Clearly Harriot has observed a single spot, or group of spots, or (as in the very first case) a single spot which develops into a group of spots; and he has added on, in proportion to the time it requires to traverse a measured arc, the times it must have required to pass from the eastern solar limb to the first recorded position, and from the second recorded position to the western limb. How he evaluated these proportional times at the limb it is impossible to say, unless further calculations can be found. He might have used a scale drawing, or a table of versed sines (or other trigonometrical tables). In view of the use of fractions, the latter method is unlikely. Taking an average of Harriot's eleven figures for the half-period, we deduce a rotation of approximately $26^{d.}$ 23.

That Harriot later improved on these early estimates is evident from a set of calculations following immediately after the observations, and two auxiliary tables. (The latter are of little moment, having been drawn up to give (i) the number of days from 1 January to the end of each month in a common and a bissextile year, and (ii) the intervals from 1 December 1611 to the end of each

month of 1612, and to 31 January 1613.) The new calculations are written in
the manuscript more or less as follows:

$$1610 \text{ Dec. } 8$$
$$1611 \text{ Nov. } 28 \qquad 355^d \text{ II } \begin{array}{|c}27\\13\end{array} +\tfrac{4}{13}$$

$$\text{Dec. } 3$$
$$\text{Dec. } 22 \qquad 385^d \text{ II } \begin{array}{|c}27\\14\end{array} +\tfrac{7}{14}$$

$$1610 \text{ Dec. } 8$$
$$1612 \text{ Dec. } 17$$

$$\text{Dec. } 21.20$$
$$\text{May } 30 \qquad 162^d \text{ II } \begin{array}{|c}27\\6\end{array}$$

There are next a large number of supporting calculations, and also, in modern
notation, calculations which may be expressed

$$386/14 = 27\tfrac{8}{14},$$
$$739/28 = 26\tfrac{11}{28}.$$

As to the earlier statements, the first is to be read '355 days separate the two
dates, and $355 = 27 \times 13 + 4$', and the others likewise, so far as is possible. In
short, the following equations are there to be abstracted:

$$355/13 = 27\tfrac{4}{13},$$
$$385/14 = 27\tfrac{7}{14},$$
$$162/6 \ = 27.$$

Were it not for the last, it could be said that Harriot might have been dealing
in half-periods. It seems obvious, however, that in some way he believed himself to have done what Rigaud said was impossible by virtue of the 'fleeting
nature of the phenomenon',[103] and compared distant observations in the hope
of diminishing the error of the inferred synodic period. How else are the calculations to be explained? On the other hand, are we to believe that he compared the Sun on widely separated dates, when between the first pair of those
dates we have no evidence that he observed the Sun regularly, and when on
some of the terminal dates (28 November 1611; 30 May [1612]; and 22
December 1612) there is no reason for thinking that he observed at all?
Harriot was not in the habit of indicating on his drawings those spots which
disappeared to be seen again later, but it seems to me certain that he did, at
least during 1612, follow spots round full circuit, perhaps helped by the approximate periodicity established earlier. The reason for this claim is that at
several points in the records there are numbers which appear to represent
counts of sunspots recorded up to that point. Each number is written at the
bottom right-hand corner of the page. There are obvious difficulties of interpretation of sunspot counts (unresolved doubles, doubtfully seen spots, and

so forth), but making due allowance for these, on referring to the drawings, the numbers seem plainly to be sunspot totals. They are:

Number	43	53	64	65	67	77	84	93	97	98	103	108
Follows obs. number	28	32	36	40	44	48	52	56	60	64	68	72
of date (1612)	14.i	20.i	31.i	5.ii	11.ii	16.ii	20.ii	2.iii	11.iii	17.iii	24.iii	30.iii

There is little doubt that Harriot was the first to attempt this sort of count. Whether he hoped to deduce a periodicity in the count we cannot learn. As Heinrich Schwabe found in the last century, the frequency was to be discovered after years rather than months of counts. Beginning his study of the solar surface in 1826, by 1843 he was able to announce a ten-yearly cycle,[104] subsequently modified to 11·11 years by Rudolf Wolf.[105] This is an involved story which there is no need to recount here, but it is worth noting that Carrington examined Harriot's sunspot records in 1857, made a copy and a duplicate copy of the drawings. One he sent to Wolf, who had earlier placed great reliance on old records, and the other he presented in due course to the Royal Astronomical Society.

If we accept Harriot's five sets of figures as his final estimates of the value of the period of solar rotation, and take their average, we arrive at a period of $27^d \cdot 154$. These early sunspot observations of Harriot's were made near the time of a sunspot minimum, when the mean sunspot latitude (regardless of algebraic sign) was in the neighbourhood of 10°. At 10° latitude Carrington found a rotation period of $27^d \cdot 06$. I have no wish to obscure the fact that there are difficulties in explaining Harriot's achievement, but under the circumstances I can see no way of denying it. Harriot must be conceded to have interpreted his observations of the solar rotation with a higher degree of accuracy by far than did any of his contemporaries, including Scheiner, who even in *Rosa Ursina* stated the period loosely as 26 or 27 days.[106] All were of course ignorant of the latitude dependence of the periodic time.

If we are to admit that the first of Harriot's deductions of a solar period (8 Dec./28 Nov.) was arrived at from observations sufficiently regular to make the result meaningful, then the price we must pay is that of crediting Harriot not only with the first, but with the first *combined* sunspot observations. These he might naturally have supplemented by the published data of other observers, as he possibly did with Scheiner's for 28 November 1611;[107] but the general conclusion is difficult to avoid, except by taking Rigaud's extreme procedure and simply denying outright that Harriot's calculations could be 'anything like a precise determination of the period of the Sun's rotation'.[108]

ON THE VALUE OF HARRIOT'S OBSERVATIONS

Harriot's drawings of sunspots are made with pen and ink on ordinary laid paper. Since, as we have already noted, they must be taken to be fair copies, we have no means of knowing whether his originals—perhaps done in pencil—showed any spot penumbrae by shading, but in a small number of cases an effort is made to distinguish the dark from the less dark regions on the ink drawings. Harriot soon realized that spots were changed in appearance when they were at the limb. 'The two occidentall were upon the edge well seen but not black' (14 December 1611; the spots 'generally seem bigger being niere [nigher] the middle than the sides' (15 December 1611); a spot near the limb was 'great long, and somewhat ragged, and not so black as the rest' (5 July 1612); 'the four on the west limb not so black as they were before' (15 August 1612); 'that nerest the limb long and dim, croked and narrower than I have noted' (15 October 1612). These are a few examples in which Harriot recorded not only what he would have expected to see, namely foreshortening of spots at the limb, but also the unexpected change in their intensity. In the last quoted example, he added to his notes a more precise drawing of the spot in question, but neither then, nor on 1 November when he again carefully drew the fine structure of a group of spots near the eastern limb, did he manage to represent the umbral and penumbral differences corresponding to his written descriptions. 'The great long one dim on the ester part', he wrote on 2 October 1612; but his drawing alone would hardly have conveyed the message. Harriot was not here entirely baulked by his direct method of observation, although had he used projection he would have been more at liberty to concentrate on detail, spot positions in that case being automatically registered correctly in the act of drawing.

Harriot recorded changes in the appearances of sunspots of the kinds indicated above—generation, growth and decay, change in intensity, local movements, edge effects, and so on. He left no explanations of the phenomena he so painstakingly recorded, and for this reason he simply cannot be compared in historical terms with Galileo, Scheiner, Fabricius, and the rest. To use a phrase from the end of his third letter to Welser, Galileo's demonstrations of the properties of sunspots set a seal on his other celestial discoveries—those, that is to say, which marked the triumph of Copernicus over the Peripatetics. Whether or not Harriot ever turned his thoughts in the same direction, we are not to know. In considering subjects as diverse as the optimum size for the mast of a ship, the maximum supportable population of the world, or the gaseous yield of a burning candle, Harriot would devise a mathematical theory almost by second nature. Sunspot records of relatively short duration do not lend themselves to mathematics, except in regard to the period of solar revolution, and in this respect it seems that Harriot exploited his work to the full, albeit in a rather mysterious way. It is possible that, perhaps prompted by Kepler, he thought there was a relationship between the planetary periods and that of the solar rotation. But there is no end to possible speculations of this sort, which can lead us nowhere, in the absence of further evidence. No astronomer has a better claim than Harriot to priority in the matter of telescopic observations of sunspots; and yet to make an important issue of this question is to be dragged into the follies of the corresponding seventeenth-century debate. There are no proprietary rights, much less any intrinsic virtue, in an act so obvious as that of raising a telescope to the Sun. When Harriot did so, he undoubtedly showed himself to be an astronomer of a high order of practical and theoretical competence, but we must conclude with regret that in the surviving records of his observations of the Sun we can see little more than his shadow.

APPENDIX TO CHAPTER 7

On the early Dutch (so-called 'Galilean') telescope, and its field of view

IN order to discuss the properties of Harriot's telescopes, and to compare them with others of the time, so far as the fragmentary information available allows, a few elementary principles must be set down.

Telescopes first clearly appear in documentary records more or less simultaneously (early in 1609 or thereabouts) in several parts of Europe, with the Low Countries as the most probable source of diffusion. In all instances, where the type of instrument is identifiable, it was that now known as 'Galilean'. This suggests that Harriot's instrument, first used so far as we know in July 1609, was of the same sort. The combination of a converging object-lens with a diverging ocular gives rise to an erect image (as opposed to the inverted image, produced by the so-called 'astronomical' or 'Keplerian' telescope, comprising converging objective and ocular). Harriot's draw-ings of the Moon and Sun as seen through his telescopes are indeed erect (i.e. looking south, they have east to the left, and often clearly marked as such), and there is thus no reason to suppose that he was using a telescope different in type from Galileo's.

This simple form of telescope has the ocular (of relatively short focal length f) inside the focus of rays from the objective (of focal length F). As in any telescopic system, a focal point of the objective coincides with a focal point of the ocular, in this case behind that second lens. The objective provides an inverted real image, and the ocular an erect and virtual final image. In so-called 'normal adjustment' object and image are at infinity, and prime-foci of the two lenses coincide, their separation being therefore L, where $L = F+f$ (accepting the convention whereby f assumes a nega-tive value). This is the only case to be seriously considered in an astronomical context, although it is admittedly possible to have the instrument out of normal adjustment, the eye being capable of accommodating a wide range of final image posi-tions. The angular magnification (m) for normal adjustment will, for the small angles with which we are concerned, be given by the ratio $-F/f$.

The image of the objective provided by the ocular is virtual, and at a distance L/m in front of the ocular; there is thus no real eye-ring with this instrument, and the eye must be close to the ocular for maximum apparent field of view, the emergent beam having its narrowest cross-section there. (The proximity of the eye to the second lens is responsible for minimizing the chromatism which would be otherwise in-troduced. That is to say, if the images in light of different wavelengths did not more or less overlap). Unfortunately, the peripheral field of view is seen only by partial pencils of light, and is less bright than the rest (see below). The lack of a clearly defined field cannot be made good by the introduction of stops, as long as the eye is close to the ocular, since there is no real image within the tube of the instrument. Blurring of the peripheral field introduces only very small uncertainties as to the meaning of figures quoted for the field by writers past and present alike.

In calculating the actual field of view (θ), let D be the diameter of the objective diaphragm (assuming it to be in contact with the lens). The size of its (virtual) image as formed by the ocular will be D/m. All rays emerging from the telescope appear to diverge directly from this 'virtual exit-pupil' (E), as we may regard it by analogy with the astronomical telescope. With the eye close to the centre of the ocular, E subtends the same angle (2 arc tan $D/2L$) at the eye as does the objective. It does not follow, however, that the eye is capable of collecting all rays leaving E. Those it collects are those capable of passing through the pupil for any given position of the eye, and what appears to be the standard argument expresses this in terms of the linear diameter of the eye pupil (p). Making use of the accompanying figure, we should on this argument say merely that the eye receives a cone of rays of angle $m\theta$ when p is equal to AA'. (Actually at the periphery only half of the pencils at A is regarded as collected, but this appears to be one chosen definition of the limit of the visual field.) Then very simply,

$$\tan m\theta/2 = (p/2)/(L/m),$$

and for the small angles involved,

$$\theta = 10800 \, p/(\pi \, L) \quad \text{(minutes of arc)}.$$

Unfortunately, this standard formula may be very far from the truth for a variety of reasons. Not only can the eye pupil never be at the ocular itself, but the eye is a lens system capable of appreciably altering the cross section of a cone of light before it crosses the plane of the iris. Most of the refraction taking place in the eye occurs in fact at the air/cornea surface, before the iris is reached. It is even more mistaken to suppose that the size of the objective, or rather of its diaphragm or mount (namely D) is immaterial to the field of view. If D/m is less than p (see the second figure), the eye can receive no full pencils of light whatsoever. The limit of such full pencils is reached when, taking the pupil to be at the ocular as before,

$$\theta = \frac{10800}{\pi} \cdot \frac{(p - D/m)}{L} \quad \text{(minutes of arc)}.$$

Changing the negative sign for a positive, we have the angle of the field which sends partial pencils into the eye, and beyond which no light is received by the eye. If there is any clear field, the ratio of partially illuminated field to clear field, along any radius of the visual field, is $2D/(pm - D)$.

Supposing, next, that the effective pupil distance from the ocular be e, it will be necessary to replace the distance L in the equation by $(L + em)$. Under the most favourable circumstances, e will be 5 or 6 millimetres, and its introduction into any calculation might affect the result considerably—by 13%, for example, in the case of Galileo's instrument of magnification 20.

Even ignoring the problem of refraction at the eye, we can see that the interpretation of statements concerning field of view—Harriot's in particular—is complicated in several different ways. Since the value of p changes with light intensity, it is meaningless to quote a value for the field of view without some indication of light conditions.

O. Källström and O. Allström have measured the field of an instrument which belonged to Gustavus Aldolphus, a telescope within a military baton, as 4·5 m at 1000 m.[109] This is equivalent to a field of about 15'·5. No comment was made on the clarity of the field selected, although it was pointed out that the field of view of the instrument φ is very limited 'owing to the small objective orifice and because the lenses are placed so far from the ends of the tube'. In fact, given no obstruction, the clear field may be calculated as nearly four times as large as that found (by day, and taking $p = e = 5$ mm.).

In discussing a telescope made by William Gascoigne,[110] S. B. Gaythorpe calculated its field of view as about 25', close to the total field we have calculated with

$p = 5$ mm. (day). For other conditions, see our table in our section on Harriot's instruments. Gaythorpe mentions that he takes the pupil aperture of the observer as $\frac{1}{8}$ inch, and makes it clear that he supposes enlargement of the pupil (to $\frac{1}{3}$ inch) with dark-adaptation to increase the field, but gives no indication of his method of calculation. The problem of the Galilean telescopic field was certainly passed over too lightly in earlier writings by G. Abetti and V. Ronchi,[111] a report on whose work was also given in English at the time by D. Baxandall.[112] It is believed that two of Galileo's telescopes (here called I and II) survive, together with an object glass III (broken) of a third. (The ocular of II is a replacement, and the precise details of the original are not known. If we accept a magnification of 30 for the complete instrument, III, we may deduce a focal length of 5·63 cm for its missing ocular.)[113] At the suggestion of George Hale, of Mount Wilson, Abetti and he initiated the study, and 'ha portato a concludere che il cannocciale I ha un potere risolutivo di 20″ e un campo di 15′, il II ha 10″ e 15′ rispettivamente'.[114] As may be seen from our table, the term $\pm D/m\varphi$ is of much less importance than is the aperture of the eye pupil. Telescope II, with the eye adapted to darkness ($p = 8$ mm, we suppose), might, it seems, provide a total field of over 30′ (taking $e = 5$ mm), or 24·6 clear. Bringing the effective pupil aperture down, however, to 3·5 mm—a reasonable figure for bright Italian daylight—we find for Galileo I a total field of 14′·2 (clear 4′·3), and for Galileo II a total field of 14′·7 (clear 9′·2). These figures suggest that the 1923 tests were made under the untypical conditions of bright daylight—not even relevant to Galileo's most important sunspot observations, which were made by projection. The figures also give incidentally some idea of the limitations of the Dutch type of instrument, with which the *area* of the unobstructed field is in one case less than a tenth of the total area seen. (As we know, the unobstructed field might in principle be entirely non-existent.)

NOTES

1. Notes to the text indicate that the discoverer of sunspots was 'Io. Fabricius de maculis in Sole. Witeb. 1611' (see below), and that the 'Hollander' published at 'Lugduni Bat. Ao 1612'. This is a reference to a rare and obscure tract by a writer calling himself simply 'Batavus', or 'Dutchman': *De maculis in sole animadversis, et, tanquam ab Apelle, in tabula spectandum in publica luce expositis, Batavi dissertatiuncula ad Amplissimum Nobilissimumque virum, Cornelium Vander-Milium Academiae Lugodinensis Curatorem vigilantissimum*, Ex Officina Plantiniana Raphelengii (Leyden), 1612, 19 pp, quarto. I have not seen this work referred to by any modern writer, but Burton's style of the previous sentence suggests that he had seen it. Raphelengius finished printing three years later with a book by the Italian astronomer Magini. 'Apelles' was part of a pseudonym of Scheiner, to whom Burton referred elsewhere, but apparently Burton was ignorant of the identity of the two.
2. 'Galilée et les taches solaires (1610–1613)', *Revue d'Histoire des Sciences*, xix (1966), pp. 306–70; reprinted in *Galilée: Aspects de sa vie et de son oeuvre*, Centre international de Synthèse, Paris, 1968, pp. 186–251. See p. 195, n. 3.
3. *Oeuvres de François Arago: Notices Biographiques*, vol. iii, 1855, p. 271 sqq.
4. From the first part (now lost) of a letter of which the remainder is British Museum Add. MS 6789, ff. 427–8. See Rigaud (cited n. 11 below) at p. 43 where the missing part is printed from von Zach.
5. *Istoria e dimonstrazioni intorno alle macchie solari e loro accidenti*, Giacomo Mascardi, Rome, 1613. Translated in S. Drake, *Discoveries and Opinions of Galileo*, Doubleday, New York, 1957. Galileo's letters are dated 4 May, 1612, 14 August 1612, and 1 December 1612.
6. *Tres epistolae de maculis solaribus* (published 5 January 1612) was followed in September by *De maculis solaribus et stellis circa Iovem errantibus accuratior disputatio*, both at Augs-

burg. The letters of Scheiner, Galileo, and of Welser to Galileo, are assembled in vol. V. of Favaro's edition of Galileo's *Opere*.

7. Two early papers are Alexander Hosie, 'Sunspots and Sun shadows observed in China BC 28—AD 1617', *Journal of the North China Branch, Royal Asiatic Society*, xii (1878), pp. 91–5; Joseph de Moidrey, 'Observations anciennes de taches solaires en Chine', *Bulletin Astronomique*, xxi (1904) 11 pp. The observations were often systematic, lasting for as much as ten consecutive days, and the spots were described in size and shape. Much further information and further references may be found in J. Needham and Wang Ling, *Science and Civilization in China*, vol. iii, Cambridge, 1959, pp. 434–6.

8. *Kosmos*, vol. iii, Stuttgart and Tubingen, 1850, pp. 412–6. See also the translation by E. C. Otté and B. H. Paul, *Cosmos*, vol. iv, Bohn's Scientific Library, 1852, pp. 379–86. This may be supplemented by G. Sarton, 'Early observations of the sunspots', *Isis*, vol. xxxvii (1947), pp. 69–71. See also B. R. Goldstein, 'Some medieval reports of Venus and Mercury transits', *Centaurus*, xiv (1969), pp. 49–59.

9. For Galileo's references to one of these early chronicles, see *Opere* (ed. Nazionale) vol. v, p. 138, and cf. his letters to Welser, op. cit., p. 117. Kepler had drawn attention to chronicles, and had actually 'restored' the text to its true form, in the light of his interpretation. See *Ad Vitellionem Paralipomena*, Frankfurt, 1604.

10. *Phaenomenon singulare Seu Mercurius in sole*, Leipzig, 1609.

11. *Miscellaneous Works and Correspondence of the Rev. James Bradley*, Oxford, 1832, to which was added *Supplement . . . with an account of Harriot's astronomical papers*, Oxford, 1833 (separately paginated), of which see pp. 17–70 on Harriot and pp. 37–8 on sunspots.

12. *Histoire de l'astronomie moderne*, Paris, 1821, p. 631.

13. All references are to MS Leconfield 241, volume 8 as now bound. Speaking generally, folio references are unnecessary insofar as observations are numbered.

14. Admittedly there were those who could reconcile an irregular outline with the notion of a stellar constitution. In a debate between a Dominican father and certain Jesuits at the Roman College in September 1612, the Jesuits said that the irregularity was due to the clustering of the stars. See Galileo, *Opere*, ed. Naz., vol. xi, p. 395.

15. MS Leconfield 241, vol. 9, rough draft of the initial leaf *De quadratura Lunae*.

16. See p. 134 above.

17. *Op. cit.*, p. 38.

18. 11 December 1611 (N.S.), 11^h 40^m 3^s. This was in error by less than an hour.

19. See below.

20. *Annales célestes du dix-septième siècle*, ed. M. G. Bigourdan, Paris, 1901, p. 34.

21. *Annuaire du Bureau des Longitudes pour l'an 1842*, pp. 460–76.

22. That is, 9 March 1611, New style. See Berthold's *David Fabricius und Johann Kepler vom neuen Stern*, Norden, 1897; see also *Der Magister Johann Fabricius und die Sonnenflecken*, Leipzig, 1894, pp. 29–38.

23. See Joseph Klug, 'Simon Marius aus Gunzenhausen und Galileo Galilei', *Bayerische Akademie der Wissenschaften, Abhandlungen* (Math.-Phys. K1.) xxxix (1916), pp. 367–8; 403–12, 443–52; 498–503.

24. Printing was begun in 1626 and completed 1630.

25. *Rosa Ursina*, p. 28. It is generally accepted that 'mense Martio anni 1610' on the same page refers to 1610/1611, or is a misprint. The date March 1611 occurs again on the second (unnumbered) page. The title of the book refers to the house of Orsini, the 'rose' being an allusion to the Sun.

26. Scheiner was perhaps the first to notice, and to name, the *faculae*, or 'little torches', the bright areas associated with sunspots (*maculae*).

27. For the letters and replies, see Galileo, *Opere*, ed. Naz., vol. xi, pp. 208–14.

28. *Ibid.*, p. 230.

29. It is amusing to consider the delicacy with which Galileo treated the naming of Jupiter's satellites. He decided at length in favour of 'Medicean' rather than 'Cosmic' that is, in favour of the Grand Duke Cosmo's family rather than simply Cosmo himself, and it was necessary to paste over a correction to the half-title of the first Venice edition of *Sidereus Nuncius* (apud Thomasi Baglionum, 1610), which is uncorrected in the Frankfurt edition of the same year.

30. See Delambre, *Histoire de l'astronomie moderne*, Paris, 1821, p. 681.

31. See Galileo's *Opere*, ed. Naz., vol. v., p. 25. Zinner's arguments were set out in appendix, H (pp. 494–6) of his *Enstehung und Ausbreitung der koppernicanischen Lehre*, Erlangen 1943, Zinner has since repeated his claims elsewhere.

32. Dame, *op. cit.*, pp. 192–4. The quotation which follows is taken from the translation of the *Dialogo* by Stillman Drake, *Dialogue concerning the Two Chief World Systems*, Berkeley and Los Angeles, 1962, p. 345.

33. See Dame, *op. cit.*, p. 194.

34. 'When did Galileo make his first telescope?' *Centaurus*, ii (1951), pp. 44–51.

35. This is reconcilable with an apparently inconsistent statement of *Sidereus Nuncius* (1610). See Rosen, *op. cit.*, pp. 44–5.

36. He arrived there before 25 July. The date depends on the interpretation of the phrase 'more than a month' in *Il Saggiatore*. See Rosen, *op. cit.*, p. 49.

37. *Ibid.*, p. 47.

38. Harriot dates it 26 July 1609.

39. Any doubt which may be thought to attach to the year should be dispelled by the statement that the Moon at the time of observation was five days old. It may be verified that this was so in 1609, but not in 1610, on 26 July.

40. For a manuscript document containing a brief resumé of Galileo's observations of the satellites from 7 January to 15 January 1610 and comparable with the first leaf of his manuscript journal of early observations (*Opere*, ed. Naz., vol. iii. pt. 2, p. 427), see Stillman Drake's 'Galileo Gleanings'—XIII. An unpublished fragment relating to the telescope and the Medicean stars', *Physis*, anno IV (1962), pp. 342–4.

41. Harriot's first observation is explicitly headed 'My first observation of the new planets'. It is copied out again subsequently with a similar heading, as the first of a numbered series of Jupiter observations.

42. British Museum Add. MS 6789, ff. 425–6. See Jean Jacquot, 'Thomas Harriot's reputation for impiety', *Notes and Records of the Royal Society*, xi (1952), pp. 164–87. The letter is dated 'Traventi, the longest day of 1610', and Jacquot's '21 June' is the date in the Gregorian calendar.

43. *Op. cit.*, p. 27.

44. Baron von Zach's very foolish inference from Harriot's use of the date 26 January 1610 to the conclusion that Harriot's first observation was made at that time is disproved by Rigaud, *op. cit.*, pp. 64–7. There is even a reference to Venice, to which Rigaud could have drawn attention, at the side of a calculation of the correction needed for longitude difference of Venice and Syon.

45. I owe the interpretation of these ascriptions to Professor Shirley.

46. Add. MSS 6788, f. 251 (six, with some pencilled attempts); f. 252 (a score or so, with further variants), and 6789, ff. 455–9 (twenty-one in pencil and two in ink).

47. Translated by E. Rosen, *Kepler's conversation with Galileo's Sidereal Messenger*, New York & London, 1965.

48. Add. MS 6789, f. 455r.

49. *Ibid.*, f. 475. It is not unlikely that further examples of this and of the Galilean anagrams will be found elsewhere in Harriot's papers, which I do not claim to have searched systematically.

50. 5 nonas Maias.

51. Mentioned by Rigaud, *op. cit.*, p. 27.

52. See n. 8. Kepler, and at first Fabricius and Scheiner, projected without lenses. It was Benedetto Castelli, Galileo's pupil, who first suggested to him the use of a telescope for projections.

53. Add. MS 6789, ff. 266–238. See especially f. 230r. On f. 239 he considers a related subject, that of burning glasses.

54. Add. MS 6787, f. 244v. Some of the drawings on the recto are also relevant, but not all are easy to interpret.

55. Drawing no. 146 is repeated on the verso, unnumbered, and this—a note to which mentions much thunder in the west—might be an original sketch. As already mentioned, we have crayon records of some of Harriot's night observations, on the quadrature of the Moon, for

example. Against the lunar observations for 23 October [1610] Harriot has added the note 'Looke the papers of obser[vation].'

56. *Op. cit.*, p. 33.

57. *Ibid.*, p. 37.

58. Delambre, *op. cit.*, p. 681.

59. Ingolstadt, 1540. Tycho later preferred a small pin-hole in a sheet of paper, perhaps because optically sound glass was difficult or impossible to obtain, especially coloured. Robert Hooke is quoted by Rigaud (op. cit., p. 33) as disapproving of 'the coloured glasses' because they 'take off the truth of the appearance as to colour', and detract from the sharpness and distinctness of the image.

60. Here and elsewhere I expand 'Chr' to 'Christopher', and substitute a reasonably intelligible punctuation.

61. 10, 12, 13, 15 September 1610, all lunar drawings.

62. About ten miles from the centre of London, and in Syon Park, which now runs along the Thames for about a mile. Across the river is the Old Deer Park containing Kew Observatory. of later fame, which is in fact only half a mile south of Harriot's place of observation.

63. See under instrument $\frac{10}{1}$ above.

64. Sunspot observations 113 (or 1, in a new numbering sequence) to 139 or 27. Some of these drawings are to a larger radius than usual.

65. Christopher is mentioned in nine of these London observations, which were probably left unnumbered because Harriot had no part in them. All subsequent satellite observation numbers are given in the form '85+9' to allow for the additional nine.

66. On 5, 8, 9, December 1611 it might have included Lower and Tooke, both named on 1 and 3 December.

67. MS Leconfield 241, vol. 12. I owe this difficult reading to Professor Shirley. According to O.E.D. 'pair of stairs' is an accepted usage, known from the sixteenth century, to denote a flight of stairs, or even a floor or storey.

68. Printed by Rigaud (from Baron von Zach), op. cit., p. 42. The original is now lost, but Rigaud identified a later part of the letter.

69. British Museum Add. MS 6789, f. 425v.

70. *Ibid.*, f. 429v.

71. See the Jupiter record of 7 December cited on p. 136.

72. See p. 137.

73. Robert Burton, for example, in the section of his *Anatomy* from which we quoted at the outset, has this footnote to the third edition (1628): 'Some of those [planets] about *Jupiter* I have seen my selfe by the help of a glasse 8 foot long'. This does not occur in the second edition (1624).

74. Francis R. Johnson, *Astronomical Thought in Renaissance England*, Baltimore, 1937. See esp. Chap. VI.

75. *A briefe and true report of the new found land of Virginia . . .* London, 1588, f. E4r.

76. Edward Rosen argues convincingly that the word *telescopium* was conceived by John Demisiani, and given currency after a banquet given by Cesi on 14 April 1611, at which Galileo was the guest of honour. A report of this occasion dated 16 April 1611 mentions Galileo as a mathematician who

observed the motion of the stars with the *occhiali*, which he invented, or rather improved. Against the opinion of all the ancient philosophers, he declares that there are four more stars or planets, which are satellites of Jupiter and which he calls the Mediciean bodies, as well as two companions of Saturn.

See Rosen, *The Naming of the Telescope*, 1947, p. 31. Rosen quotes from a letter from Welser of 20 May 1611, also mentioning that Galileo showed to the guests the satellites of Jupiter, 'together with a number of other celestial marvels', *ibid.*, p. 35.

77. Galileo did not analyse his data at this time, but Simon Mayr quoted 13', 8', 5' and 3'. See Rigaud, *op. cit.*, p. 30.

78. Thus on 16 March 1611 he gives the distance of a satellite as 'about 5 diameters', alternatively '9' or 10''. Earlier, on 28 November 1610, he put a satellite '1½' a [Jove] or diameter Iovis a [Jove]'.

79. *Op. cit.*, p. 24.

80. Add. MS 6786, f. 269r and v. Since he also read Galileo, it would be very surprising if he did not apply Galileo's very obvious method for calculating the field.
81. In a bright Sun the pupil might have been 2 mm in diameter, but with a hazy or clouded morning Sun between 3 and 6 mm, according to circumstance.
82. *Op. cit.*, p. 35.
83. *Op. cit.*, p. 24.
84. His circumstances were nevertheless clearly better than Lower's in Traventi. See p. 150 above.
85. See p. 141 above.
86. See for examples the records for 20 February, 27 March, 12 April, 31 March, 7 June, 1612.
87. See Appendix.
88. Essential bibliographical sources for these instruments are given in the Appendix above. All measurements are given in our table in millimetres, as taken or converted from the sources. Note that speaking generally, Galileo stopped down his object lenses to about half their diameters. Figures quoted here are for the clear apertures as stated by Abetti and others.
89. Harriot is known to have been in the employ of Henry Percy at least as early as St. George's Day 1593, when a payment was made to him by the Earl. Percy probably disposed of the sphere in 1600, when he needed money for a military expedition to the Low Countries.
90. See, for an illustration and further details, R. T. Gunther, *Early Science in Oxford*, vol. ii, 1923, pp. 148–50.
91. They show, for instance, the Copernican system for precession.
92. Letter to Harriot, 11 June 1610, Brit. Mus. Add. MS 6789, f. 426r: 'I have supplied verie fitlie my want of a spheare, in the desolation of a hogshead; the hopes thereof have framed me a verie fine one'. In his letter of 6 February 1610 he had asked Harriot to tell the bearer, Vaughan, 'how to provide himselfe of a fit sphere', and how it should be designed (*ibid.* f. 427v).
93. *De astrolabo catholico*, 1550.
94. See my 'Werner, Apian, Blagrave, and the meteoroscope', *British Journal for the History of Science*, iii (1966–7), pp. 57–65, esp. note 8.
95. Quoted by D. B. Quinn and J. W. Shirley, 'A contemporary list of Hariot references', *Renaissance Quarterly*, xxii, No. 1, Spring 1969, p. 13.
96. For 2 July–31 August 1612, London and Syon.
97. *Dialogue Concerning the Two Chief World Systems*, Stillman Drake's translation, p. 345.
98. It seems probable that it was Passigiani's observations of the elliptic trajectories of sunspots which first led Galileo to realize the inclination of the solar axis. See the letter of Cigoli to Galileo of 23 September 1611, *Opere*, ed. Naz. vol. xi, p. 212.
99. *Observations of the Spots on the Sun*, 1863, pp. 221; 224.
100. See Galileo's first and third letters to Welser (4 May and 1 December 1612), trans. Drake, *Discoveries and Opinions of Galileo*, New York, 1957, pp. 95; 136. All Galileo's and Scheiner's letters are printed in vol. v of the Ed. Naz. of Galileo's *Opere*. Scheiner quoted one period of $15^d 2^h 22^m$ (i.e. 22 'scruples'), but he also believed that there was a variation in period and distance from the ecliptic, and that this was evidence for the extra-solar character of the spots.
101. *Ibid.*, p. 102, and again in his second letter, of 14 August 1612, p. 106.
102. *Op. cit.*, p. 39, note n.
103. *Op. cit.*, p. 40.
104. 'Periodicität der Sonnenflecken', *Astron. Nachrichten*, xxi (1844) p. 234.
105. *Neue Untersuchungen*, 1852, p. 249.
106. *Op. cit.*, p. 215.
107. See p. 133 above.
108. *Op. cit.*, p. 40.
109. 'The telescope in the baton', *The Optician*, Nov. 25 and Dec. 2, 1949.
110. 'On a Galilean telescope made about 1640 by William Gascoigne, inventor of the filar micrometer', *Journal of the British Astronomical Assoc.*, xxxix (1929), pp. 238–41.
111. G. Abetti, 'I cannocchiali di Galileo e dei suoi discepoli', *L'Universo*, Anno IV (Sept.

1923) no. 9; V. Ronchi, 'Sopra i cannocchiali di Galileo', ibid., (Oct. 1923) no. 10, summarized in 'Le caratteristiche dei cannocchiali "di Galileo" e sulla loro autenticita', *Rendiconti della R. Accad. Naz. dei Lincei*, xxxii (Nov. 1923) pp. 339–43. A French translation of Abetti's paper is in *Ciel et Terre*, Anee XL (Jan. 1924) no. 1, p. 12.

112. 'Replicas of two Galileo telescopes', *Trans. of the Optical Society*, xxv (1923–4), pp. 141–4. Note that he there warns against some errors in an earlier paper.

113. The fact that the Dutch type of telescope is inherently inexpensive explains the relatively large numbers of such instruments mentioned in the writings of Harriot and Lower, Galileo and others. We know, for example, that Galileo's first instrument was of magnification about 3; that on returning to Padua he made one of magnification 9 (*Sidereus nuncius*) and another of 20; and that he observed Jupiter on 7 January 1610 with one of magnification 30. He made many others, for mention of which see Ronchi's article in *L'Universo*. It seems that Galileo's highest magnification was 33. Objective III is supposedly that with which Jupiter's satellites were discovered. It was presented by Viviani to Leopoldo de' Medici, who had it mounted in its present ornamental frame.

114. Ronchi, in the second article cited, p. 339.

BIBLIOGRAPHY

I. 1580–1700

A. PRIMARY MANUSCRIPTS AND SIGNATURES

Alnwick Castle:
  Syon House MSS
  G. II.1.a. Signature of Harriot on lease. 7 July 1600.

British Museum:
  Additional MS.   6782/a, ff. 1–253.
                   6782/b, ff. 254/504.
  Additional MS.   6783/a, ff. 1/213.
                   6783/b, ff. 214–426.
  Additional MS.   6784/a, ff. 1–215.
                   6784/b, ff. 216–413.
  Additional MS.   6785/a, ff. 1–220;
                   6785/b, ff. 221–441.
  Additional MS.   6786/a, ff. 1–280.
                   6786/b, ff. 281–561.
  Additional MS.   6787/a, ff. 1–289.
                   6787/b, ff. 290–578.
  Additional MS.   6788, ff. 1–567.
  Additional MS.   6789, ff. 1–538.

Guildhall Library, London:
  The will of Thomas Harriot.
  Archdeaconry Court of London, Certified Copy.
  Archdeaconry Court of London, 1618–26/7, ff. 71–72.

Hatfield House:
  CP 42/36   11 July 1596. Letter, Harriot to Sir Robert Cecil, on updating of maps.
  CP 52/101   3 July 1597. Letter, Harriot to Sir Robert Cecil, requesting his signature on a paper to Ralegh.
  CP 114/40   1605 [Nov. or Dec.] Harriot to Salisbury asking release from prison.
  CP 114/61   16 December 1605. Petition of Harriot to Privy Council from Gatehouse prison.

National Library, Vienna:
  Cod 10703,   B1. 318–382. Eigenhandig. 2 December 1606, London. Letter from Harriot to Joannes Kepler in Prague.
  Cod 10703,   B1. 384–385. Eigenhandig. 13 July 1608. Syon. Letter from Harriot to Joannes Kepler in Prague.

Oslo University Library:
  Copy of Vitellio, *Opticae libri decem* ed. F. Risner, (Basiliae, 1572) contains tables of refraction written by Harriot.

Petworth House:
  HMC 240, ff. 1–170. *Canon Nauticus.*
  HMC 241/I   Algebra, Geometry, Calendar, Conic sections.

HMC 241/II	Calculations from observations of Hannelius, Copernicus, Brahe, the vernal and autumnal equinoxes, solstices, orbit of earth, length of year.
HMC 241/III	Kepler, *de Stella Martis.* Snellii, *Eratosthenes Batavus*
HMC 241/IV	Constellations, chemical papers, miscellaneous calculations, Jupiter's satellites.
HMC 241/V	Triangles.
HMC 241/VI	Projectiles, center of gravity, reflexion of bodies; *Doctrine of Nautical Triangles Compendious.*
HMC 241/VII	Comets of 1607 and 1618.
HMC 241/VIII	Observations of sunspots.
HMC 241/IX	The moon.
HMC 241/X	Letters.

Public Record Office:
C 24/372/125   Lawsuits v. Ralegh, Harriot's testimony, 1610
C 24/372/126
St. Ch. 8/260/4

B. SECONDARY MANUSCRIPT REFERENCES

Alnwick Castle:
  Alnwick MSS.   7: f. 286, 288
                 9: f. 122.
  Leconfield MSS.   1620–1629
  Syon House MSS. – Household Accounts.
  U. I. 2:   t, gg, kk, hh, rr.
  U. I. 3:   e, o, x, ah, ap, ar, ax.
  U. I. 4:   f, n, z, am, as, ax.
  U.I. 50:   a5, a7.

Bodleian:
  Aubrey MS. 13, f. 342. 20 July 1683. Wallis letters to Aubrey, 1684.
  Clarendon I, f. 54. 27 July 1608. Letter to Harriot, in Latin, from Alexander Lower.
  Rawlinson B158, ff. 152–3. Gossip about Harriot and his friends.
  Savile 09, 22 March 1677. Manuscript notes of John Wallis on Harriot, prefixed to his copy of the *Artis Analyticae Praxis*, 1631.

British Museum:
  Additional MS. 38170, f. 92. Harriot agent to Ralegh in settling compensation for loss of Sherborne.
  Birch MS. 4394–4396. Papers of Walter Warner.
    4395: 92. Original draft of Preface to *Artis Analyticae Praxis* by Torporley.
    4396: Letter; Aylesbury to Northumberland about costs of publishing Harriot's *Artis Analyticae Praxis*.
  Harley 6001, ff. 1–40 (copy).
  Harley 6002, ff. 1–57 (copy).
  Harley 6083, ff. 1–455 (copy—some Harriot materials).
  Harley 6848, ff. 185–186.
  Sloane MS. 2086, f. 57. Notes on Harriot's illness by Mayerne.
Inscription in *El Viaie Que Hizo Antonio de Espeio in el Anno de Ochenta y Tres. . .* (Paris, 1586). Harriot gave this book to J. Dee, noted on the title page on January 29, 1590. This copy in British Museum: C. 32. a. 32.

T.H.—12

Guildhall:
> MS. 4421–1 St. Christopher-le-Stocks Registers 1558–1653. Record of Harriot's burial in the Choir, the Chancel, 3 July 1621.

Hatfield House:
> CP 196/131 Petition of William Floyer for title to Abbey of Molana.
> CP 115/21 Persons to have access to Sir Walter Ralegh in the Tower.
> CP 134/86 Interrogatory of Carlton on Harriot Nov. 1605. Holograph of King James.
> CP 113/63 Sir Thomas Smith to Salisbury on search of Harriot's lodgings and study at Syon.

Lambeth Palace Library:
> Carew MS. 604, ff. 195–196. Letter from Cecil to Carew, 1 October 1602.

National Library, Vienna:
> Cod 10703, B1. 378–380. Letter from Kepler to Harriot in London, Oct. 1606. Prague.
> Cod 10703, B1. 383. Letter from Kepler to Harriot in London, 2 August 1607. Prague.
> Cod 10703, B1. 386. Letter from Kepler to Harriot in London, 1 September 1609. Prague.

Public Record Office:
> SP/216 [Gunpowder Plot]
>> ff. 112, 113, 113x: Examination of Earl of Northumberland, 23 November 1605.
>> f. 122: Examination of Nathaniel Torporley, 27 November 1605.
>> f. 125: Second examination of Earl of Northumberland, 30 November 1605.
>> f. 137: Examination of Sir William Lower, 2 December 1605.

C. BOOKS AND PRINTED REFERENCES

1. *Acknowledged by Harriot (c. 1603)*
See Quinn-Shirley, 'A Contemporary List of Harriot References', *Renaissance Quarterly*, 22 (1969), 9–26.

[1] HARVEY, Richard, *A theologicall discourse of the Lamb of God* (London, 1590).

[2] HOLINSHED, Raphael, *Chronicles* (London, 1587).

[3] ANGLERIUS (PETRUS MARTYR), *De orbe nouo decades, octo*, edited by Richard Hakluyt (Paris, 1587).

[4] NASHE, Thomas, *Pierce Penilesse his supplication to the devil* (London, 1592).

[5] PARSONS, Robert, *Elizabethae. . . edictum. . . cum Responsione* (Augustae, 1592; Lugduni, 1592; Romae, 1593).

[6] FORMAN, Simon, *The groundes of the longitude* (London, 1591). Harriot the 'unbelieving S. Thomas.'

[7] HOOD, Thomas, lost work on longitude.

[8] ——, *The use of the two mathematicall instrumentes, the cross staffe and the Jacobs staff* (London, 1592).

[9] HAKLUYT, Richard, *Principall navigations*, 1st edition (London, 1589) includes reprint of *Briefe and true report*, and Ralph Lane's 'Discourse of the first colony'.

[10] HARRIOT, Thomas, *A briefe and true report of the new found land of Virginia*, (London, 1588). *A briefe and true report of the new found land of Virginia* (Frankfurt, 1590), with the illustrations of John White (Harriot captions) engraved by Theodor de Bry. Also published in Latin, French and German.

[11] Unidentified.

[12] TANNER, Robert, *A briefe treatise for the ready use of the sphere* (London, 1592).

[13] PARSONS, Robert (John Philopatris, pseudonym), *An Advertisement written to a secretarie of my L. Treasurers of Ingland* (1592).

[14, 23] HUES, Robert, *Tractatus de Globis et eorum Usu* (London, 1594).

[15] HARVEY, Gabriel, *Pierces supererogation* (London, 1593).

[16] PLAT, Sir Hugh, *The jewell house of art and nature* (London, 1594).

[17] MORE, Richard, *The carpenters rule* (London, 1602).

[18] SCALIGER, Joseph Justus, *Cyclometrica*, 2nd edition (Lugduni Batavorum, 1594).

[19] DAVIS, John, *The seamans secrets* (London, 1595). Joins Harriot with Dee as cunning mathematicians.

[20] KEYMIS, Lawrence, *A Relation of the Second Voyage to Guiana* (London, 1596). Includes dedicatory Latin poem *Ad Thomam Hariotum & universae Philosophiae peritissimum*, also reproduced in Hakluyt's *Principal Navigations*, III (1600).

[21] WYFLIET, Cornelis van, *Descriptionis Ptolemaicae augmentum sive Occidentalis notitia brevis commentario* (Louvain, 1597).

[22] BARLOW, William, *The navigators supply* (London, 1597).

[23] See [14].

[24] CHAPMAN, George, *Achilles Shield* (London, 1598). Prefatory poem, 'To my admired and soule-loved friend Mayster of all essential and true knowledge, M. Harriots'.

[25] TORPORLEY, Nathaniel, *Diclides Coelometricae seu Valuae Astronomicae Vniversales* (London, 1602).

[26] GILBERT, William, *De magnete* (London, 1600). Harriot a skillful navigator.

[27] HAKLUYT, Richard, *Principal Navigations*, 2nd edition (London, 1598–1600). Dedicatory epistle of second volume (1599).

2. *Other*

BRERETON, John, *A briefe and true relation of the discoverie of the north part of Virginia* (1602).

CHAPMAN, George, *Translation of the Whole Works of Homer* (London [1611]). Preface indicates he conferred only with Harriot and Hues in making his translation.

CORBET, Richard, *Certain Elegant Poems* (London, 1647). Contains 'A poetic letter sent from Dr Corbet to Sir Thomas Aylesbury. Dec. 9, 1618 on the occasion of a Blazing Star', which praises Aylesbury and Harriot.

GIBSON, Thomas, *Syntaxes Mathematica* (London, 1655).

HALLEY, E., 'De Numero Radicum, in Æquationibus Solidis ac Biquadraticis', *Phil. Trans. Royal Society*, XVI (1686–87), 391.

HARRIOT, Thomas, *Artis, analyticae praxis, algebraicas nova methodo resolvendas* (London, 1631).

READ, Alexander, *The Chirurgicall Lectures of Tumours and Vlcers: Delivered... in the Chirurgeans Hall these three yeares last past, viz. 1632, 1633, and 1634* (London, 1635). See p. 307.

WALLIS, John, *A Treatise of Algebra, both Historical and Practical* (London, 1685), ——, *Opera Mathematica* (Oxford, 1693), II. Preface, 206, 207–13.

II. 1700–1900

A. MANUSCRIPTS

Bodleian: Rigaud 9, ff. 1–6. S. P. Rigaud's notes on Harriot.
    Rigaud 35, ff. 100–329.
    Rigaud 50, ff. 49–69.

B. BOOKS

AUBREY John, *Brief Lives*, 1669–1696. Ed. Andrew Clark, 2 vols. (Oxford, 1898); I, 284–7.

BIRCH, Thomas, *The History of the Royal Society*, 2 vols. (London, 1756). I, 120, 126, 309; II, 410.

EDWARDS, Edward, *The Life of Sir Walter Ralegh*, 2 vols. (London, 1868). Important correspondence, passim.

FONBLANQUE, Edward B., *Annals of the House of Percy*, 2 vols. (London, 1887).

GLANVILL, Joseph, *Plus Ultra, or the Progress and Advancement of Knowledge since the days of Aristotle* (London, 1668). See Ch. IV.

HALLIWELL, James Orchard, *A Collection of Letters Illustrative of the Progress of Science in England from the Reign of Queen Elizabeth to that of Charles II* (London, 1841).

HUTTON, Charles, *A Mathematical and Philosophical Dictionary*, 2 vols. (London, 1796). Reprints von Zach's 1788 account of the Harriot papers.

LAGRANGE, Joseph Louis, Count, *Oeuvres de Lagrange*, 14 vol. (Paris, 1867–92), IV, 539.

MONTUCLA, Jean Etienne, *Histoire des Mathématiques*, (Paris, 1799–1802), II, 105–8, 115–20.

MORGAN, Joseph, *Phoenix Britannicus: Being a Collection of Scarce and Curious Tracts* (London, 1732), 368, poem on Harriot's death.

Nouvelle Biographie Générale (Paris, 1858), vol. 23, 450–51 on Harriot.

RALEGH, Sir Walter, *History of the World*, ed. William Oldys, 11th edn. (London, 1736). Discussion of Harriot, 184–5.

RIGAUD, Stephen P., 'Account of Harriot's Astronomical Papers', in *Supplement to Dr. Bradley's Miscellaneous Works: with an Account of Harriot's Astronomical Papers* (Oxford, 1833), 1–70, and 5 plates.

STEVENS, Henry, of Vermont, *Thomas Hariot*, privately printed (London, 1900).

WOOD, Anthony à, *Athenae Oxonienses*, (London, 1721), vol. 1, 459–62. *Athenae Oxoniensis and Fasti Oxonienses*, 2 vols. (London, 1815).

C. PERIODICALS

BESSEL, F. W., 'Berechnung der *Harriot*schen und *Torporley*'schen Beobachtungen des Cometen von 1607', *Monatliche Correspondenz*, X (1804) 425–440.

RIGAUD, Stephen P., 'On Harriot's Papers', *Royal Institution of Great Britain Journal*, II (1831), 267–271.

——, 'On Harriot's astronomical observations contained in his unpublished manuscripts belonging to the Earl of Egremont', *Proceedings of the Royal Society*, III (1830–37), 125–6.

ROBERTSON, A., 'An account of some mistakes relating to Dr. Bradley's astronomical observations and Harriot's MSS', *Edinburgh Philosophical Journal*, VI (1822), 313–318.

ZAH, F. X. VON, 'Beobachtungen des Uranus; ... und Anzeige von den in England aufgefunden Harriotschen Manuscripten', *Astronomishches Jahrbuch für das Jahr 1788* (Berlin, 1785), 139–155.

——, 'Mémoire sur la nouvelle planète Ouranus', *Mémoires de l'Académie de Bruxelles*, V (1788), 22–48

——, 'Etwas aus den, von Herrn von Zach in Jahr 1784 in England aufgefunden Harriotschen Manuscripten, vormemlich Original-Beobachtungen der beyden Kometen von 1607 und 1618', *Astronomischen Jahrbuchern, erster Supplement-Band* (Berlin, 1793), 1–41.

——, *Allgemeine geographische Ephemeriden* (Weimar, 1798), 1, 230, 484, 635.

——, 'Etwas von *Hevelius und Harriot's* Handschriften', *Monatliche Correspondenz*, VII (Gotha, 1803), 36–60.

——, *Correspondence astronomique, geographique, hydrographique et statistique du Baron de Zach* (Genoa, 1822), 105–138

III. SINCE 1900

A. BOOKS

BAKELESS, John, *The Tragicall History of Christopher Marlowe* (Cambridge, Mass., 1942), 2 vols. See I, 105, 111, 128–30, and 134–37.

BATHO, G. R., *Household Papers of Henry Percy* (London, 1962).

BRADBROOK, Muriel C., *The School of Night* (Cambridge, 1936). Harriot references passim; brief account, 9–11.

BROOKE, Charles F. T., *The Life of Marlowe* (New York, 1938), 98–100.

CAJORI, Florian, *A History of Mathematical Notations*, 2 vols. (Chicago, 1928). I, 199–201; II, 115–117.

CORBITT, David L., Ed., *Explorations, Descriptions, and Attempted Settlements of Carolina, 1584–1590* (State Department of Archives and History, Raleigh, N. C., 1948).

COTTER, Charles H., *A History of Nautical Astronomy* (New York, 1968).

EIFERT, Virginia L. S., *Tall Trees and Far Horizons: Adventures and Discoveries of Early Botanists in America* (New York, 1965), 1–22.

GLASER, Anton, *History of Binary ond other Nondecimal Numeration* (privately printed, 1971). Harriot mentioned as first to develop binary system, 10–13.

GUNTHER, Robert W. T., *Early Science in Oxford*, vol. II (Oxford, 1923). Account of Harriot and telescope, 293–294.

HILL, Christopher, *Intellectual Origins of the English Revolution* (Oxford, 1965). Chapter VI: 'Ralegh-Science, History and Politics', 131–224. Sect. II, 139–45 devoted to Harriot. Other Harriot references passim.

HULTON, Paul and QUINN, David B., *The American Drawings of John White,1577–1590*, 2 vols. (London and Chapel Hill, 1964).

JOHNSON, Francis R., *Astronomical Thought in Renaissance England* (Baltimore, 1937), passim. Main entry 226–9.

KARGON, Robert H., *Atomism in England from Harriot to Newton* (Oxford, 1966).

LEFRANC, Pierre, *Sir Walter Ralegh Ecrivain: l'oeuvre et les idées* (Paris, 1968), references passim; main entry 344–352.

MCLEAN, Antonia, *Humanism and the Rise of Science in Tudor England* (New York, 1972).

MERSENNE, P. Marin, *Correspondance de P. Marin Mersenne*, edited by Cornelis de Waard and others, 12 vols. to date (Paris, 1932–72). References passim.

NICOLSON, Marjorie, *Science and Imagination* (London and Ithaca, N.Y., 1956). Harriot as a possible link between Kepler and Donne.

QUINN, David B., *The Elizabethans and the Irish* (Ithaca, N.Y., 1966). Harriot's residence at Molana Abbey noted, 115–6.

——, *Raleigh and the British Empire* (London, 1947). Harriot's role in Ralegh's colonization ventures.

——, *The Roanoke Voyages, 1584–1590: Documents to Illustrate the English voyages to North America under the patent granted to Walter Ralegh in 1584*, 2 vols. (London, 1955). Reprints *Briefe and True Report* with notes. For Harriot, see especially, 'Thomas Harriot and John White', vol. I, 35–60.

RUKEYSER, Muriel, *The Traces of Thomas Harriot* (New York, 1971). A poetic and

literary account, but sensitive and effective in developing a sympathetic understanding of Harriot.

STRATHMANN, Ernest A., *Sir Walter Ralegh: A Study in Elizabethan Skepticism*
(New York, 1951). Harriot references throughout as representative on new
scientific skepticism.

TAYLOR, E. G. R., *The Haven-Finding Art* (New York, 1957).

——, *Late Tudor and Early Stuart Geography, 1583–1650: a Sequel to Tudor Geography, 1485–1583* (London, 1934).

——, *The Mathematical Practitioners of Tudor and Stuart England* (Cambridge,
1954). Narrative 3–162. Practitioners, 165–431. Lists brief biographies of 628
mathematical practitioners arranged roughly chronologically.

WATERS, David W., *The Art of Navigation in England in Elizabethan and Early
Stuart Times* (London, 1958).

YATES, Frances A., *A Study of 'Love's Labour's Lost'* (Cambridge, 1936). Harriot as
a member of Ralegh group satirized by play.

——, *Theatre of the World* (Chicago, 1969).

B. PERIODICALS

BATHO, G. R., 'The Library of the Wizard Earl: Henry Percy, Ninth Earl of Northumberland (1564–1632)', *The Library*, XV (1960), 246–261.

CAJORI, Florian, 'A Reevaluation of Harriot's *Artis Analyticae Praxis*', *Isis*, 11
(1928), 316–324.

CROMBIE, Alistair C., PEPPER, Jon V., QUINN, David B., SHIRLEY, John W., and
TANNER, R. C. H., 'Thomas Harriot (1560–1621): an original practitioner in the
scientific art', *Times Literary Supplement*, London (Oct. 23, 1969), 1237–8.

CUNNINGHAM, Dolora G., 'The Ralegh Group and the History of Elizabethan
Skeptical Thought', *American Philosophical Society Yearbook* (1968), 551–552.

GEORGE, F., 'On Harriot's Meridional Parts', *Journal of the Institute of Navigation*,
9 (1956), 560–569.

GLASER, Anton, 'Binary Arithmetic from Hariot (ca. 1660 A.D.) to the Computer Age'.
Paper presented at the Second International Congress of Mathematical Education, Aug. 29–Sept. 2, 1972 at the University of Exeter, England.

HARRINGTON, J. C., 'Archeological Explorations at Fort Raleigh National Historic
Site', *North Carolina Historical Review*, XXVI (April, 1949), 127–149.

JACQUOT, Jean, 'Thomas Harriot's Reputation for Impiety', *Notes and Records of
the Royal Society*, IX (1952), 164–187.

JONES, Phillip S., 'Historically Speaking: the Binary System', *Mathematics Teacher*,
XLVI (December, 1953), 575–77

KARGON, Robert H., 'Thomas Hariot, the Northumberland Circle, and early
Atomism in England', *Journal of the History of Ideas*, XXVII (1966), 128–136.

KORBLER, Juraj, 'Thomas Harriot (1560–1621), fumeur de pipe, victime du cancer?',
Gesnerus, IX (1952), 52–54. Puts forward the theory that Harriot might be the
first person known to die of cancer caused by smoking a pipe.

LOHNE, Johannes A., 'Dokumente zur Revalidierung von Thomas Harriot als Alge-
braiker', *Archive for History of Exact Sciences*, III (1966/67), 185–205.

——, 'The Fair Fame of Thomas Harriott: Rigaud *versus* Baron von Zach',
Centaurus, VIII (1963), 69–84.

——, 'The Increasing Corruption of Newton's Diagrams', *History of Science*, VI
(1967, issued Sept., 1968), 69–89. Harriot and theory of trajectories discussed,
76–77.

——, 'A Note on Harriott's Scientific Works', *Centaurus*, VII (1961), 220–21.

——, 'Regenbogen und Brechzahl', *Sudhoff's Archiv*, XLIV (1965), 401–415.

——, 'Thomas Harriot als Mathematiker', *Centaurus*, XI (1965), 19–45.

——, 'Thomas Harriott (1560–1621), The Tycho Brahe of Optics', *Centaurus*, VI (1959), 113–121.

——, 'Zur Geschichte des Brechungsgesetzes', *Sudhoff's Archiv*, XIVII (1963), 152–172.

——, 'Thomas Harriot', *Dictionary of Scientific Biography*, VI (1972), 124–129.

MEE, Arthur, 'Carmarthenshire and early telescopes', *Transactions of the Carmarthenshire Antiquarian Society*, IV (1908–9), 43–44. Refers to the astronomical interests of William Lower.

MORLEY, F. V., 'Thomas Hariot – 1560–1621', *The Scientific Monthly*, XIV (January, 1922), 60–66.

NICOLSON, Marjorie, 'The "New Astronomy" and English literary imagination', *Studies in Philology*, XXXII (1935), 428–462.

PEPPER, Jon V., 'A Note on Hariot's Method of Obtaining Meridional Parts', *Journal of the Institute of Navigation*, 20 (1967), 347–349.

——, 'Harriot's Calculation of the Meridional Parts as Logarithmic Tangents', *Archive for History of Exact Science*, IV (1968), 359–413.

——, 'The Study of Thomas Harriot's Manuscripts: II. Harriot's Unpublished Papers', *History of Science*, VI (1967, published Sept., 1968), 17–40.

——, 'Letter from Nathaniel Torporley to Thomas Harriot', *British Journal of the History of Science*, 3 (June, 1967), 285–90.

——, 'Harriot's Work on the True Sea-Chart', *Actes du XIIe Congrès International d'Histoire des Sciences Paris 1968*, IV (Paris, 1971), 135–138.

PLOMER, Henry R., 'The Will of Thomas Harriot, Mathematician and Astronomer (1560–1621)', *The Home Counties Magazine*, VIII (1906), 240–47.

QUINN, David B. and SHIRLEY, John W., 'A Contemporary List of Hariot References', *The Renaissance Quarterly*, 22 (1969), 9–26.

QUINN, David B., 'The Failure of Raleigh's American Colonies', *Essays in British and Irish History in Honour of James Eadie Todd* (London, 1949), 61–85.

——, 'Thomas Hariot and the Virginia Voyages of 1602', *William and Mary Quarterly*, 27 (1970), 268–81.

REINHOLD, Robert, '20th Century Discovers an Elizabethan Genius', *The New York Times* (Apr. 8, 1971), p. 39.

——, 'Rediscovering an Elizabethan Genius', *International Herald Tribune* (Apr. 13, 1971), p. 14.

ROBERTSON, Jean, 'Some Additonal Poems by George Chapman', *The Library*, second series, XXII (June, 1941), 168–176. Identifies two portraits, the Delaram engraving and the Trinity College portrait, as possibly Harriot.

SADLER, D. H., 'Calculating the Meridional Parts', *Journal of the Institute of Navigation*, 6 (1953), 141–7.

SANDISON, H. E., 'Arthur Gorges, Spenser's Alcyon and Ralegh's friend', *Publication of the Modern Language Association of America*, XLIII, 3 (Sept., 1928), 645–671. Calls Harriot the 'true and loving friend' of Sir Arthur Gorges.

SCRIBA, Christoph J., 'Wallis und Harriot', *Centaurus*, X (1964/5), 248–57.

SEATON, Ethel, 'Thomas Hariot's Secret Script', *Ambix*, V (1953/6), 111–114.

SHIRLEY, John W., 'An early experimental determination of Snell's Law', *American Journal of Physics*, XIX (1951), 507–8.

——, 'Binary Numeration Before Leibnitz', *American Journal of Physics*, XIX (1951), 452–4.

——, 'George Percy at Jamestown, 1607–1612', *The Virginia Magazine of History and Biography*, 57 (July, 1949), 227–44.

——, 'Sir Walter Ralegh's Guiana Finances', *Huntington Library Quarterly*, XII (1949), 56–69.

——, 'The scientific experiments of Sir Walter Ralegh, the Wizard Earl, and the Three Magi in the Tower, 1603–1617', *Ambix* IV (1949–51), 52—66.

See also Quinn, D. B. and Shirley, J. W., supra.

STROUT, Eugeny, and MOORE, P., 'The Very First Maps and Drawings of the Moon', *Journal of the British Astonomical Association*, LXXV (1964/5), 100–105.

TANNER, Rosalind Cecily H., 'On the role of equality and inequality in the history of mathematics', *British Journal for the History of Science*, I (1952), 159–69.

——, 'Thomas Harriot as Mathematician: A Legacy of Hearsay, Part I', *Physis*, IX (1967), 235–47.

——, 'Thomas Harriot as Mathematician: A Legacy of Hearsay, Part II', *Physis*, IX (1967), 257–92.

——, 'La place de Thomas Harriot dans l'histoire de la médecine et de l'astronomie', *Gesnerus*, XXIV (1967), 75–77.

——, 'The Study of Thomas Harriot's Manuscripts: I. Harriot's Will', *History of Science*, VI (1967, publ. Sept., 1968), 1–16.

——, 'Nathaniel Torporley and the Harriott Manuscripts', *Annals of Science*, 25 (1969) 339–49.

——, 'Thomas Harriot and Marinus Ghetaldi', *Jugoslavenska Akademija Znanosti I Umjetnosti*, (Zagreb, 1969), 161–170.

——, 'Un mathématicien à son médicin: lettres de Thomas Harriot à Théodore de Mayerne', *Actes de la Société helvetique des Sciences naturelles 1970*, 195–197.

TAYLOR, E. G. R., 'Hariot's Instructions for Ralegh's Voyage to Virginia', *Journal of the Institute of Navigation*, V (1952), 345–50.

——, and SADLER, D. H., 'The doctrine of nauticall triangles compendious', *Journal of the Institute of Navigation*, VI (1953), 131–47.

VACCA, G , 'Sui Manoscritti Inediti di Thomas Harriot', Extract from *Bollettino di bibliografia e storia della scienze matematiche*, Feb,/Mar., 1902.

WALLIS, Helen M., 'The first English globe: a recent discovery', *Geographical Journal*, CXVII (1951), 275–90. Describes the Molyneux globe discovered at Petworth.

WHITE, George W., 'Thomas Hariot's Observations on American Geology in 1588', *Transactions of Illinois Academy of Science*. 45 (1952). 116–21.

INDEX

NOTE: This is a selective rather than a full index, and is weighted to show Harriot as a scientist.

Abetti, Giorgio, 150, 160

Acosta, José de, *Historia natural* (1590), 12–13

Adams, Randolph G., 19

alchemy, 110, 111, 114, 142

Alexandro, Alexander ab, 94, 95

algebra, 7, 8–10, 100, 101

Algonquian language, *see under* Indians, American

Alhazen (Ibn al-Haitham), *Kitāb fi-1 manāzir* (*c.* 1030), 2, 87 *n 13*

al-Kindī, 131

Allen (Alleyn), Thomas, 97

Alnwick Castle, 22, 33 *n 50*, 116

altitude, meridian, 55, 56, 58, 65, 67, 85, 87 *n 8*; tables and diagrams, illustrating the schema, 68; latitude from, 55; schema for observations, 66

Amadas, Philip, 17, 38, 39

Amazon R., 12, 13, 36

amplitude, 72; calculation of, 72–3; (fig.), 73; of the sun, 54; tables discussed, 72–3, 74, 89 *n 39*

Amsterdam, 110, 127 *n 40*

Annales Regi Francorum, 131

Apelles, *see* Scheiner, Christoph

Apian, Peter (Apianus, Petrus), *Astronomicum Caesareum* (1540), 140

Arago, François, 129, 130, 133

Aristotelians, 108, 110, 132

Aristotle, 109, 118

armillary sphere, 150, 164 *nn 89, 92*

Arundel, earl of, *see* Howard, Thomas

astrolabe, 55, 58–61, 150–1

atheism, 23, 24, 25, 27, 93, 108

atomism, 4–5, 107–16, 118–20; Harriot's view of, 115

Atomists, ancient, 109, 110

atoms, 5, 108, 110, 112, 115, 118—19

Aubrey, John, 30, 94, 107, 110, 117, 125 *n 6*; *Brief Lives* (1898), 19, 116, 120–1

Aylesbury, Sir Thomas, 51, 97–8, 116, 117, 121, 126 *n 36*

Azores (Asores), Islands of, 12, 37, 88 *n 29*

Babylon, 8

back staff, 15, 20, 87 *n 9*

Bacon, Sir Francis, vi, 29; *Novum organum* (1620), 7

Bacon, Roger, *Opus tertium* (1267), 97

Baines, Richard, 23–4

Barberini, Maffeo, 135

Barlow, William, *Nauigators supply* (1597), 81, 85

Barlowe, Arthur, 17; Virginia voyage (1584), 38, 39, 43

Barrow, Isaac, *Lectiones geometricae* (1670), 86

Bible, 5–7, 108, 109

Bill, John, bookseller, 94–5

binary numeration, Harriot's discovery of, v, 10

Blackwater R., 20, 21, 22

blood circulation, Warner's treatise on, 120–3

Blundeville, Thomas, *His exercises* (1594), 77, 85, 87 *n 4*

Bodleian Library, vi, 95, 150

Bodley, Sir Josias, 150

booklists, bookseller's, 75, 94, 95

Bond, Henry, *New booke of gauging* (1634), 85

Borough, William, 57; *Variation of the cumpas* (1581), 71, 72

Bourgoignon, Nicholas, 43

Bourne, William, 57, 143; *Regiment for the sea* (1574), 56, 67

Brahe, Tycho, 63, 147, 163 *n 59*

Brett, Alexander, of Dorset, 26

Browne, Maurice, 37, 38

Bruno, Giordano, 108, 109—10, 113, 114, 125; *De la causa* (1584), 120; *Spaccio de la bestia trionfante*, 125 *n 9*

Bry, Theodor de, 50, 51; *America, part i* (1590), 19, 46, 47, 51

Buckner (Bookener), Thomas, 31, 32, 34 *n 87*, 98

Burton, Robert (Democritus Junior), *Anatomy of melancholy* (1621), 129, 160 *n 1*, 163 *n 73*

Busby, Richard, 19, 126 *n 39*

Butler, Michael, 38

cancer, Harriot's final illness, 93–4

Canon triangulorum nauticorum, Harriot's table of cosines, 77

Carew, George, 16, 26

Carleton, Dudley, 28

Carmarthenshire, Wales, 28
Carolina Outer Banks, N.C., 40–1, 42, 49; Indians, 50
Carrington, Richard, 152, 155
Cassini I (Gian Domenico), 140
Catesby, Robert, 28
Catholic faith, 6, 13, 20, 27, 113
cause, philosophy of: Bruno's, 109; Warner's, 119
Cavendish, Sir Charles, 109, 117, 121, 127 nn 40, 45
Cavendish, William, earl (later duke) of Newcastle (d. 1676), 109, 117, 121, 124
Cecil, Robert, earl of Salisbury (d. 1612), 12, 27, 48
Cerne Abbas, Dorset, 24
Chapman, George, poet, 114
Chesapeake Bay, Virginia, 41, 44
China, 130
Cholmeley, Richard, 23
Cigoli, Ludovico Cardi de, 134
circulation of the blood: Warner's theory of, 120–3; Harvey's discovery of, 121–2
Clerke, Agnes, 92, 104 n 8
Collins, John, *Marriners plain scale new plain'd* (1659), 86, 127 n 41
combinatorics, vi, 96, 100
comet of 1607, 11
compass, magnetic, 19, 20, 55, 56, 58, 72, 85, 88 n 23, 143; deviation of, 72, 73; point of, 57; raising or laying a degree of latitude (table), 75; rhumbs in, 57
complex (noetic) numbers, 101
Copernicanism, 4, 6, 7, 107, 108, 110, 130, 135, 152
Copernicus, Nicholas, 1, 5, 6, 63, 64, 110, 156; 'Commentariolus' (1530), 65; *De revolutionibus* (1543), 1, 5, 6, 65
copper, 49, 50
Cortes (Curtis), Martin, 57, 69, 74; *Arte of nauigation* (1561), 69
Coygnet, Martin, 76, 89 n 45
cross staff, 11, 20, 55, 58–61, 63, 70, 85
Cysat, Johannes Baptista, 134–5

Dame, Bernard, 129, 135
Danchaster, *see* Hay, James
Davis, John, navigator, 32 n 15, 55, 84, 85, 87 n 9
dead-reckoning, 56, 64, 87 n 7
declination of the sun, tables discussed, 54, 58, 63, 64, 65, 85
Dee, John, 54, 75, 84–5, 89 n 59, 143; 'Canon gubernauticus', 84; 'Paradoxall compass', 85
deism, 108
Delambre, Jean-Baptiste, 131
Demisiani, John, 163 n 76

Democritean philosophy, 108, 111, 113
Democritus, Junior, *see* Burton, Robert
Descartes, Rene, 3–4; *Principia* (1644), 127 n 57
Devereux, Robert, earl of Essex (d. 1601), 26
Digges, Leonard, *Prognostication* (1555), 89 n 40, 143
Digges, Thomas, 74, 108, 143
Diophantus, 8–10
Douglas, John, navigator, 57, 62
Drake, Sir Francis, 37, 42, 43, 45
Durham House, 18, 25, 38, 49, 53 n 58, 64

Elizabeth I, queen of England (d. 1603), 22, 32, 38, 96, 98, 110; death of, 26; friendship with Ralegh, 24
Elizabeth, princess, daughter of James I (d. 1662), 95, 96, 105 n 28
energy, primal (*vis*), philosophy of: Hill's, 111, 112, Warner's, 114, 118, 119–20, 124
Epicurus, 5
Essex, earl of, *see* Devereux, Robert
Essex House, 142
Etzlaub, Erhard, 84
Euclid, *Elements* (c. 300 B.C.), 8

Fabricus, David, *Prognostication* (1615), 133–4
Fabricus, Frisian Johannes, 129, 132, 133–4, 138, 156; *De maculis* (1611), 133
Fernandes, Simon, 37
Fernándes de Quirós, Pedro, *Terra australis incognita* (1617), 95
Fernández de Oviedo, Gonzales, *Historia natural de las Indias* (1526), 42
Florence, 11, 135
Florida, 46, 52 n 38
Floyer, William, 21
Frampton, John, 12
France, 2, 32 n 1, 64, 94, 113, 134
Frankfurt, 46, 47, 95

Galileo, Galilei, v, 2, 4, 11, 115, 129–36, 140, 145–6, 152, 153, 156, 161 n 29, 164 n 88; association with Harriot, 136–9, 145–6, 147, 162 n 39; extant telescopes of, 144, 149–50, 160; observer of Jupiter's satellites, 136, 137, 145, 161 n 29, 162 n 40, 163 n 76, 165 n 113; sunspot observations, 129, 131, 152; *Dialogue* (1632), 4, 135, 152; *Il saggiatore* (1623), 136; *Sidereus nuncius* (1610), 136, 137, 138, 144
Gascoigne, William, 149, 159
Gaythorpe, S. B., 159–60
Gemma Frisius, Reiner, *De catholico astrolabio* (1556), 69, 151
Gilbert, Adrian, 25
Gilbert, Bartholomew, voyage (1602), 49
Gilbert, Sir Humphrey, 18; voyages, 37–8

Gilbert, William, 10; *De magnete* (1600), 110, 114

Gosnold, Bartholomew, voyage (1602), 49

Greaves, John, 140

Gregory ,James, 86, 90 *n 67*

Grenville (Greinvile), Sir Richard, 18, 20, 45, 47, 84

guards, 69–70: greater and lesser, 56, 67

Guiana, 12–13, 16, 25, 31, 48, 57

Gunpowder Plot (1605), 27–9, 49, 98; Harriot interrogated, 28–9

Gunter, Edmund, 77, 86, 89 *n 46*

Gustavus Adolphus, of Sweden, 149, 159

Hakluyt, Richard, of Oxford, 15, 17, 19, 37, 43, 46–50; dedication to Ralegh, 18; *Principall navigations* (1589), 18, 19, 43, 46; *Principal navigations* (*1598–1600*), 19, 43

Hale, George, 160

Halley, Edmond, 85–6

Hancock, Edward, secretary to Ralegh, 26

Handson, Ralph, *Nauticall questions* (1614), 71

Harington, John, 1st baron Harington (d. 1613), 95

Harington, John, 2nd baron Harington (d. 1614), 95–6

Harriot, Thomas (1560–1621)

birth, 17; education, 17, 36; final illness and death, 29, 31, 93–4; will (1621), 1, 4, 31, 35 *n 88*, 91–9, 116, 149

teacher of navigation, 1, 21, 38, 48; role in Virginia, 18, 22, 36–51; survey of Virginia, 40–3; chronicle, 20, 43; mathematical navigation, *see* writings, *Arcticon*; employment under Ralegh, 16–32, 48, 49, 108; charges of impiety, 23–5, 107; employment under Northumberland, 22, 25, 27–8, 30, 49, 94, 97, 98, 108; questioned about Gunpowder Plot, 28–9; imprisonment, 28; failure to publish, 4, 87 *n 5*, 129–30; scientific contributions, 2–4, 9–10, 132–3, 136–57; *see also under* binary numeration; moon; satellites, Jupiter's; sunspots; telescope

associates, *see* Allen, Thomas; Aylesbury, Sir Thomas; Bill, John; Buckner, Thomas; Dee, John; Harington, John; Hill, Nicholas; Hues, Robert; Percy, George; Protheroe, John; Sydney, Sir Robert; Tooke, Christopher; Warner, Walter; White, John

correspondents, *see* Cecil, Sir Robert; Kepler, Johannes; Lower, Sir William; Torporley, Nathaniel

writings: 'Arcticon' (*c.* 1584), 17, 38, 58, 61; *Artis analyticae praxis* (1631), 5, 7–8, 94, 101, 103, 116; *Briefe and true report* (1588), 1, 12, 13, 18–20, 43–7, 50, 91, 125 *n 9*, 143; 'Doctrine of nauticall triangles compendious' (1594), 75–83, 100–101, 115, 137–8; 'Instructions' (1595), 57–75, 85, 88 *n 24*

Harrison, John, watchmaker, 56

Harvey, William, 117; discovery of circulation of the blood, 120–2; *De motu cordis* (1628), 121

Hay, James, viscount Doncaster (Danchaster), 16

Henry, prince of Wales (d. 1612), 96, 105 *n 29*

Hermeticism, 108, 109, 113, 114, 126 *n 12*

Hernandes, Francisco, 42

Heydon, Sir Christopher, 137, 143

Hill, Nicholas, 108–14; primary constituents of nature, 110–14; *Philosophia* (1601), 110–14; Mss., 126 *n 12*

Hipparchos, 69

Hobbes, Thomas, 109, 114, 117, 121, 124–5; *Works*, 124

Holinshed, Raphael, *Chronicle* (1587), 18

Howard, Charles, earl of Nottingham (d. 1624), lord high admiral, 26, 97

Howard, Thomas, earl of Arundel (d. 1646), 17

Hues (Hughes), Robert, 29, 30 ,77, 94, 98, 116; *Tractatus de globis* (1594), 30

Humboldt, Alexander, 130–1

Hyde, Edward, earl of Clarendon, 97

Ibn al-Haitham, *see* Alhazen

Ibn Rushd (Averroes), 131

Indians, American, 13, 19, 47, 49, 50; Harriot and language of, 13, 18, 19, 39–40, 48, 49, 53 *n 62*; tribes Harriot may have studied in 1585, 41; *see also* Manteo; Powhatan; Wanchese

Inquisition (Holy Office), 134

Ireland, 20–2, 42, 64

Isleworth, 22, 27, 34 *n 86*

James I, king of England (d. 1625), 21, 26, 27, 28, 50, 95, 96, 98

James R., 36, 41; Indians of, 49

Jamestown Colony, 49, 51

Jefferys, Nicholas, 24

Jessop, John, 24

Jesuits, 130, 134, 161 *n 14*

Jupiter, satellite observations ('Jovial Planets'), 11, 34 *n 57*, 136–7, 141—8, 150

Kepler, Johannes, v, 6, 11, 114–15, 131, 132, 137, 156; correspondence with Harriot, 2,

3, 4, 108, 115, 138; *Conversation with Galileo's Sidereal Messenger* (1610), 11; *Dissertatio* (1610), 138, 144; *Epitome astronomiae Copernicanae* (1617), 95; *New astronomy* (1609), 6, 11; *Optics* (1604), 2, 3

Keymis, Lawrence, 17, 25, 48

Kocab (*Ursa Minoris* β), 56, 67

Kyd, Thomas, 23, 24

Lactantius, 6, 7

Lane, Ralph, 19, 22, 41, 42, 43

latitude, raising or laying a degree of (table), 75

L'Ecluse, Charles de, 47

Le Moyne, Jacques, artist, 46

Leibniz, Gottfried Wilhelm, 9

Leicester, earl of, *see* Sydney, Robert

light, philosophy of: Harriot's, 115; Hill's, 110, 111, 112

loadstone, 19

Locke, John, 114

locomotive faculty, Warner's view of, 123–4

logarithms, Warner's canon, 117, 128 *n 62*

London, 21, 23, 26, 28, 37, 42, 53 *n 62*, 94, 95; Harriot moved to, 17, 36; telescopic observations from, 142, 143

London Pharmacopeia, 95

Lower, Sir William, 8, 28, 132, 141, 142, 146, 150; correspondence with Harriot, 4, 7, 10, 11, 92, 104 *n 9*, 107, 114, 115, 125 *n 1*, 129–30, 136, 143, 164 *n 92*

Lucretius, 5

Mace, Samuel, voyage (1602), 49

Magini, Giovanni Antonio (Maginus), 133, 160 *n 1*

Malapert, Charles, 134

Manteo, an Indian, 18, 39

maps: arctic, 84; moon, vi, 150; world (1569), 89 *n 57*; (1599), 48, 90 *n 61*

Marlowe, Christopher, 23–4

Mars, 11, 137, 148

Martyn, William, 105 *n 26*; *Kings of England* (1615), 95

Martyr, Peter (Anglerius), *Decades* (1555), 15, 18; (1587), 18

matter, philosophy of: Bruno's 109; Hill's, 110, 113; Warner's, 114, 118–19, 120

Mayer, Tobias, 56

Mayerne, Theodore Turquet de, 92, 93–5, 98, 104 *nn 10, 16*

Mayr, Simon (Marius), *Prognostication* (1613), 134; *Mundus iovalis* (1614), 134

Medina, Pedro, 57

Mercator, Gerhard, 76, 84

Mercator chart, 73, 84–7, 87 *n 4*, 89 *n 57*

Mercurius gallo belgicus, 95

meridan, 76, 77, 80

meridian line, 81–2, 86; augmentation of (fig.), 81

meridian scale, 84

meridian zenith distance (MZD), 67

meridional parts (mer-parts), 78, 82, 83, 86; D. longs on the 7th rhumb (table), 84; tables of discussed, 54, 75, 77, 80, 84–5

Mersenne, P. Marin, 109, 117

Mexico, 42

Molana Abbey, Ireland, 21–2

Monardes (Monardus), Nicolás, *Joyfull newes* (1577), 12

Monteagle, Lord, 28

moon: first drawing of surface, 136, 141; first telescopic observations of, 115; Harriot's observations of, 32 *n 13*, 33 *n 16*, 132, 136, 141, 147, 148, 162 *n 55*; Italian drawings of, 136; mapping of, vi, 150

motion, philosophy of: Harriot's, 115; Hill's, 114; Warner's, 119–20

Munster Plantation, 20, 22

Myrtle Grove, Youghal, 20

Napier, John, *Mirifici logarithmorum canonis descriptio* (1614), 85, 86, 87 *n 5*

Nashe, Thomas, poet, *Pierce pennilesse* (1592), 125 *n 9*

nautical triangle: definition of, 76; diagrams, cases of, 78; on the globe, 76; solutions of, 77–80; *see* Harriot, 'Doctrine'

navigation, 1, 18, 21, 37, 38, 48, 54–7

negative numbers, 9–10, 101

Neo-Platonism, 108, 109, 111, 113, 120, 126 *n 12*

Newcastle, earl of, *see* Cavendish, William

Newport, Christopher, 49, 50

Newton, Sir Isaac, 86

Nicholas of Cusa, 110

noetic (complex) numbers, 101

Norman, Robert, *Newe attractive* (1581), 71

Norman, Thomas, clergyman, 25

Norris, Richard, *Infinite secants of an arch* (1685), 86

North America, 18, 36, 38, 39, 45, 46, 48, 49, 50, 51

Northumberland, earl of, *see* Percy, Henry

Nottingham, earl of, *see* Howard, Charles

numerical signs: addition, 9; exponents, 9, 102; 'Gemini' equality sign, 153; inequality, equality, 1, 9; multiplication, 9; radical, 9, 101; subtraction, 9

Nunez, Pedro (Petrus Nonius), 55, 59; *De arte atque ratione navigandi* (1546), 74, 87 *n 10*

Tratado da esphera (1537), 89 *n 58*

Oldys, William, 'Life of Ralegh' (1736), 30, 34 *n 82*

optics: Hobbes' treatise on, 117; Warner's papers on; 117, 121; *see* refraction
Oriel College, Oxford, 17, 32 *n 1*
Orinoco R., Brazil, 12, 13, 36
Oughtred, William, 85–6, 99
Oviedo, *see* Fernández de Oviedo

pain, philosophy of: Hill's, 112; Warner's, 123–4
Paris, 43, 46, 94, 110
Parsons, Robert, *Elizabethae angliae reginae* (1592), 23
Passigmani, Cresti da, 134
Payne, Robert, 109, 117, 121
Peele, George, poet, 25
Pell, John, 19, 30, 97, 99, 117, 120, 127 *nn* 40, 45, 128 *n* 62
Percy, Henry, 9th earl of Northumberland (d. 1632), 4, 22–30, 49, 97, 98, 99, 110, 114, 116, 120, 125; acquires Syon House, 4, 26; association with Harriot, 22, 25, 27–8, 30, 49, 94, 97, 98, 108; imprisoned in Tower, 28, 49, 98, 116, 122
   Algernon, son of Henry and 10th earl (d. 1668), 116
   Dorothy, daughter of Henry, 96, 105 *n 35*
   George, brother of Henry, 49–50, 53 *n 62*, 66
   Thomas, cousin of Henry, 27–8, 98
Perham, Sir Edward, 16
Petworth House, 22, 30, 91, 98
Pitiscus, Bartholomew, *Trigonometry* (1614), 71
plane chart, 76, 84, 85
Plotinianism, 114
pole star (*Polaris*), 54, 56, 67, 69, 72, 74; table of allowances, 70; (fig.) 71; *see also* guards
Polter, Richard, *Pathway to perfect sayling* (1605), 85, 88 *n 15*
Popham, Sir John (d. 1607), lord chief justice, 27
Portugal, 1, 13, 37, 64, 67
Powhatan, Indian chief, 50
Powhatan, Indians, 49
projection, stereographic, 54, 83; of the rhumb lines (fig.), 74
Prothero(e), John (d. 1624), 98, 99, 106 *n 43*, 116, 121; son John, 99
Prutenic Tables, 63
Ptolemy: astronomy of, 31; refraction table discussed, 2–3; *Geographia* (1462), 69
Purchas, Samuel, 50–1; *Pilgrimage* (1613), 51; *Pilgrimes* (1625), 51

Quir, *see* Fernándes de Quirós, Pedro

Ralegh, Carew, 24

Ralegh, City of, 44
Ralegh, Sir Walter, 1
   association with Harriot, 16–32, 37–8, 48, 49, 108
   dedication to, 15, 18
   rise to power, 18, 23; patent (1584), 20, 38, 39, 44, 49; knighthood, 18; voyage to Guiana (1595), 25, 48, 57; voyage to Cadiz (1596), 48; promoter of Virginia voyages, 17–18, 42–6, 49; Irish colonial venture, 20–2; early will (1597), 25–6, 49
   fall from grace: marriage, 24, 25; 'School of Atheism' investigation, 23–5; imprisonment, 24, 26–7, 30, 49, 116, 122; trial for treason, 26–7; execution, 16–17, 31
Ralegh, Walter (son), 25
Read, Dr. Alexander, 94; *Chirurgicall lectures* (1635), 29–30, 34 *n 79*, 93–4
Recorde, Robert, 9, 103, 108; *Whetstone of witte* (1557), 9
refraction: Harriot's work on, 87 *n 13*, 115; sine law of, 3–4; tables of Harriot, Ptolemy and Witelo discussed, 2–3; table for the sun and fixed stars discussed, 85; Warner's table discussed, 117
Reinhold, Erasmus, *Prutenicae tabulae* (1551), 63
Rheticus, George Joachim, *Narratio prima* (1539), 69
Rhind Papyrus, 8
rhumb, 76, 78; tables of discussed, 85
Rigaud, Steven P., v, 75, 92, 131–3, 137, 140, 144–7, 153–5; *Account of Harriot's astronomical papers* (1833), 101
ring, sea, 55, 58–60; (fig.), 55
Risner, Friedrich, ed. *Treasury of Optics* (1572), 2, 3
Roanoke, Virginia: colonists, 20, 43; Indians, 41; island, 42; river, 41, 50
Rome, 113, 134, 135
Rothmann, Christopher, astonomer, 63

Smith, Thomas, customer of London, 37
Smith, Sir Thomas (son), merchant, 33*n49*, 37
Snell (Snel; Snellius), Willebrord, 2, 86; *Erosthenes batavus* (1617), 95; *Observations* (1618), 95
soul, philosophy of: Bruno's, 109–10; Hill's, 112
South America, 13, 36, 48
space, philosophy of: Hill's, 110, 113; Warner's, 114, 118
Spain, 12, 13, 37, 43, 63, 64, 67, 69; war with, 21, 26, 45
Speidell, John, *New logarithmes* (1619), 85
Spenser, Edmund, poet, 22
'spring clock', 19, 20, 144

staff, excentricity of, 62; (table), 62; parallaxis of, 60, 61–2, 70; (fig.), 62
Stevens, Henry, *Thomas Hariot and his
Associates* (1900), v, 91–100
Stifel, Michael (Stifelius), 9, 10, 102, 103
Strachey, William, 'Historie of travell in
Virginia Britania' (1612), 51
Stukely, Sir Lewis, 16
sun: annual motion of (fig.), 64; axis of,
152, 164 *n 98*; azimuth of, 71, 151; declination tables discussed, 54, 58, 63, 64,
65, 85; eclipse of (1585), 40; ecliptic line,
151-2; Ephemerides of, 85; longitude of
(fig.), 65; rotation of, 151–5, 156
sunspots, 107, 115; definition of, 131; history of observations, 130–1; early observers of, 134–5; first printed account of
telescopic observation, 133; Harriot's
first observation of, 132, 138; Harriot's
methods of observation, 139–41; value of
Harriot's observations, 155–7; Galileo's
observations of, 129, 131, 135–6; counts
of, 154–5; solar rotation, 152–5, 156
surplus of the horizon, 60, 70; (table) 61;
(fig.) 60
Sydney (Sidney), Robert, Viscount Lisle,
earl of Leicester (d. 1626), 96, 97, 121
Syon House, Isleworth, 22, 26, 28, 31, 49,
50; Harriot's residence at, 4, 26, 27, 28,
30, 33 *n 49*, 34 *nn 62, 86*, 49, 53 *n 58*, 93,
96, 98, 116, 139, 141, 142, 163 *n 62*

Tarde, Jean, 134
telescope (cylinder, instrument, perspective
glass, perspective trunk), 1–2, 11, 19–20,
107, 115, 117, 141–4; Dutch or 'Galilean',
136, 145, 149–50, 158–60, 165 *n 113*;
(diagram) 144; Galileo's use of, 11, 136,
149–50, 165 *n 113*; Harriot's use of, 2,
32 *n 13*, 115, 141–50; 'Keplerian', 158;
variety of words for, 144, 163 *n 76*
Thames, R., 4, 163 *n 62*
Thorndyke, Herbert, 117, 127 *n 41*
'Three Magi', 30, 116
'Three Seas Marriadges', 59
Throckmorton, Sir Arthur, 26
Throckmorton, Elizabeth, 23, 24, 25
Thynne, John, of Longleat, 37
time, philosophy of: Hill's, 110; Warner's,
118
Titchbourne, Sir Benjamin, 27
tobacco, 24, 93
Tooke, Christopher, 99, 132, 141, 142
Torporley, Nathaniel, 10, 28, 29, 94, 108,
115, 137; executor of Harriot will, 4, 98,
99, 116; transcriber of Harriot's mathe-
matical papers, 5, 96, 97, 100–103, 105 *n
22*, 106 *nn 47, 48, 50*; *Synopsis of the con-*
troversie of atoms, 5; *Corrector analyticus*,
107
Tower of London, 26, 27, 28, 29, 30, 31,
35 *n 86*, 49, 98, 116
Turner, Peter, physician (d. 1614), 92, 93,
142
Turner, Peter, mathematician (son), 104 *n 13*
Turner, Samuel (son), 93, 104 *n 13*

vacuum, existence of, 110, 115, 120
Venus, 31, 131, 133
Vere, Edward de, earl of Oxford, 110
Vesalius, Andreas, *On the structure of the
human body* (1543), 14
Viète (Vieta), François, 7–8, 9, 10, 96, 99;
In artem analyticam isagoge (1591),7
Virginia, 36, 51; colonies (1585–6), 18, 20,
31, 40–2, 43; (1587), 43–4; voyages
(1584), 17, 21, 38–40, 43, 47; (1585), 18,
21, 38, 39, 40, 43, 44, 98; (1586), 43, 47–8;
(1587), 21, 43–4, 32 *n 9*; (1588), 43, 44–5;
(1590), 38, 43; fauna, 13, 41, 42; flora, 12,
13, 41–2, 52 *n 19*; Indians, 13, 41, 47–8,
49–50
Virginia Company, 50, 51; charter, 49, 50
vis, see energy, philosophy of
Vitelo, Vitellio, *see* Witelo
von Zach, F. X., *see* Zach, F. X. von

Wales, 11, 28, 94
Wallis, John, 'Concerning the collection of
secants' (1685), 86
Wanchese, an Indian, 18, 39
Warner, Walter, 24, 25, 29, 30, 31, 94, 97,
99, 114, 117, 126 *nn 36, 39*, 127 *nn 41, 57*,
137; association with Harriot, 108–9,
116; definitions of time, space, matter,
energy, 114, 118–20; papers of, 108, 116,
117, 120, 128 *n 64*; printed *Praxis*, 105 *n
22*, 116; treatise on vital functions, 117,
120–5
Welser, Mark, 133, 134; correspondence
with Galileo, 130, 135, 152, 156; correspondence with Scheiner, 133, 140
Wheatley (Wheately), apothocary, 92
Whiddon, Jacob, navigator, 57, 59, 62,
88 *n 29*
White, John, 17, 19, 38, 43–4; association
with Harriot (1585), 38, 40, 41, 45; drawings in Virginia, 19, 41, 42, 45, 47, 50,
52 *n 19*; Virginia voyage (1587), 44–5;
map, 41
White Thomas, 124
Witelo (Vitellio), *Ten books on optics* (1572),
2, 3, 87 *n 13*
Wococon, Virginia, 40, 41
Wood, Anthony à, *Athenae Oxoniensis*
(1691), 30, 107, 127 *n 41*

Wright, Edward, 54, 67, 77, 83, 85, 86, 87 *nn 4, 5*, 88 *n 21*; *Certaine errors in nauigation* (1599), 67, 70, 77, 85

Wright-Molyneux world map (1599), 48

Wytfliet, Cornelis van, 51

Youghal, Ireland, 20–2

Zach, F. X. von, v, 91, 162 *n 44*

Zamorano (Samerano), Rodrigo, *Compendio* (1581), 69

Zinner, Ernst, 134